The Ends of Our Exploring

THE ENDS OF OUR

HOOLEY McLAUGHLIN

EXPLORING

Ethical and Scientific
Journeys to Remote Places

Malcolm Lester Books

Canadian Cataloguing in Publication Data

McLaughlin, Hooley Michael Graham, 1949–
     The ends of our exploring : ethical and scientific journeys
     to remote places

Includes index.
ISBN 1-894121-10-4

1. McLaughlin, Hooley Michael Graham, 1949 –
– Journeys – Siberia.
2. Science and philosophy.
3. Philosophy, Modern – 20th century.
4. Philosophy, Canadian – 20th century.
I. Title.

B67,M32 1998   501   c98-931762-5

The epigraph on p. vi is reprinted with the kind permission of
Faber and Faber Ltd. It is taken from *Four Quartets, Collected
Poems 1909 –1962* by T. S. Eliot.

Book design: Gordon Robertson

Malcolm Lester Books
25 Isabella Street
Toronto, Ontario M4Y 1M7

99 00 01 02 5 4 3 2 1
Printed and bound in Canada

For Danielle

We shall not cease from exploration
And the end of all our exploring
Will be to arrive where we started
And know the place for the first time.

– T. S. ELIOT, "Little Gidding"

CONTENTS

ACKNOWLEDGEMENTS

MY MEMORIES of the events in this book are personal. I thank those friends and colleagues who have shared in my adventures. Sasha brought me through physical and intellectual journeys unharmed, but changed. Monty indulged my curiosity at risk to himself. Joann, Tom, Heinz, Paul, Ché, Roshelle, Dharma, Nicola, Sid, Gretchen, Baiba, John, Joe, Dirk, and many others travelled with me in one way or another, and made me think more carefully about my life and work. I know their recollections will not always match mine, but then "truth" is relative and is definitely a product of the exchange between the observer and the observed. I hope they enjoy the stories and my philosophy.

For my initiation into science, I am indebted to Richard Liversage, who indulged my approach to laboratory work. And I am immeasurably grateful to Bill Stauble for guidance into deeper thoughts during more recent years.

I will be forever in debt to my publisher, Malcolm Lester, for the thoughtful discussions, the opportunity to write, and his enthusiasm for the project. His staff have been uniformly helpful and supportive throughout the writing of the book. I am immensely appreciative of the chance to work with my editor, Alison Reid, who taught me to think clearly about how I am portraying my ideas. I also want to thank my designer, Gordon Robertson, and my indexer, Chris Blackburn, who both interpreted the spirit of the book so well.

My family is intimately woven into the stories. During the writing of the book, I was encouraged and moved by their presence, their support, and our mutual memories. Levi and Reuben were travelling companions. Levi's humorous insights into cultural diversity helped me to take a more relaxed view of things. Reuben and I had long conversations together about the ethics of science in the late twentieth century, which I will always remember. Gabrielle inspired me with her courageous approach to life, and my granddaughters, Na'ama and Chavva-Tal, are with me daily during the writing, reminding me what really matters. And I will always be grateful to my father, Ted, for his insights into maps and world travel. Danielle has been with me throughout the time span of the stories in the book—thirty years of my life. Her love, support, and imagination over that period are the reason the book was written at all.

INTRODUCTION

WHERE AM I TAKING YOU on my journeys? We start in Siberia on the Ob River, heading into a remote edge of northern Asia. The landscape belongs to another culture, and as I move through it, I slowly realize that I cannot understand or even *see* the people of this foreign civilization from my perspective as a western scientist and museum curator.

It was 1990, and I had been promised a trip to the major centres of Europe, to visit the great museums that display the science and technology of our western culture. But it was not to be. My colleagues would go to Paris and Amsterdam and Munich and Barcelona and London, but I was told I was needed in a team leaving for the Soviet Union, to work on a project that no one could precisely define. Somehow, during a period of three weeks, we had to travel to meet people in northern Siberia and then create a museum exhibition for presentation in Toronto. There would be three of us going; Fiona was to be project manager, Jim the designer, and I would be the content co-ordinator—the curator. I didn't want to go. Siberia felt like a cold and unlikeable place, filled with industrial wastelands and native people who wore fur year-round, who were locked into a pre-scientific culture. But that trip up the Ob marked a change in my understanding. No, I didn't go to Europe then, but I put into perspective the Europe that is in me.

I am taking you through my route to personal discovery. Journeys to remote places in the world are intertwined with the process of my philosophical development as a scientist. The journeys, physical and intellectual, are revealed to the reader as a series of small adventures, first a story of one of my travels and then a discussion of the relevant science or philosophy. The result is like a long braid, a helix of ideas and experiences that fall into place one after the other, each new passage reinforcing the message of the one before. Themes will appear and later be repeated in other forms; stories will be revisited from many angles, each time emphasizing some new aspect of my personal discovery.

During my short stay in Siberia, I began to see that the world we live in is made up of maps. We apprehend the reality around us as maps— maps that act as models of that reality, that overlie the unknown with comfortable preconceptions, that act as templates for shaping a safe and familiar sequence of events in the future. Maps reflect our way of thinking, our culture, and because they are derived from such singular and idiosyncratic apprehensions, experienced individually or collectively as members of a particular group, one person's or one culture's map cannot match the map of another. People in the same corner of the earth can live out their lives guided by maps that do not overlap. I found reindeer herders who still follow the animals' annual migration up into the Yamal Peninsula of Siberia, threading their way through the melting permafrost of the twentieth-century gas-drilling stations. The two civilizations, one ancient and one modern, never see each other. And from my scientist's perspective, it was easier to decipher the modern gas-drilling stations. The map of the gas fields of the Yamal was laid out in a way that I could understand—it stood eight feet high on the office wall of the director of mining. But the map of the reindeer herders I met consisted of a daily routine, a pattern that stretches over time, and that one could not be drawn and mounted on an office wall.

My journey is also an intellectual discovery, finding the maps that guide western scientists in their work. The philosophical works of the thinkers of the west, like the great museums of Europe that I missed when I went off to Siberia, hold the artifacts of our civilization. They stand as proof that we are unravelling the mysteries of the universe. We in the west have a hierarchical view of ideas, of civilizations, of all living things, a view that extends to our perception of the very people of the earth. I am inviting you to explore the origins and the implications of this European way of thinking through an examination of scientific theories and practices over the past centuries. Most of our philosophical history is a conflict between those who would try to fix a higher meaning or purpose to the ascent toward perfection that they choose to see in the evolution of all living things, and those who assert that the logic of change and evolution resides within nature as they attempt to refute the existence of a "designer" who guides all processes and events.

I am taking you on journeys where even the philosophers and scientists, despite attempts to eliminate our need for purpose, will be seen to be perpetuating that same flawed "argument from design." For most thinkers of the western world, the map is laid out before their journey even begins. The map substantiates the concept that all things are thought to be headed in a direction that requires that they be shaped or designed to "fit in." The famous attempts to invent models that would include random actions and thus demonstrate an *unpredictable* evolution of living things are also born of the western mission to perpetuate the hierarchy; theories such as those that describe evolution as the adaptation of random life forms to the environment are nothing more than disguised arguments from design. In Charles Darwin's world, the living beings must be moulded or shaped by a landscape that is waiting like a grand designer, a destiny that is not to be avoided. It is the belief in the map that is the downfall of most attempts to defy the teleology that lies at the heart of western thought. For Darwin and others, the ultimate design is not to be questioned—the living beings of the earth will fit in or they will die. Even for thinkers who live strictly within the world of ideas, their cerebral experiments must also compete in the established *intellectual* realm. No matter what our activity, be it physical or intellectual, there is no escaping the map of western civilization, exemplified by the pyramid with the ideal of humankind at the top.

Argument from design is "teleological" thinking, the term derived from Aristotle's description of the various causes that can describe actions and processes. Scholars using teleological arguments examine the end point, $τέλος$, of a series of events and deem that to be the force that drives all activity. Teleological thinking demands an answer to the question "why?" Thus an animal that is a swimmer is seen to have had an evolutionary history "designed" to lead to that *future* end point. Darwin's concept of evolution through the adaptation of random life forms to the environment was thought to move us away from that unfortunate destiny-based approach. But when you see the world as a series of maps laid out for us by western thought, you see the pitfalls in that argument. Where is the randomness when you accept that there is a landscape into which the random living things must adapt? It is no different with civilizations. In Darwin's time as now, the expectation was for all cultures to see the obvious superiority of European civilization and allow the map of European intellectual history to be the template for culture.

Teleological thinking, the argument from design, an argument that accepts an unseen map that dictates acceptable tastes and culture, and an argument that camouflages a hidden desire for purpose, guides much of our thinking today. A desire for a human-shaped universe traps us in the belief that all living forms, civilizations, and even scientific ideas are heading toward some perfect pinnacle of perfection, and that this is a reality within our abilities to satisfy. This belief has led to the notion of European superiority, and it is the basis of much of the prejudice we see today, prejudice that is justified by the philosophers and thinkers who shape our civilization.

I have found my route to this understanding tortuous, for it has entailed facing my own prejudices and misconceptions. I am taking you through journeys that have helped me to understand my own acceptance of this style of thought, this teleology that underlies my education as a scientist and thinker. My trip to Siberia is followed by more journeys to Moscow and Leningrad in the winter. I was struck by the effect that cold and hunger and isolation had on my behaviour. On one trip, I took a train from Moscow to Leningrad; it was a journey into a cold hell. My friend Sasha and I walked for hours after the train trip and met people who told me stories that I never want to hear again, about how the cold, their imprisonment in the Gulag of Siberia, or their deprivation during the siege of Leningrad fifty years ago led them to do things that would not be countenanced in any "ideal" civilization. And there are other journeys. I will not forget my walk along the Gulag railroad, where I confronted my personal feelings of exhilarating power, feelings that I imagine such a vast enterprise must have elicited in Stalin, but an enterprise that enslaved so many people. While I was writing the book, I visited the devastated downtown core of Johannesburg, where I met a man who invited me into his shanty home in a ruined turbine building. On another occasion, in the opulent living quarters of a Saudi Arabian prince, I met a household servant whose attentions forced me to examine my attitude toward slavery; I discovered that I enjoyed feeling important and deserving of his servitude, despite my belief that human hierarchies are oppressive and wrong.

In Washington I witnessed a black man take part in an experiment on brain imaging. He was the subject of the experiment, but he was mentally ill, and I wonder how we can accept his participation as the act of a fully aware colleague in our collective scientific pursuit of knowledge. Although we are all colleagues because we are all living together in this world, I question the attitude that encourages us to strive to be superior to our fellow human beings. I question the map that guides our actions in this western civilization. I submit that it leads us into ethical dilemmas. Yet we think it is reality, the only map that exists. Why should our belief in the hierarchy of all things be the only model or map that guides us into the future?

In our *intellectual* pursuits, we often try to understand the world from a position *removed* from immediate experience. We scientists and philosophers consider ourselves superior to the life around us. As a result, we are defining our civilization with an artificial, preconceived map. And it is a map that does not do justice to the true dialectic of our everyday experience.

There are alternatives to teleological thinking. Some of my journeys have been very private ones. Not long after my trip to Siberia, I went alone into the northern lakes of Ontario by canoe. I wanted to be by myself to think. I learned that each stroke of the paddle was a shaping event, that I was interacting with the living world. We were having a very intimate dialectical interchange, the water and I; we were making the map. The maps that result from personal encounters exemplify a non-teleological approach. When we permit the influence of those more dialectical exchanges, there are no preconceptions by which we are moulded and shaped. And so I believe there is a way to lead us out of this dilemma of imposed maps and the never-ending climb toward an ideal pinnacle of civilization and thought. The maps made by native hunters in the north of Canada provide another example of non-teleological thought. They are not "to scale," they do not agree with the professional mapmaker's aerial views, but they do represent the physical and emotional experience of the paddler who will spend many hours on one day making his way down a river filled with rocks and rapids, and on the next will relax on an open lake with a soft breeze that will carry him effortlessly home. Our journeys over the earth are experienced directly. A day spent dodging rapids and rocks will seem a lot longer and more difficult than a day spent sailing over a calm lake. We are creatures that flourish in the intimate interactions of life.

CHAPTER ONE

SIBERIA

It is not down in any map; true places never are.
— HERMAN MELVILLE, *Moby Dick*

1

I T IS MORNING.
"*Nah leeyeh´va!*" I swing the wheel to the left. "*Nah prah´va!*" I swing the wheel to the right. "*Preeyah´ma!*" I am learning the words for left, right, and straight ahead. Under the command of the captain, I steer the sixty-foot boat toward the harbour at Pitlyar, a village in northern Siberia.

We have commissioned the crew to take us to meet the Khanti and Nientsi people who travel from their winter settlements to follow the reindeer. Every summer, reindeer and people from across Siberia move north into the tundra.

Our boat trip is elaborate. It has taken a lot of effort on the part of our Russian hosts. When we first set out last evening, I felt I had been a little too demanding, but the night we have just passed has taken away my brief feelings of guilt. Our companions from Moscow, Sasha and Tatiana, saw no problem in inviting Alexander, a local government representative, and his wife to travel with us, in quarters cramped and inadequate for even four passengers. Altogether, we number seven. Fiona and Jim and I are here from Canada, looking for artifacts to put into a museum display on northern Siberia. This was intended to be a good time for us all, and it would have been if there had been any room to lie down in the sleeping compartments, or any air to breathe. Cigarettes and talking and singing and vodka drinking had gone on all night, our sixth night of interrupted sleep since arriving in the Soviet Union. But there really is no night here, no morning, no afternoon, no evening. The sun is always up.

2

It has been a day's journey from Salekhard, a city near the mouth of the Ob River on the Arctic Circle. I turn the wheel over to the captain just as we enter the final bend of the river. Steering the boat under his instructions has been exhilarating, and it has revealed a curious phenomenon. Normally, I have great trouble telling my left from my right. When someone yells, "Turn left!" while I am driving, I am just as likely to turn right. I have heard that this is not uncommon. But here in Siberia, everything is new for me. Travelling in a foreign language, I can now tell my left from my right. I feel confident in my ability to navigate. But I am not entirely sure where I am going.

There is a lot of light, the white brilliant midsummer sunlight of the Arctic. The waves are huge and the boat shifts over them uneasily. The engines churn, slow down, reverse, and churn again. Dock workers guide us in with sticks, large tires cushion us as we gently hit the wooden dock.

3

Today, the Yamal area is known for natural gas reserves, not especially for reindeer. But reindeer are still herded by northern peoples from Norway to the far east of Siberia. The Yamal is just one region among many. Back in Salekhard, in the office of Vasily Pochibekin, the director of all the drilling and mining in the region, we discuss the number of oil and gas fields. Yes, there are many of them—oil to the south, and gas fields to the north and east, in the Yamal and nearby regions; and yes, the drilling is bringing prosperity. The socialist proscription against conspicuous wealth and the encouragement of social equality do not hold here in Siberia. The leather chairs are sumptuous, and the control of the director is absolute and offhand. Because he likes the fact that my first name is a rude word in Russian, Pochibekin lends us a bus with a driver for our stay. It is the size of a city bus. Looking out, we see people standing at muddy crossroads, bewildered but resigned as we drive by. No one complains here. Vehicular travel and gas drilling on the Yamal are melting the permafrost. Some people say that the Yamal could melt away entirely, into sodden muck. Because tire tracks leave impressions that last for at least fifty years, maybe a giant meltdown is not so far-fetched. But no, there is no danger to the environment, we are told. And yes, local Nientsi and Khanti people are offered work too, not just Russians from down south.

4

We are shown Pochibekin's eight-foot-high map. Sculpted from wood and highlighted with gold paint, it covers a large section of one wall in the director's office. The map depicts the Yamal peninsula and regions immediately to the south and shows one thing only: the natural gas fields. It seems as if half the Yamal peninsula is covered by the gas reserves. The director of operations has shown little emotion during our meeting, but now, standing next to the map, he cannot hide his pride. Yes, it is his goal to tap the entire region in as efficient and scientific a manner as possible. He has engineers working closely with him, and co-operative ventures with foreign firms are now allowed. He has what he needs to make this happen.

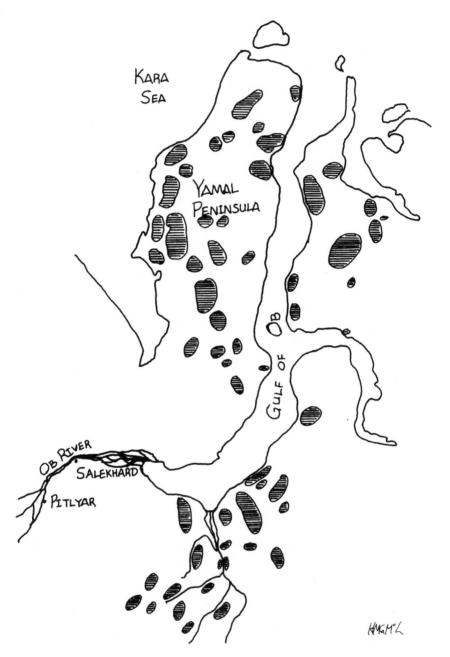

Vasily Pochibekin's map of the natural gas fields in the Yamal Peninsula and surrounding regions, as shown to me in 1990. The map stood eight feet against one wall of his office. (Gas fields are indicated by the shaded areas.)

5

Maps reveal the shape of a civilization, a society. But maps cannot be easily read by those who are not members of that society. A map placed on the surface of the earth can overlap other maps. It can occupy the same space as the map of another civilization, but the different maps may touch only at a few key points. The everyday activities and interests of people are what make each map distinct. People in any culture are focused on activities that occupy their waking hours. The activities of every person in a community can be added to those of fellow workers or neighbours. Together, the people make up the culture, the civilization. If the Yamal looks like feeding grounds for reindeer, then it is that and nothing else for most of the day. If the day is spent drilling for gas and taking messages from directors far away from the Yamal itself, then the map of the Yamal is seen as gas-drilling stations and pipelines. Do these people even see each other? Of course they do sometimes, but they can only communicate when there is time and when there is an opening, a link between the two worlds occupying the same position on the surface of the earth.

6

This is the north, and it is cold and snow covered for much of the year. I am thinking that is why things are not all that dirty, or at least not as dirty as I had expected along this industrial and polluted river route. Today, there is a windblown look to the hillsides. And there are a few trees. Coming south to Pitlyar, we have just crossed the tree line. The river is fast and huge, but not as wide as it was at the mouth. Back there, in Salekhard, we could barely make out the northern reaches of the Ural Mountains across the water on the European side.

7

The harbour is an eddy-formed pocket in the river's bank, protected by hills that deflect the fast-moving water. Finding a place to settle on the Ob's banks is so unlikely, we are told, that they named this place Pitlyar. It means "Falling from the Sky to the Sea," a reference to its divine origins. There was snow at Salekhard, and here there is frozen ground. The harbour water appears to be gelled. Refuse from a few barges, some stray boards, and odd pieces of garbage float turgidly on its slick cold surface.

8

The evening before the boat trip, we swam in the river. After too much vodka, and that unrelenting sunlight, we looked out the hotel window and decided. We walked over the sands at the shore, ankle deep in murky muck, and eventually made our way into water deep enough for swimming. It was so cold that we couldn't smell the stink. We couldn't feel the oily water on our skin. It felt almost cleansing. We swam for over half an hour to entertain the local people, who had come out to watch us. I don't think anyone had willingly swum there before.

9

In the world of maps, it is not only a spatial overlapping that takes place. There is also an overlapping of time. The reindeer herders and the gas drillers both have to work in the summer. But for them, having to share a given time and space leads to less communication, not more. In the minds of many of the people involved in this emerging clash of cultures, the gas drillers are not competing for resources needed by the reindeer herders. They are drilling *beneath* the earth. Neither do gas men mind the herders, who appear and are gone the next day.

10

I had expected worse. Pitlyar is a muddy village, but the journey here was far filthier. This is strange country, where the Russians treat the land as if it were put here for working in and on but not for cherishing. On the way to Salekhard from Moscow, we landed in Ukhta. We stayed for the better part of a day, fogged in. Stiff from an all-night flight, flying low over the trees and mountains in a noisy vibrating aircraft, slung into a canvas hammock of a seat, baggage piled high around us, we had emerged hoping to lie down anywhere, on the floor if necessary. But the floors were filthy, and the seats were all occupied by travellers from across the Soviet Union. They had been waiting for days for travel accommodations for themselves and their families. The airport food was indescribable—greasy slabs of fat and equally greasy bread. Plugged toilets had forced people to relieve themselves in the adjacent hallways; piles of paper used for personal hygiene completed the terrible scene. And yet, oblivious to the pale, tired, hungry faces of the people on the benches around us, Tatiana demanded that a table and chairs be set up in the middle of the main room. There, in front of the counters with the slabs of grey chicken and unidentifiable meats for sale to the travellers, she laid out sausages, soft cheeses, cognac, bread and caviar for our breakfast. "Ah," she sighed in gratification over the food. "Eat!" The juxtaposition was so ludicrous that I did, despite my feelings of guilt.

11

The reindeer herders see the Yamal as a long trail, a line that tracks around obstacles if necessary, but characterized by a continuous non-stop movement to the north and back again. Only a complete barrier would cause them to take notice. At the moment, the fact that such a barrier may be growing is irrelevant to people who see their lives in terms of seasons, who are regulated by time and not by alterations to spatial maps that delineate the ownership of territories on the surface of the earth. To people following a narrow migration path, a barrier is only real once it has pinched off the last openings. Until that final act of closing, the linear map of the herders is not interrupted. I am reminded of the way our cat goes in and out the front door. Since it is an aluminum screen door with a pneumatic device, it takes time to close. The cat waits until the last second before the door shuts and then dashes through. For him, his route from outside to inside, his mapping of the world, is essentially the same whether the door is wide open or only a little bit open. "Get in here! I can't wait all day!" Of course, not everyone is completely oblivious to what is happening. In 1990, we met Khanti and Nientsi people struggling to maintain territory that would be reserved for the exclusive use of National Minorities. Two years before, there was a successful ban on heavy transport across the tundra; tire tracks were fast becoming permanent bog holes. However, interference with future drilling stations was another perhaps more likely impetus for the change in transportation policies, as muddy reaches of melting permafrost are not the best conditions for setting up a natural gas operation. Despite some political activism, the Khanti and the Nientsi are by and large unaware of the changes coming. The screen door has not completely closed—they haven't yet noticed that their environment is being destroyed.

12

I stare at the map of the Yamal. Gas-drilling stations are signals of modern progress. But what about an older science, what about the Nientsi and Khanti reindeer herders, what about those who must follow the traditional migration routes? The reindeer travel into the Yamal peninsula and nearby tundra zones during the summer months. They feed on the plants that grow for a short time on the permanently frozen ground. What do they do now? How do they manage now that the Yamal has become an obstacle course? We are told what we are told by everyone, by the Khanti people in Pitlyar and by the Nientsi people we meet in Salekhard, and here by the director of gas and oil drilling: the reindeer follow the traditional paths and move *around* the gas-drilling sites. Pochibekin offers to fly us in by helicopter to see the moving bands of Nientsi and Khanti people with their reindeer. Will we be able to land the helicopter and talk with them? No, and it may be hard to find them in one trip. As we become interested, the offer seems less firm; maybe it would be better to speak to people closer by. But for now the reindeer do still move through the Yamal.

13

Perhaps their reception of us would not be all that friendly. Later, on the boat, we travel farther north toward the Ob's mouth, where it opens into a long saltwater gulf before joining with the sea. Seeing a small settlement of Nientsi *tchum*s (shelters made of reindeer skin hung on wooden poles), we attempt to land to meet the people. Maybe the reindeer are not far away. The boat grounds itself on a rock and we are trapped. The waves buffet the boat but we don't move. The constant revving of the engines, first in forward and then in reverse, has no effect. We try long poles and then yelling for help. One lone spokeswoman waves us away—she looks worried. The crew members tell us that there are probably only women and children in the settlement. They are not even coming to the riverbank to see us. After a while, I can hear our captain's voice over the sound of the wind and water—his threats have become a little heavy. He wants someone on shore to help secure a rope to one of the rocks. The woman gets into a canoe and begins to paddle out to us. Just then, we free ourselves and she turns quickly back to shore; not wanting to risk another landing on the rocky coastline, we leave her behind.

14

For the gas drillers, the Yamal is as it appears on the wall in Pochibekin's office in Salekhard. It has a distinct size and shape. Things have a position. They do not move. There may be new spots to put on the map, but the old spots remain. The engineers can measure distances using instruments on the map itself. And their map creates its own history; you can read the history by noting the dates of the gas drilling. For the Khanti and the Nientsi, history is recorded at each annual reindeer migration. For them, there is no map as seen from the air, no map of the trails between the impassable mud stretches of long past, no photograph showing the routes laid out between the gas fields. There is only the daily journey, along a route measured not by distance but by time.

I am struck by the contrast of these two maps—the Yamal of the gas fields and the Yamal of the reindeer. For me, this is a door to understanding the maps that guide our lives and the maps that we make from the world we live in.

15

A map is not an abstract notion. Maps are drawn, in physical space, on paper, or are described using stories about real events and people. And, by and large, the physical manifestations of maps, our stories, do reveal a great deal about the nature of our lives, about our past and our future aspirations.

Maps do not reveal reality, they are only *filters*. No map can show the reality that even one person is aware of, let alone the reality perceived by everyone in a society, the collective reality of people with individual priorities. We see things and events, and we experience our daily lives through our respective filters. Part of this filter is derived from our cultural inheritance, and part is more personal, related to the way we were treated as children or reflecting the issues that occupy our daily lives. The filters of office workers are not identical to those of auto mechanics or agricultural workers, even if they have been raised in the same families and have been shaped by the same cultures. The way we travel through our daily lives dictates the shape of our reality.

16

One at a time, the bricks are taken from the barge next to us in the harbour. Khanti women, wearing dresses made of cloth with their traditional geometrical patterns, kerchiefs and boots, old women and young women, lift the heavy bricks from the piles on the barge, walk over the wooden plank joining them to the shore, and lay the bricks carefully onto the piles accumulating there. There are about twenty of these silent workers. No men take part in this exercise. Russian men nonchalantly watch over the activity, occasionally glancing at the women like efficiency experts monitoring an assembly line. At this rate, I estimate, it will take them all day, if they take no rests. The bricks are heavy. The women make no noise. The men smoke and joke with one another.

This scene is not really so unlikely, I try to tell myself, although I can feel that it is not unimportant to me and that I am studying it carefully. The Khanti men have left with the reindeer in April or May, and some of the women have stayed behind. I am not told why, although I ask. I suspect it is because their families need the money.

17

On a later trip to the U.S.S.R., in winter, I remembered that image of two Russias, two worlds living side by side in Pitlyar harbour. The January of 1991 was bitterly cold. Two of our Russian friends had come down to Moscow to meet us, and we proposed to take them out for a meal. The hotel staff would not permit ordinary Russians to enter, so we bribed them with American dollars. Lyudmila and Anna feasted with us. For US$50, about five months' pay for a hotel worker at that time, we were given so much food that the dishes had to be piled three deep over the entire surface of the table. Five soup bowls were filled with black caviar. Fresh vegetables and fruits, the rarest of foods in Moscow that year, vied with delicious dishes of fish and meat for our attention. To the two women, it was horrifying. They stuffed their pockets with food to take back to Siberia. Even the reindeer were dying of cold and hunger that winter, they told us.

18

Pochibekin understood the process of mapmaking intrinsically. He did not clutter up his map, the reality he had forged in the Yamal. He did not indicate, near the site of one major gas field on the Taz River, the lost settlement of Mangazeya. Mangazeya was settled in 1601 by the Pomori sailors coming from the White Sea. This was the first of the European settlements and was only recently rediscovered, but this was not of concern to Pochibekin. Nor were the routes through the tundra where the Pomori dragged their ships overland in order to avoid the northerly sea trip through the ice. He did not show the seasonal habitats of reindeer, or Arctic hare and fox, or of the musk ox reintroduced to nearby Arctic regions from North America in 1945, after what is thought to be a three-thousand-year extinction in Siberia. He did not show the movement of snow and ice, he did not show the tundra plants and their spring flourishing, he did not show the shipping routes down the Ob from the oil fields further south, and he did not indicate the oil spills that were flooding large areas to the south. He did not mark the railroad that was started by Stalin but never completed, its remains crossing the north of Siberia, one section within a short drive of Pochibekin's office. He did not indicate the Gulag camps along Stalin's railroad where the prisoner workers died of cold, overwork, and starvation. He did not feature the communication lines that his own workers have with the rest of the world in order to do their job, to maintain a semblance of family life. He did not even indicate the plans for pipelines or the loading points for future shipments of liquefied gas. The only thing that mattered was the sucking of the earth itself, not the ultimate delivery of fuel for use by people across the Soviet Union. Nor, as we have seen, did he indicate the routes taken by traditional Nientsi and Khanti reindeer herders.

19

In Pitlyar, we are in a pioneer village. The buildings are made of log and the transport is horse and ox-drawn cart. There are chickens and pigs running loose from makeshift corrals made of a few rails of wood. Trees are scarce; wood for fences is a low priority. We are told that logs and boards have been transported here from the south. Judging by the look of the cabins, I would say that must have been many years ago. We meet the head of the local Soviet, Olga Polna. There is a line of small tables set perpendicular to the front of a much larger desk and chair, a layout I had seen in every government office so far, from Moscow to Salekhard. Several telephones of different colours are the main adornment of the desk itself. Olga settles into the large chair; Lenin's picture is behind her. We sit at the tables, in small low chairs, across from one another. If someone were to walk in during one of these official Soviet meetings, he would think that the important person behind the desk was not actually participating, and that we had been given the room for our own get-together. Applying for permission to interview some of the few Khanti people remaining in Pitlyar during the reindeer migration is a formality, but it is taken very seriously. We cannot visit them without the presence of the official head of the local Soviet.

20

We are invited to meet the schoolchildren. The classroom is airy and bright, and the children are very busy with their work. But something is wrong. "Where are the Khanti children?" I am asking the teacher. She looks away from my eyes; Olga answers. We are told there is a policy that allows the children to be taken by helicopter in early June to join their families on the migration routes. It is obvious that there are two communities living side by side in the village, two communities that are somewhat assimilated with each other, but they maintain long-held separate traditions. And for several summer months, the communities occupy a different physical space.

21

Was Pochibekin right? Was his limited point of view an asset in understanding the Yamal? Could we ever understand a map that confronts us with everything from Mangazeya to Stalin's railroad? It would have to be broken down into separate components. But even then, this collection of maps would not be any one person's or any one culture's "reality filter." It could not accurately depict the information to the satisfaction of the many mapmakers coming from many cultures.

22

With Olga guiding us through the muddy streets, we visit a Khanti family, and we spend the rest of the morning learning to set up a *tchum*, the reindeer-skin tent that acts as a nomadic home during the migration season. Inside the *tchum*, with the white light from outside illuminating the rich reds and browns of the skins, I sit a few moments with the old man, Lazarus. He is happy. It has been a long time since he last took the reindeer skins from the storage shed. When we asked for a *tchum* demonstration, there was a long discussion within the family. The skins were reverently carried into the sunlight and unwrapped, laid out on the grass, and inspected, and even sniffed for signs of decay. What is it like for these Khanti people, now that the Russians have chosen to live with them? The muddy streets of the village are a mosaic of Russian and Khanti families. Since the early 1700s, the reindeer have been semi-domesticated, living in corrals during the winter months, fed with grasses and hay stored in the village. Since that time, Russian immigration has also been a part of the lives of these northern people. First the Pomori people came from the White Sea region. Then came further waves. By far the most traumatic was the Gulag relocation during

Stalin's time. And today, the gas and oil fields bring Russian men who come for six-month stints to make three to four times their normal pay. They live in rough conditions and they pay little attention to their new neighbours. But the oil and gas drillers are not living in this village. Here in Pitlyar, the Russian people have established themselves for a variety of reasons. Since the late 1950s, the population of Russians has risen tenfold; now they far outnumber the indigenous groups. They are here for good, it seems. Years ago, the Pomori sailors set this trend for permanent encampments. On arriving, the sailors dismantled their ships in order to provide wood for building homes in the treeless north.

23

Science, as we have come to know it in western culture, is characterized by asking questions. The background of the questioner will dictate the nature of the questions. Personal backgrounds produce variances between questioners, between scientists. And the most significant differences are seen between questioners who have had disparate cultural upbringings.

Questions lead to models of reality, or maps of the world around us. I am searching for the maps that reveal the nature of our civilizations. Ultimately, I am searching for a very precise kind of map—I am a scientist; I use concepts that have been developed by scientists over the history of science, and as a scientist, I am looking for the maps that represent our understanding of the physical and natural world. I believe that these maps will tell me much of what is *wrong* with our collective approach as scientists, because I believe that these maps act as *a priori* templates for our actions, dictating the routes we take, shaping our questions, and predetermining the answers. Knowing the qualities and the biases of the maps of our civilization will tell me a great deal about our goals, our prejudices, and our political hierarchies.

24

Alexander is on the roof of the log cabin where Lazarus and his wife and grown daughter live. He is rifling through the storage bins in an attic space in an attempt to make us believe that he can find good material for our upcoming museum display. He is a scientist too, he seems to be telling us. Our Khanti hosts want to sell to us. It is a rare opportunity to make money, and they do not seem to mind the intrusion. Alexander looks well rested, despite having spent the night drinking vodka and singing on the boat. He's wearing reindeer antlers on his head. "Hey, Jim! Take my picture! Look, look at me!" Jim's Polaroid camera is a hit. It was useful earlier in getting us through a security check in Bykovo airport on the outskirts of Moscow. Not wanting to put our photographic film through the X-ray scanners, we bribed the guards to let us through the back way. Jim took their pictures, complete with automatic weapons at the ready, and left them the photos.

Now Lazarus is looking at me expectantly. "They are willing to take money," Olga assures us in Russian when we hesitate to hand over wads of virtually worthless banknotes. Lazarus accepts our rubles and smiles happily. The whole episode is a little disturbing.

25

Science is governed by the culture of a rather narrow group of people, those educated in European-style universities. We read the same books, we aspire to the same professions, we like the same recreational activities. Today, however, many of us pride ourselves in being the kind of people who investigate other ways of seeing things. So, for example, I acknowledge the need to preserve rain forests and to retain the knowledge embedded in the cultures of the rain-forest people, or for that matter the need to preserve the northern tundra and the knowledge of the people who live there—the knowledge intrinsic to the living systems of the earth itself. A few years ago, I did not pay much attention to the ecological patterns of nature around me, but I have added them to my repertoire. I am confident that my approach is open-minded and inclusive. But am I also aware of my blind spots?

26

Later in the day, we make our way back to the boat, loaded down with useless scruffy fur clothing and a few good pieces of carved wood. Some of the wooden carvings are from Hartegenov, a local wood sculptor, who works in a small room littered with shavings. Most of the Khanti and Nientsi arts and crafts we have seen in the region have been cute—chintzy dolls' faces and fake tools. Hartegenov's are not. He is a living artifact, a find; he was worth coming for. So was *tchum* building worth the trip. It will not be until years later, however, that I will realize what had really been of value for me on this journey.

27

The impending demise of the reindeer and their herders in the gas fields of the Yamal shows that Pochibekin has not learned; he has not listened to the local concerns, and he has not examined the effects of his actions. The development of oil and gas resources is problematic. Perhaps there are solutions that can accommodate the traditional lives of the people of the north. Perhaps not. But one thing is sure, we say, we who consider ourselves enlightened—we must consider all the factors together. Maybe the oil and gas drilling will have to be stopped, at least in certain specified areas, as the Nientsi and Khanti people in the Yamal for Future Generations group have asked, or maybe it is reindeer herding that will end. Whatever the outcome, we inform everyone that we ask for only a complete review of the facts.

But stop. For me, the Yamal story is not an exercise to stimulate thoughts about bringing cultures together in order to provide for a new understanding. This is a noble cause, but it misses the point.

Rather than dwelling on good intentions, what can I really learn from the maps?

The two Yamal maps occupy the same territory on the face of the earth but do not mesh. A new combined map would be as cluttered as the one Pochibekin did *not* make. It might contain everything from Mangazeya to Arctic hares. It would be unusable. More than likely a new map for the colliding cultures would be unrecognizable and unreadable. It would be a map for a future world, a future culture that does not yet exist. And that culture may never exist; it may be a physical and philosophical impossibility.

I say the maps are too far apart. They follow different routes into the discovery of reality.

28

There are no pure ideas that are without a cultural connection. Our robust models of reality appear to us to be reality itself, the only true reality. The powerful filter of western science has led to the belief that there is only one true map. We believe we are unveiling Nature herself.

This is where our problems start. Stephen Hawking verbalizes the thoughts of many of us who feel we are on the pathway to "truth." In his words, we believe we are approaching an understanding of "the mind of God."[1] Many scientists working in the world of science today assume that we are close to understanding everything. Beliefs like this make it difficult, if not impossible, to see the maps or the realities of the other, often older, cultures around us.

29

When we arrive back at the harbour, now late in the day, the Khanti women are still unloading the bricks. The sun is not exactly oppressively beating down here, it is just that in the far north the summer light is constant and bright. I am tired from doing very little. The women are moving slowly, oblivious to their surroundings. With all the log houses I have seen, I wonder what the bricks are for. I never did find out.

30

Just how far have we all really come in this European civilization of ours? We believe that our actions are taking us to the heights of discovery, the ultimate understanding of our "place in the universe," and this understanding rests on a belief in one kind of map. The methods of science have been so successful that we dream of understanding everything. But this means the "things" have to be there to be understood; they must stay in their places waiting to be discovered. This is the true underlying meaning of "finding our place in the universe," the meaning behind finally knowing "the mind of God." How far has this brought us since the days Europeans refer to as the Dark Ages: everything in its place, set in a hierarchy, one above the other, reaching from the lowest minerals to the ultimate level of God?[2] The mere fact that "God" is mentioned speaks less to scientists like Hawking giving a passing nod of respect to their philosophical roots than it does to their still believing in the hierarchy of existence as expounded by the masters of the institutions of the Middle Ages.

31

For me, visiting in 1990, the existence of two worlds in Siberia is made even more evident when I am told that young men and women choose more and more not to travel with their families into the north with the reindeer migration. Young women in particular are leaving the traditional ways of their indigenous families and are seeking education and employment in the larger centres. They see no chance for assimilating one world into the other. They opt for the one with less physical hardship. Lazarus and his small family gave up the annual trek eleven years before our visit. Putting up the *tchum* for us was his first taste since that time, and he looked dreamy and happy sitting in it.

32

The speech by Ulysses in Act 1 of Shakespeare's *Troilus and Cressida* exemplifies the roots of our western civilization. Ulysses reveals a structure that is both a metaphor and a literal manifestation of the cultural map. This mapping has changed little, if at all. We still place everything in an order, where its position in the hierarchy, its "degree," as Ulysses puts it, is an essential part of the structure of our world.

> The heavens themselves, the planets, and this centre,
> Observe degree, priority, and place,
> .   .   .   .   .   .
>   but, when the planets,
> In evil mixture, to disorder wander,
> What plagues and what portents! What mutiny!
> What raging of the sea! Shaking of earth!
> Commotion in the winds!
> .   .   .   .   .   .
> Take but degree away, untune that string,
> And, hark, what discord follows![3]

Ulysses' speech refers to calamities that occur when the map is rearranged. The calamities tear the fabric of reality itself. The seas rage, the earth shakes, and the winds blow. For Ulysses, the mapping of reality is reality itself and must not be tampered with. There cannot be any alternative map. If there were alternatives, then the map could not be reality. It would lose its power over the things and people of the world.

33

Despite the new European methods for corralling reindeer in the winter months, and despite the modern centralized slaughterhouses for reindeer meat production, and especially despite living as neighbours in the numerous pioneer villages, the Russians from the south and the indigenous people of the north live apart. I can see the Yamal through the two maps. There are the gas drilling fields, all that Pochibekin can see when he thinks of the Yamal. And I see the traditional migration routes of the reindeer. Or do I see? The pairs of eyes I need to see these two maps are very different from one another.

34

There can be no alternatives. That is a tenet of mapmakers, who choose one cultural perspective only when describing the surface of the earth. In *hoping* for cross-cultural communication, the European mind reveals its true configuration—we do not even accept the concept of another map. "Communication" between cultures equals assimilation of all cultures into the European mode; that is what we mean by cross-cultural communication. This is most true of the enlightened thinker, because it is that person who speaks volubly about bringing together the peoples of the world to speak on an "equal basis." Yet if we all come together, what will be the common language, and what will be the common, mutually acceptable, map? In this respect, considering the true lack of communication that is likely to be experienced when cultures come together, Pochibekin was right. His needs were simple and he was not burdened with false attempts at cross-cultural communication. The fact that he was also instrumental in the demise of a local civilization attests to both the strength and the singularity of his personal reality as well as to his lack of understanding of the need to accept the possibility of another point of view.

35

As I look over the photographs I took during my visit to Pitlyar in Siberia, I am struck by my own scientific blind spots. What was it that took me so long to learn after my return? One photograph in particular

now haunts me. We visited the sculptor Hartegenov in his home in Pitlyar. In the picture I am holding in my hand, he looks tired and trapped
in his tiny log house. The rooms were barely adequate for his wife,
small daughter, and mother-in-law, but he had taken over one end of
the kitchen as a studio. He had a stack of wood and was in the middle
of a number of carvings, some big and some small. There was no mis-
taking the poverty of his situation, as there was little furniture other
than the benches he had carved himself, and only a wood stove for
heating. The walls had been patched with flattened tins and dirt mixed
with mossy plants.

36

Western science brooks no substitutes. The hierarchy of all things,
living and dead, is absolute. This is particularly noticeable in the study
of living things, which includes the examination of human beings. In
the eighteenth century, the Swedish naturalist Carolus Linnaeus began
a detailed classification of the differences among the many forms of
plants and animals. By classifying animals and plants, he was continuing the European tradition of putting things in their place. During the
century that followed Linnaeus, new evidence revealed changes in the
qualities of the various species of the world and their distribution over
geological time. Georges Cuvier (1769–1832), the French anatomist,
father of comparative anatomy and palaeontology, in looking at the
fossils of extinct animals and plants that appear sequentially in the geological strata, proposed that major catastrophes may have taken place,
after each of which new life forms emerged. The Scottish geologist
Charles Lyell (1797–1875) suggested that instead of mass extermina-
tions, life may be characterized by the continual demise of species followed by the creation of new ones. It should not be supposed that
either scholar felt that there was evidence of the creation of new forms
from some extraordinary act of God. Rather, scientists were slowly
developing the concept of an evolutionary model. Charles Darwin
brought about a new understanding in the nineteenth century when he

developed "evolution" within the parameters of his proposed theory of natural selection. Essentially, he put the engine of evolutionary change into the organism itself. Each living being, acting as an individual, would compete for living space, would be treated well or badly by the local environmental conditions, and would either die, taking its traits with it, or procreate, extending its particular line of characteristics. Slow changes, rather than catastrophic shifts, distinguish Darwin's view of evolution, but the central concept of change over time, central to the theories of Cuvier and Lyell, is preserved in his approach.

For most people who study the history of science in the west, Darwin was responsible for a major revolution in scientific thought.[4] He firmly established the concept of evolution. Some would say that he helped to move scientists away from the tendency to think of organisms as part of a grand design prescribed by a God-like process where there is an end point toward which all change is headed. It is the belief of most scientists today that the theory of evolution, centred as it is on the random natural selection process, dictated by the accumulated actions and histories of many individuals in a population of a given species of animal or plant, precludes the existence of any *a priori* design. After all, if a butterfly that is dark in appearance is better camouflaged from bird predators when it sits on the dark brick of a polluted English mining town, one can hardly connect the success of its progeny to a predetermined plan. English mining towns are unlikely to have been predicted in a grand design for butterflies. To accept the existence of grand design, after all, would mean an equal acceptance that every action of any living thing is predestined, and this does not fit well with the central western philosophical belief in "free will."

37

We had come into town as if from Mars. No one knew we were coming, we stayed only a short time, and we had big demands. We asked Hartegenov if he would be willing to come to Toronto to help us with our display on the Yamal region of northern Siberia. He declined at first, saying that his little daughter would miss him if he were gone for too long. We listened to his concerns and told him to think about it.

38

Darwin was one of the boys. He went to the same schools, read the same books, and he had the same aspirations as generations of scientific and philosophical scholars before him. And Darwin took it upon *himself* to describe his theories as "revolutionary." In the conclusion to *The Origin of Species*, he states:

> When the views advanced by me in this volume, and by Mr. Wallace, or when analogous views on the origin of species are generally admitted, we can dimly foresee that there will be a considerable revolution in natural history.[5]

Darwin's acceptance of the mantle of revolutionary was in keeping with his role as a major player in the science establishment. It was an expected reward for his labours of genius, however humbly enunciated by Darwin himself, and however much he includes the works of others such as his contemporary, the Welsh naturalist Alfred Wallace. He was a part of an elite and therefore perfectly suited for the role of "leader" in science. But his scientific views were not particularly unorthodox or revolutionary, since science was and is characterized by a pursuit of ever more defining descriptions of the nature of things. Scientists have developed a tendency to label new theories, along with their creators, as "revolutionary." However, often neither the theories nor their authors are especially revolutionary.

39

I had arrived in Siberia on a scientific mission, bearing the full weight of the European scientific attitude. I was trying to be completely objective and removed from strictly human concerns. As content co-ordinator and curator for the museum exhibition, I had the responsibility of assessing the various components we were "collecting," and I felt that Hartegenov's presence was essential. And despite what we told him, I did not want him to help us to create the display—I wanted him to be the display itself. He is a Khanti sculptor and therefore could represent the people we were focusing on in the exhibition, and his work is comparable to much of the best I have seen from the native people of our north. Like the sculpture of Canada's Inuit, his work depicts the lives of the northern people, a culture that is rapidly disappearing. But did I really understand what I was doing?

40

Darwin could expect to be taken seriously as a leader of science. His new theories were a grand synthesis of concepts that had been developing over the two centuries preceding his work. But did they deviate from the cultural map of western thought? I would suggest that to be truly revolutionary, a theory would have to move away from the primary cultural map of the time. Darwin himself, as a scholar, showed little deviation from the normal trajectory of a career in science. He aspired to his expected station in life and did what is expected of scientists—he proposed a new hypothesis. His "degree," as Ulysses would put it, is not in jeopardy. His theory of evolution, on the other hand, does introduce an apparent shift away from the expected order of things. Or does it? Certainly, the theory of the evolution of one species to another could be thought of as challenging the prescribed order of things. However, it could also be seen as simply another take on the traditional viewpoint. In Darwin's theory, there is no dissolving of the concept of separate species, each with a place in the world. The fact that some species disappear and new ones appear as the physical situation changes does not radically alter the prevailing image of the world, no matter what mechanism is chosen. The new world view, after Darwin, fits in nicely with the map that is fixed in the mind of the traditional educated European: there are separate species, each with its place in the cosmos, a cosmos that is based on a hierarchy, rising from the lowliest slime to the European human at the top.[6]

41

I collected him. In the exhibition, staged the following year in Toronto, Hartegenov did appear. He carved his wood for the education and entertainment of the curious public. He spoke no English and therefore was in a world of his own, dutifully creating his native Siberian pieces. I paid for his time, but could I justify the act? He had left his small daughter behind, and he came for the money.

42

The hierarchy is preserved. The ordered positions held by all living things, some creatures always superior to others, are inherent in the design of the theory of evolution. Even considering the randomness of natural selection, animals and plants are conceived by scientists and the rest of us as being arranged in order of degree, the simplest leading to the most complex. Thus, the more recent developments in animal-hood or planthood are not seen as simply random mutations well adapted to their environments. The creatures that have appeared most recently on earth are seen as *advances* in design. The old concept of everything in its place is preserved, as is the medieval notion of a ladder of importance or value in the order of things, from the lowliest to the highest. This concept is accepted easily by us all, including scientists, because it fits the map within which we work and think. And because it fits so well, we do not even notice our acceptance of it. This blindness is evident even at the elevated level of natural philosophy, where, we would hope, the clearest thinking on the nature of things should take place.

43

Darwin's view of the natural order, and the superiority of one living thing to another, comes out most clearly in his descriptions of the nature of humans. In *The Descent of Man and Selection in Relation to Sex*, his position is revealed in this statement about women:

> Woman seems to differ from man in mental disposition, chiefly in her greater tenderness and less selfishness. . . . It is generally admitted that with woman the powers of intuition, of rapid perception, and perhaps of imitation, are more strongly marked than in man: but some, at least, of these faculties are characteristic of the lower races, and therefore of a past and lower state of civilisation.[7]

The belief in the order of all things, including human "races" as they ascend, in degrees, from animals, was a part of the world in Darwin's time. Charles Lyell, a compatriot of Darwin's, along with other contemporary scientists, like the biologist Thomas Huxley, championed his theories:

> The difference of brain is so great between the European & the Bushman as to show in this, as well as in mental capacity, a wide range. The difference in the brain of a Bushman & a Gorilla is, says Prof. Huxley, less than between an Orang & a Lemur.[8]

I would have to ask, how far have we come from these ideas? We still believe in putting things in their place, and honour the degree or station of every living thing and every human being. If this is not so, why do we preach the superiority of western methods in science and technology, and why are most of the powerful positions in the world of science and technology held by people of European descent?

As we examine the nature of science, will we achieve an understanding of the natural world, or will we merely reach another form of understanding, an understanding of *human* ideas in the *human* world? Will the natural world remain hidden under the layer of human concerns and human expectations that characterizes the activities of our scientists? Will we begin to see that we are mapping the world, modelling it in a way that we can understand and decipher, a mapping shaped by humankind, a distortion that reveals our biases, a distortion that is nevertheless comfortable and familiar to us? And will we ever consider this map to be only one way of seeing things? Will we recognize our limitations and acknowledge the existence of other points of view? Or will we remain deluded and think we understand reality through our science, unbiased and unaffected by human concerns and prejudice?

44

What I learned in Siberia was this: no idea, not even a scientific idea or concept, can be considered to be derived from pure reason. My lofty goal of using Hartegenov to bring attention to the issues of modern industrial life as they impinge on the lives of traditional peoples did not come without subjective interpretations. My "collection" of Hartegenov occluded the very message I had hoped to deliver. But my map did not coincide with Hartegenov's, and I did not understand what I had done. I believed then that my scientific observations and collections in Siberia had no immediate moral value in themselves. I thought that the moral framework for my exhibit lay in the *delivery*. I thought the people who would come to see the exhibition would be compelled to reflect on the sad state of affairs today. I was wrong. I could not divorce the delivery of the exhibition in Toronto from the collection process that preceded it in Siberia. All ideas and all actions have a moral value. When we stay within our own culture this is true, and it is doubly true when we cross cultural boundaries. I had crossed the boundary between cultural maps, and I was not even aware of it. I could not see that I was transporting Hartegenov from his map into mine, where he was placed on a low rung in the human hierarchy, where he was a display for an exhibition. I could not see that because I did not recognize the fact that there are different models of reality, different maps for different cultures. I had assumed that there could be dialogue between two cultures, on a level playing field. I did not realize that I had assimilated Hartegenov and that I had left him with no control. And ultimately, it did not matter that the aim of the exhibition was a lofty criticism of the modern developments in the north.

45

This is what happened: I was so affected by my visit to the Khanti people that I wanted to bring back a living piece of it. But was Hartegenov's presence in Toronto really giving us a viable piece of Siberian life? During the time that he was here, it became increasingly difficult for me to enter the exhibition hall that housed the displays on Siberia. He would not talk, but he came dutifully each day to be on public view. He looked worse than when we met him that day in Pitlyar. I was relieved when it was time for him to return to the Soviet Union. We had not communicated at all during his stay. In my opinion today, our cultural maps were so far apart as to yield only the barest minimum of possible contact. For me, at least, bringing Hartegenov to Toronto did not add life to the display. It added an atmosphere of death.

46

In 1904, the anthropology department of the St. Louis World's Fair put on display an African man known as Ota Benga, as a representative of primitive humankind.[9] People came to see him as if he were an animal in a zoo. He was one of many others representing the peoples of the world, including Inuit, Zulus, Ainu, and native people from South and North America. About the same time, Robert Peary, the Arctic explorer, brought six Inuit to New York City to be studied by scientists at the American Museum of Natural History. They were kept in the basement of the museum, where they drew large crowds who attempted to see them through a grating above a basement window. Only one of them survived to return to his native Greenland.

47

The moral dilemma I experienced during the exhibition has been pivotal. In going to Siberia, I used a cultural mindset born of western science. I saw situations that were inequitable on a human level. I sought to bring the elements together so that people could assess the plight of the native people of Siberia in the modern industrial context. In so doing, I was drawing the maps, superimposing them and analyzing their interrelationships. As the mapmaker, I was in control of the final outcome, and my actions in curating the exhibition dictated the interpretations I wanted to make. I felt superior to the mapmakers of the gas fields of Siberia who left out so much local history and culture. But in the end, I was as blind as Pochibekin.

48

Has my Yamal map changed?

I imagine going back to Pitlyar. I am taking the same boat up the Ob. The river is still polluted. There are many foreign oil and gas ventures in the region. The reindeer are suffering from the lack of tundra range in the summer. The Khanti people have less and less to do with their time. In Pitlyar harbour, women continue to unload barges in the Arctic sun. Sasha told Fiona that Alexander is becoming an entrepreneur. Alexander is a survivor. In 1990, he was the local representative to the meetings of the Supreme Soviet in Moscow, and now he is one of their major capitalists. Alexander wants to turn the boat rides up the Ob into part of his tourism empire. I can also recommend the beaches.

Hartegenov is on display in his own village now. He is one of the attractions for foreign visitors. His home is still cold in the winter, but there is talk of bringing in satellite TV.

CHAPTER TWO

NORTHERN
ONTARIO

Something really does happen to people who go to
the north—they become . . . in effect, philosophers.

– GLENN GOULD, on "The Idea of North"

49

WHAT IS A TELEOLOGICAL EXPLA-
NATION? It is one that answers the
question "why?" Teleology is the
study of why, derived from the fourth of Aristotle's original classification of the four causes: 1. What is something made of? 2. Where does
something exist in space—what is its form? 3. What is the origin of
something, or from whence did it come? 4. Why is it here—or what
is its purpose?[1] The fourth cause, the "final cause," is the source of
much mistaken discussion on the nature of living things on the earth.
When we ask, "Why is the neck of a giraffe long?" we are making
the assumption that there has been a determination by a designer to
develop this long neck, with an ultimate purpose in mind. Scientists
easily dismiss the existence of a designer because they see this as an
invitation to religious believers. Religion has no place in science. This
is virtually a law of modern science. So, no grand designer, please, we

say. However, I believe that the processes we accept in modern science have within them a hidden final cause, a hidden purpose or destiny that we cling to, despite our apparent rejection of a grand design. The landscape or environment is there; it lies in wait like a grand template, and we perceive that the giraffe grows into it, fitting in with the formal design of the world, the hierarchy of living things. Random steps may take it there, but the landscape is waiting to receive successful applicants in the evolution of life.

As I contemplate the control that the perceived grand design has over my life, I think of the journeys I have taken. I know that at times I live as though the map had been laid out for me to follow. And then sometimes the opposite is true. There are times when I know that I am making the map in front of me one step at a time.

50

The hat is perfect. Without it, the left side of my face would have been frozen by now. The wind is coming from the north and is carrying tiny ice pellets. The hat has a wide brim and its canvas material acts as the right sort of soft shield. It has a cord to keep it on my head. I have adjusted the hat so that it faces the wind. I haven't been able to change its position since the wind whipped up, because I have had to paddle steadily, with no resting between strokes. Each and every time I must use a J-stroke, driving the canoe forward and then correcting the trajectory. The waves are high. I must hold the canoe at 45 degrees off the wind direction. This allows me to push the bow of the canoe through the waves and avoid being totally broadsided. The waves rock me dangerously as a result of the angle of my course, but going straight on is a greater risk. I know that if I try to face the wind and the waves head-on, the canoe may shift ever so slightly and I will be off in another direction, having swung around in one motion. I guide the canoe in a slow arc around the head of the lake to the opening of the river. It is a long project. The water is very cold, and my muscles are aching.

51

Natural selection provides apparent answers to the teleological quandary, but for me the answers are not completely satisfactory.

To illustrate Darwin's model of evolution, let's imagine we have an island where several species of frogs live. One type lays its eggs in the shallow water of a quiet pond. Another stays in the trees, putting droplets of sticky fluid on the underside of leaves in the spring. There is a frog that carries its eggs on its back, keeping them moist and safe until they are ready to start living on their own as tiny froglets. And there is one frog that holds the eggs and the tadpoles in its mouth. How did these various frogs come to be? According to the concept of adaptation to the environment, there was a selection of the traits that are successful. How does this occur?

52

I reach the end of the lake and stop for a while on the beach at the mouth of a river. I think for a minute that the wind has died down. But it takes very little wind to make a lake passage nearly impossible for a solo canoeist. The waves have white tops, and the ice pellets continue to rain down. It has taken me over an hour to cross the lake, and I have three hours ahead of me on the river. Only then will I be able to make camp on one of the near islands in the next lake. In between, along the riverbank there is swampland and dense forest. I estimate four hours to sundown. I would have started earlier, but after packing in the morning, I took five hours to drive up from Toronto, then another two hours to settle things with the canoe outfitters. Nevertheless, I think I should have tried to set off earlier. The environment is exerting its selective pressure on me; the going is harder than I had anticipated.

53

To begin with, there was one type of frog. Let's say that it is the one that lives in a pond and lays eggs in the water. Frogs are not all identical to one another; they vary slightly from generation to generation, depending on their parentage. And over a long time period, small mutations occur, and more extreme variations to the basic frog appear. New types of frogs have to compete for space in the pond with the old frogs. The newer ones may be successful, perhaps because they mature more quickly and are therefore less likely to be eaten by passing fish. Or they may be less successful, possibly because they are brightly coloured and easily found by wading birds. On our imaginary island, we will assume that the old frogs do not maintain their sovereignty over the pond. The new frogs with the shorter egg stage, the shorter maturation time, are more successful breeders, so they dominate the space available and force the old frogs and the other hopefuls into extinction. For now, the new frogs are the best adapted to the local environment.

54

This is fishing season, late May. I watch as a motorboat starts across the water toward me. It will take the three fishermen about ten minutes to complete the same crossing, and they will be in their camp within the hour. Three other fishing parties passed me before on the lake; fishermen are very "advanced" life forms, it would seem. I am one of very few canoes in the area, but, I tell myself, I should find no trouble isolating myself from the noise and the traffic.

55

Some new frogs are more radical. One type has sticky footpads, which are useful when the frogs grapple for a good position during mating.

The sticky feet also allow them to climb up trees by the shore.

The island environment begins to change. The pond starts to dry up. There is only room for some of the pond frogs to lay eggs. The others die out. But the radical new frogs have special abilities that work well under the drought conditions. As they breed in their isolated population away from the pond, the formerly rare traits become common characteristics. Other populations also begin to appear under these new, drier conditions. While the tree frogs lay their eggs in puddles of dew, other frogs carry their eggs in their wet mouths. Still others move into a nearby stream and carry their young under the skin of their backs until they can handle the swift waters themselves. These are not clever stratagems; they are chance traits that a few of the frogs had in their repertoires. Slight variations in the genetic backgrounds are brought to light under new extreme environmental conditions. Natural selection has allowed these few frogs to continue while others die out. Isolation and mating within their separate groups over countless generations leads to the different frog *populations* living as separate *species*.

56

The fishermen have stopped their motor and are now squatting on the beach. They have a detailed topographical map of the river and surrounding lakes laid out in front of them. "It's over to the left—that's where the river runs, eh!"

His partner disagrees. "Jeez, I been here last year and you weren't. Map or no map, we're gonna go to the right."

I can't talk to these people, although I grew up in a town where I spoke their language. I feel nervous and hope they will ignore me. For the first time on the trip, I am afraid. I'm alone, surrounded by people who think someone in a canoe is strange. I do know that the guy reading the map is correct. They should go left, but I really don't care. By the time they realize their mistake and turn back toward the correct channel, I will have only gone a short distance myself. Let them suffer a little. Meanwhile, I fiddle with my gear, trying to look as if I can't hear them.

57

The frogs were not "designed" to fit the environment. They did not acquire traits for a final purpose. Under the concept of natural selection in the evolution of a species, the frog carrying the eggs in its mouth did not develop a large mouth so that it could carry the eggs in the event of some future drought. There was no designer that decided these things. The physical trait is random, and it came in handy for the frog when a drought did come. There are usually some members of a population with traits that prove useful in a changing environment. If they can breed under the new conditions, a new population begins, one distinguished by this formerly rare physical characteristic.

The teleological argument would have it that the end result, success as a mouth-breeder, was the goal to which the mouth-breeding frog aspired. The problem with this argument is that it requires the frog to predict its own future. Natural selection in the tradition of Darwin provides an alternative to this designer concept. But there is another form of teleology, more subtle, a teleological trap that even Darwinian natural selection cannot avoid. The belief in a natural environment that has habitats lying in wait, environments waiting to "adapt" animals and plants, is also teleological.

58

I ease into the river. It is not fast moving. I can guide myself fairly well. It winds in big loops through wet areas of bulrushes and arrowroot. A couple of years before this canoe trip, when I was taking the boat ride up the Ob in Siberia, that river was an ocean of waves and wind. Coming back from Pitlyar, we had to anchor midstream to weather ten-foot swells. It took two hours before we could continue. But this river in the north woods of Ontario is small and winding and the bulrushes on the swampy banks stop all wind. I am not tossed on the waves at the whim of the weather and the terrain as I was on the Ob. The river is so narrow that I can immediately sense the effects it has had on the land around me, and the canoe, in turn, has an effect on the river. In the narrow passageway of my route, the canoe shapes the water into a trough ahead of me, creating a watery channel that guides me around the bends.

59

The believer in natural selection expounds on the concept of adaptation. Under the new drought condition on our island of frogs, variations of frog adapt into the drier environment. They find their place in the new setting. There may be no master designer, working from final causes, involved in the direct making of the various frog types, but there is the natural setting lying in wait. For the believer in Darwin's natural selection, the landscape is a patient template. From this adaptationist point of view, certain physical conditions of the earth accept or reject organisms that seek to prosper within their boundaries—a dry island acts as a *moulder* of the population of frogs, accepting as successful applicants those with traits that permit them to raise their young in droplets of fluid under leaves or in the sticky gelatin on their backs or in the moist confines of their mouths. In the final analysis, I consider this model of life to be as teleological as a belief in a grand designer.

A dry island is seen as an environment that leads to predictable organismic change. The *static* environment acts as a design tool. Believers in creationism think of God's first actions as being the final determinant of all forms on earth. Believers in adaptationism imagine that nature moulds the shape of animals and plants over evolutionary time. Both creationism and adaptationism are teleological. The conditions of a static world, with a place for things to be, or to potentially aspire to, typify both approaches.

60

When you are sitting in a canoe alone, you sit in the bow seat, turned around to face the stern. Normally, there are two people, and the one in the stern finds it easier to steer. Being close to the back end of the canoe means every stroke of the paddle changes the direction. A stroke straight down the left side swings you off to the right. A J-stroke moves you to the left. The person in the bow seat is closer to the midpoint of the canoe, where the paddle strokes have less effect on direction. Paddling alone, sitting the "wrong" way around in the bow seat, I am even closer to the centre of the canoe than the bow person in a two-person team. Guiding the canoe is very difficult in this position, so I rely on a sort of trick. The bottom of the canoe is relatively flat, with a keel. The sides join the bottom in a very abrupt curve. If I lean the canoe over a little on its side, I can use the curve of the side as a kind of secondary keel. Going around bends in the narrow river then becomes a matter of pushing forward as fast as possible, forming a channel with the second "keel." The rest of the canoe follows the preformed channel for the duration of the stroke. In effect, the canoe is shaping the river for a brief period of time. The river itself curves first to the right and then to the left, again and again. The canoe leans over to one side during the entire course of my run down one section of the river, so I cannot change my paddle from side to side at each bend. I use the side of the canoe in different ways, depending on the slant of the turn. The river is very receptive to being shaped by my efforts, and I begin to make some headway.

The motorboat returns from behind, passing me with a slow wash that destroys my swooshing channel formation. I kneel toward the centre to avoid shipping water. "G'afternoon," I say, but they look at me, unhearing. One touches his peaked cap in grumpy greeting. The sound has disturbed the red-winged blackbirds that fly up from the rushes. I wonder if these fishermen ever see the blackbirds or even the huge herons that park at many of the bends in the river, standing and waiting for passing fish or frogs.

61

This is 1992. Perhaps I have been inspired to be an adventurer because of travelling with Sasha in the Soviet Union in 1990. Sasha swam with us in the freezing Ob, but it was nothing for him; he floated on his back and spurted water for our entertainment. Sasha had spent years as an Arctic explorer, searching for lost trails of people like Franklin and writing books about his travels. "We only did not sleep all at once because we are waiting many times on ice beers," he said to me. It took a while to realize he was not talking about drinking beer. Every day was spent avoiding polar bears on the barren ice, and one person had to be awake at all times, standing guard with a gun. But then Sasha's life in Moscow was not so peaceful, either. I ate with his family one evening in winter. He writes in a corner of the living room, his little son watching videos next to him. They have one and a half bedrooms. This is very good by Moscow standards. What a change from a Moscow apartment to the vastness of the Arctic.

I met many of the explorers from his group. One of them, Dmitri, led the Russian half of a joint Canadian-Russian expedition set up to walk across the pole in 1988. Dmitri is a proud man who wants to prove he is the meanest and toughest person alive. When he came to Toronto in September of 1991, just after the tanks had rolled into Moscow, he sported a tank-tread mark down the entire left side of his face. "Barricades!" he said with a grin. He is like one of the fishermen, surly and rough, but then I look at my gear in the canoe. I have a wooden paddle, a wooden food box filled with bread, packaged meat, fruit, and dried ready-to-make meals. The motorboat people have a freezer box filled with, I know, steaks and pork chops and beans and bacon. They have Gore-Tex rainwear. Once, when my wife, Danielle, and I were travelling this way in spring many years earlier, we peeked into one of their camps. They had beer, wonderful food, and even a battery-operated TV. I have no Gore-Tex; I wear five layers of cotton and wool, with a rubber poncho on top. Dmitri and his Russian teammates shunned the Canadians' special artificial-fabric parkas on their trek over the pole, and they gave up on the carbon-fibre skis. The Russians used wooden skis, and they ate only fatty Russian foods. The fishermen could never exist if they had to live like Russians. They are only trying to look rough and tough, like a Dmitri. I am more like Dmitri than he is like these fishermen.

62

In the early 1980s, I worked on a model for the embryonic development of living things. I did it in conjunction with Ellie Larsen, a geneticist who studies the early life stages of fruit flies. Our model attempted to explain the nature of developmental change with respect to the interaction of genes within their limited miniature world. We saw development as a river that flows down through a landscape, creating its own channel. The river curves and loops and eddies on the banks and brings down rocks to form rapids. The landscape is not static. In other words, it is a dynamic player responding to an organism's developmental and genetic changes. This is a model for the development of an animal or plant over a single lifetime, but it can just as easily be applied to the evolution of a species. The constant play between organism and environment means that there is no static environment waiting to act as a template to shape evolution. This way of seeing things is not teleological. It is an alternative to a strict Darwinian model.

Sometimes, models such as the one Ellie and I worked on are described as "dialectical." The Russians of the 1990s are dialectical, no matter how much they protest against communism. After all, they have had decades living with the concept of dialectical materialism as defined by Marx and Lenin. I began to understand them as we worked together. I went to Moscow on my own in January 1991, staying in the Communist Party residences on Leningradski Prospekt—one of the spokes of road that radiate out from Moscow to all parts of the Soviet Union. This one goes in a straight line all the way to Leningrad. I had a narrow bed, a desk, a lamp, and a radio with three buttons for stations pre-selected for me by the Party. Every evening there was a broadcast from Radio Moscow in English. As I listened late one night, I was brought tea. *"Chay, tovarish?"* said the woman who wheeled the samovar to my door at midnight. In the morning and before bed, I met in the cafeteria with people from Cuba, Angola, and China. The revolution in all its ascetic and uplifting glory was here.

63

A river shapes its banks. As it slips around a bend, the water on the inside curve moves more slowly than the water pushing against the outside curve. Surface water flowing more quickly on the outside curve turns under and creates a secondary current. The constant action of the river water shapes the bank. Over the years, the erosion of the bank on the outside curve increases and increases, and the deviation in the river's course becomes very pronounced. Ellie and I used the river's actions as an illustration of what we think is happening to an organism developing as an embryo. The growth in a budding chicken embryo wing, for example, will create a small micro-environmental zone. The micro-environment in turn will affect all activities of the cells and tissues in the area. The action is reciprocal: the growing tissue creates an environment, and in response, the newly formed micro-environment affects the subsequent growth in the limb bud, and on and on, a constant contrapuntal relationship. It is very much like a river that is initially guided into a course to the sea by the surrounding land formations, but that, in turn, shapes the land around it as it flows over the years.

64

Did we become Russian while visiting, and did that way of thinking stick a little? Or were we already predisposed to it? Once, while sitting in our bus, the one loaned to us by Pochibekin, just outside the hotel in Salekhard, Fiona said that Sasha had been by. I asked her, "What did he say? Are we going to stay here tonight or are we moving on?"

"He said we are waiting any minutes," she told me in a flat voice. She had lost all ability to find our constant frustrations funny. We were no longer in control of our environment. We did not know what was coming next. We did not see the aerial view of the map of our journey through Siberia, a map marked with a beginning and an end point. We submitted to the flow; "any minutes" was a constant explanation.

65

I paddle into the centre of the river at each bend, trying to avoid the shoreline on either side. The slow inner curve will drag me to almost a stop, and the water at the outer part of the turn is too fast—it will swing the back of my canoe around.[2] On some outer turns, the water is so swift that it will carry me into a water current that turns under at the shore, directing me head-on into the bank. In a larger river I would be swamped, caught in a whirlpool of colliding currents.

The herons sit at the slow inner sections of each curve, waiting for the helical currents at the river's edges to carry fish and other small prey their way. Owing to my caution, I steer close to the inner sections of the river's curves, where I find myself within a foot or two of one of the silently standing herons, both of us idling in the doldrums. With effort, I pull heavily on the paddle, launching myself back into the flow.

66

Didn't these people know that it was all over, that the regime that started with Lenin was coming to a close? Outside, people were starving in the streets; inside, we had chicken to eat and there was even beer. Because it was stored outdoors, the beer was frozen, but it was refreshing. I drank a quart bottle on an empty stomach, sitting next to five Cubans who were drinking a lot more than I was. Finishing, I deciphered the label—14 per cent alcohol content. I could not walk; I stood up and almost fell onto the table. The Cubans laughed and then ignored me.

67

In a dialectical landscape, the end is not known because there is no predetermined map. The map is always changing in response to the actions of the travellers. There are local goals, related only to the actions of the moment. The global political changes being predicted by the American media in 1991 were not necessarily going to happen. The dynamics between the organism and its environment could lead to a number of outcomes. Going out one evening to find western news, I travelled by taxi to a foreign hotel. CNN was reporting the Gulf War. The western view was that everything would come out as predicted; the map was reliable and we were all just players on a stage. What a contrast to my Radio Moscow reports later in the evening in my residence room. The Gulf War reports were not nearly as reassuring there.

68

In the 1930s and '40s, the Scottish embryologist C. H. Waddington described the embryonic development of an organism as a landscape of channels, like riverbeds, flowing downhill.[3] If you imagine a ball being set randomly at the top, you can mentally follow it, choosing first one channel and then another, finding the easiest route down the hill. Any change to the path of the ball requires a serious perturbation of its progress. Ellie and I perceived the landscape as having channels as well, but we filled it with active stuff, like water, dynamic fluid that changes the channel as it moves down.

There are other, more favoured, models for development. On the whole, scientists prefer to believe that shape is predetermined by, and is decipherable from, the genetic makeup of an animal or plant. But there is the alternative that Ellie and I championed: if a change is made to the environment, the genes will be influenced by this and their actions will have an effect that is different from what would have happened if the landscape had remained static. And the changes to the environment come about from a number of sources—including the growth of the organism itself. In other words, genetic effects are not particularly predictable; the genetic component is "simple-minded," dependent on local conditions, and is not a "blueprint" for the shape of an animal or plant.[4]

69

The canoe has become stuck on a beaver dam that straddles the entire width of the river. The dam was broken through during the rush of water after the recent spring thaw, but the remaining mat of woven sticks has affected the course of the river, and most of the water is spilling through the beds of rushes to either side of me. "Damn!" I define the problem. I get out into the freezing water and heave the canoe over. My leather boots fill with water, but the multiple layers of socks soon become a nice covering of warm fluid, a kind of primitive wetsuit effect.

70

At a meeting of scientists and students in Toronto in the early 1980s, I heard a talk by James Watson, director of the Woodshole Laboratories in Massachusetts for years, and until recently head of the Human Genome Project.[5] Back in the eighties, he was studying proteins. He estimated that there were approximately two thousand major proteins that typify the average cell. "Find them and get their coding down," I remember he said, "and you will know how a cell works!" Could this be the same Watson who solved the double helix riddle of DNA and who received a Nobel Prize for the work along with Francis Crick? How absurd, I found myself saying at the time.

Watson and others believe that the channels in the landscape are preset. Oh, you can change course, but the change will be to another preformed channel. Even more extreme, they believe that the proteins just have to be named to produce a picture of living systems; the trees just have to be labelled and categorized and you will have a picture of the forest. Are the interrelationships of the trees to each other, and their relationships with the animals and the insects and the sunlight and the flowering meadows not important? What about the effects of the roots growing into the earth and the trees' branches shading the nearby landscape?

In the twentieth century, we are governed by "grind and find" scientists. Students of nature grind up living material and search for biochemicals—proteins, genes. They theorize that the presence of a certain protein or gene will tell them all. But surely it depends on *where* these items occur in the internal environment of an organism. Grind and find shows no concern for the intimate dialectical relationship that exists between the proteins, genes, and the other components of the dynamic, constantly changing microenvironment inside an animal or plant.

71

As I paddle downstream, I imagine a landscape where the river has little or no effect on the banks, a pure channel that would satisfy the average scientist. Cement. A cement canal that guides the waters down smooth-faced troughs toward a final destination. What if they fixed up this river like that? In this natural river, there are so many bends that it is hard to navigate at times. A cement channel would allow me to find my way and would stop the river from pushing the bends out farther and farther. Some of the bends extend so far that ultimately the river folds itself double and cuts off the loop. These orphaned loops can be connected to the main river channel for a long time and can pose a navigational hazard for someone unfamiliar with the region. The loops are constantly forming and being cut off in this river. They cannot be found on any map; no mapmaker could keep up with them. And they are extensive. "Which way now?" my sons and I said to one another back in 1987, when we were confronted with an unexpected fork along the same river. We were confident, having read the first one correctly, the one the fishermen misread on my 1992 journey. But we spent an hour travelling through miserable bug-infested swamp, only to find ourselves back where we started.

72

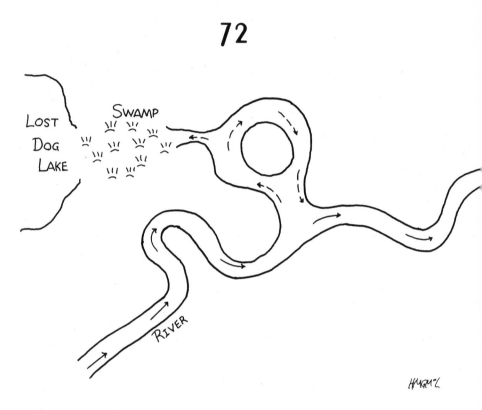

The river is a dynamic living organism. It is affected by the topology of the terrain through which it flows, but, in turn, the river also has an effect on the riverbed. Over countless years, the loops of the river shift the banks, constantly changing their position. As a loop becomes more and more pronounced, for example, a river can pinch off a section of its length. My sons and I encountered just such a configuration. An aerial viewpoint would show something like the drawing I have made here—a loop cut off from the main flow of the river—but still connected to the river—leading to a dead end (in this case, taking us to a marshland that is sometimes navigable and sometimes not).

When you are inside the river system itself, it is not so easy to discern the loop that is being cut off from the main channel of the river.

The map of the orphaned loop shows that the paddler is confronted with three channels, and only one can be the right one. The main channel is the one with the most flow, but in late summer, when we were there, the flow differences between the three channels are almost indiscernible. We chose the left-side channel and it was the wrong one. We spent an hour travelling around the loop and into Lost Dog Lake. Coming back, we ran the risk of becoming even more lost—we could mistakenly have gone down another wrong channel, perhaps going back down the same incorrect left-side channel we had tried the hour before or even going back *up* the river (all bends of a river look the same in that marshy environment). In a canoe, however, travelling back up the wrong way in the main stream of a river is quite detectable. Travellers in a motorboat, who could not so easily detect the gentle current of the late-summer river, would not necessarily be so lucky, because it is possible to travel around a loop and become totally disoriented. The experience is an illustration of the intimate relationship between an organism and the landscape. In this case, the organism is the river.

73

Scientists have spent considerable time apparently moving away from the philosophical pitfalls of teleology, only to find themselves back where they started. Somehow the grand design, the ultimate purpose to it all, is a constant requirement of those who seek to decipher the universe.

Einstein once said that he did not like quantum mechanics because the theory predicted that the nature of an object could be affected by the "decisions" or the experiences of another distant object. This was "spooky." "I cannot seriously believe in [the quantum theory] because it cannot be reconciled with the idea that physics should represent a reality in time and space, free from spooky actions at a distance."[6] Einstein did not believe that God "played dice" with the universe. What did he want to believe? Certainly there is a transformation of the image of reality in his relativity theory. However, it is a transformation of the shape of the universe only. Everything is still in its place, governed by contiguous relationships, connected in a fabric of time and space. This "fabric" of reality can be stretched and distorted by reference frames that differ in relative velocities, but they maintain an order and a position relative one to another. Like Darwinism, Einstein's relativity theory was a great leap out of the clockwork world of the preceding centuries. But in the Einsteinian universe, there is still the need to define reality in terms of the outcomes, the final design; the particles that make up the universe can be defined by their histories. Their trajectories can be followed backward in time and presumably all their actions can be calculated, although that calculation is very complicated. Despite the bold philosophical steps taken by Darwin, Einstein, and others over the past 150 years, we are left with a universe that is not much different from that described by René Descartes in the seventeenth century, a universe where all things, including thoughts, are seen as mechanistic devices.

74

There is a roar ahead of me. I manoeuvre the canoe to the side of the river, weary even with this effort because I am slowly becoming aware that the sun is moving into late afternoon and I haven't even made it to the first portage. Another disruption of my watery pathway, navigated with such an expense of energy, I do not need.

The noise is the same fishermen who have passed me twice before, but this time they are coming from the other direction. What is going on? They stop when they come alongside me. "Pardon me," the older one of the pair stammers, "didn't we see you before?"

"Yes," I reply.

"Well, where exactly are you going, if you're coming back, eh?" He says this with uncertainty, trying not to admit his own confusion but clearly wanting help. They had gone into one of the loops and returned going the wrong way, back up the river. A canoeist never makes this mistake, as each paddle stroke is an effort, revealing the direction of the river's flow. They must have gone down the same dead end to Lost Dog Lake that I took with my sons a few years back. I wonder how they could have dragged the heavy motorboat, which has a much deeper draft in the water, over the shallow swamp that makes up most of that detour. We had had trouble with a canoe, but then I remember that it is early springtime and the water levels are very high, and the dead-end routes are even more numerous. My sons and I had gone in to Lost Dog Lake during late summer when the river level was quite low.

75

I am reminded of a trip I took by train from Stavanger, Norway, to Oslo in 1995.

The journey is an overnight one. I stand in the corridor outside my sleeping compartment watching the sun go down and the landscape passing into the distance to my left. After a sleep of eight hours, I awaken and begin to prepare for the coming day. I crawl out of bed and decide to keep the curtains closed for a little while. I am standing at the tiny sink in my compartment, shaving, when I hear the train staff banging on the doors and opening them to shout at the passengers to prepare for arrival in Oslo in one hour's time. I am gratified that I have thought to lock the door with the dead bolt, since I am stark naked. A few seconds later, the door is opened wide by a porter who is shouting orders at me in Norwegian, the lock obviously offering no resistance to her key. As amazed and somewhat traumatized as I am by this unexpected intrusion, I find myself gazing in amazement past the porter at the landscape outside the corridor window behind her. It is not going from right to left as I had imagined it all night in my dreams; it is now going from left to right. I panic for a moment, wanting to ask the porter for help in orientation. Under the circumstances, I say nothing and she bangs the door shut and continues down the way with her partner, no doubt disturbing other unsuspecting passengers.

I was musing over the entirely internal feelings of motion one has. To me, as I looked toward the corridor outside my room, Oslo was to the right, not the left. To the fisherman, the destination lake was straight ahead, so why, he had asked me, was I heading in the opposite direction in my canoe? Like the fishermen who made the unintended and disorienting side trip, the train obviously went off the main track in the middle of the night, when the engine was switched from front to back. We were still going to Oslo, although I do confess I wondered for a few minutes if I had slept through the exchange in the Oslo trainyard and was heading back to Stavanger, so deeply entrenched was my personal sense of the forward motion established the night before.

76

As I am writing this chapter, I am told of an interesting experiment that has been conducted recently in Switzerland.[7] It is a real blow to those who would have an ordered universe, a universe that is predictable and accessible to calculations. In Geneva in 1997, experimenters sought to validate some of the principles of quantum mechanics.

Erwin Schrödinger, the Austrian physicist (1887–1961), described the particles of the universe as probabilities, not pure objects. Furthermore, he surmised that any given object could maintain an existence in two states—for example, it could be simultaneously alive and dead. The mere act of perceiving an object, of even looking at an object, could define which of those states it would present to the observer. Thus we have a universe that does not consist of simple billiard balls bouncing off one another in a complex, endless series of exchanges— endless but decipherable if you have the time and patience. No. We now have a universe in which reality depends on *whether* you choose to look. There are probabilities, not fixed perfect realities.

But maybe the weirdest images of this new universe, so divorced from the one where everything has its place relative to everything else, are those of objects that affect each other at a distance. Einstein based his relativity theory on the fixed speed of light. This constant holds the framework of the relative universe together. As one approaches the speed of light, the time and space it takes to get somewhere shrink. But there is this limit. You cannot go faster then the speed of light. But does this always apply? Despite the restriction of light speed, can some objects affect one another instantaneously over large distances?

In 1926, Schrödinger noted that the quantum mechanical theory allowed for a single quantum state to be spread across two objects. In Geneva in 1997, experimenters produced two photons[8] linked together in a single "entangled" state. They were sent in opposite directions over fibre-optic lines to two villages, ten kilometres apart. An analyzer in one village detected one of the photons—or not—depending on the setting of the instrument. (A photon has a random choice to be detected or not depending on its energy and the setting of the analyzer. Effectively, for the experimenters, the state of a photon's polarization or some such property depended on the interaction between that photon and the analyzer in the destination village.) In the Swiss experiment, the photon at the *other* village was always affected by what its twin did, *at the instant of its twin's action*: we have a universe in which objects distant from one another can remain "entangled," occupying, in a manner of speaking, the same "space." This is instantaneous action at a distance. Furthermore, when the Geneva experimenters changed the setting of the instruments at one of the destination villages, this caused a change in both photons instantaneously. This means that measurable properties of an object do not necessarily exist before measurement. We have a universe that is not quantifiable and that cannot be traced backward in time from the present; we cannot decipher the history of billiard ball collisions after they have been scattered to the corners of the table. This reverse engineering so valued by scientists is therefore questionable—revealed as a dubious method for accounting for the physical events we see in the universe, a product of the unwarranted desire for a strict mapping. It assumes the presence of an ordered universe that may not exist. The reality we see in front of our eyes, in our end of the universe here on earth, may be under the immediate influence of events that cannot be seen by us, events occurring in some distant galaxy. A universe that does not consist of contiguous components, and whose constituents can change at any moment owing to the actions of distant "twins," cannot

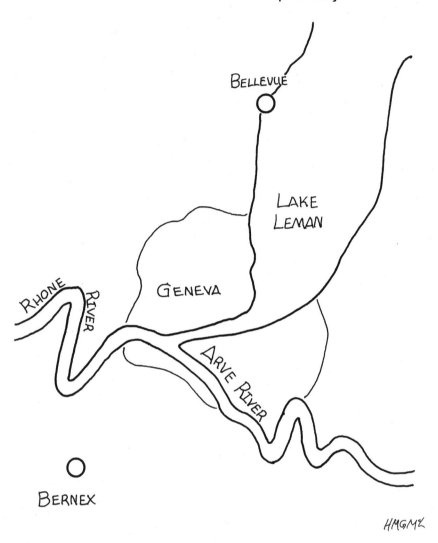

Entangled photons were sent from Geneva to the two villages, Bellevue and Bernex, in the 1997 quantum mechanics experiment.[9]

be mapped at a global level. Only local interactions can be accounted for—and even those can be measured in only a limited fashion. Taking into consideration the basic tenets of Schrödinger's theoretical viewpoint, only local, dialectical maps will have any chance of approximating reality.

77

Perhaps it is not so unlikely that the quantum mechanical theories developed in post–First World War Germany. Their emerging empire defeated, Germans saw new ephemeral concepts emerge. No firmly mapped reality exists; causality is linked to the observer. The institutions that sought truth have been proven false, and a new view of reality takes over.

"Downstream is this way!" I say to the fishermen, pointing. They realize I may be right but are totally baffled. I paddle around a couple of bends and nod to them as they now catch up to me again from behind, having decided to take my advice after all. "See, there's the first portage down the way a bit," I say, relieved for my own sake at the sight of the marker about a quarter of a mile down an unusually long stretch ahead of us.

78

When Ellie and I described our stream, our river, of embryonic development, we paid attention to all sorts of watery phenomena. Eddies and rapids are important metaphors, because they symbolize for us physical conformations of the developing organism; they literally depict the two-way exchange, the reciprocal contrapuntal action, of the dialectical morphogenesis[10] we were describing in our model of animal development.

The rocks are carried down the stream by the force of the water, and then, in their turn, the rocks become obstacles to the movement of the water itself. In an embryo, tissue can grow in response to genetically controlled growth cues, and in turn, the built-up tissue itself creates a new micro-environment in which the gene-tissue intercommunication is altered. Just as there is a constant dynamic relationship between the river and the riverbed, there is a constant interplay between the genes and the flesh and bones of the living organism.

79

The rocks in the stream also have an effect on the canoe. Before reaching the portage, I must steer into the Vs, avoiding the rocks that have been carried down the river. At the second portage, which comes all too soon after the first, I debate going down part of the way through the rapids. It is tricky as a solo canoeist, and the water is like ice. After a few rocks and a near miss, I pull up to the shore and start the portage. The packs are heavy, necessitating my taking three trips, counting the canoe. My back and arms are aching when I am done.

The fishermen have simply dragged their boat, filled with gear, over the ground, like the Pomori sailors on their way to Mangazeya in northern Siberia, over three hundred years ago. This looks idiotic to me, but I consider the possibility for next time.

80

Travelling through rapids does give me the sense of our theoretical model. This past summer Danielle and I spent a day going down a fast shallow river with plenty of rocks. We skimmed by hundreds of them. "Why didn't you tell me that rock was coming!" I yell. We are caroming off a smooth but treacherous boulder.

"I did!" She's right, she did, but I have to vent my impatience and fear somehow. The rocks are all manifestations of the theory; the river is a playground of eddies and Vs brought about by years and years of water carving out for itself a passage in the stony landscape.

Alone, it is no playground. I begin to wonder if I should have stopped at the liquor store along the highway like all the other northern migrants—anything to dull the pain at this point. The acetaminophen with codeine is buried in my pack. As the fishermen disappear into the last stretch of the river, I hear their loud voices. They are drunk.

81

As I head into the lake, I am confronted with the reality of the map we carry within us as we journey. It is like the maps of the native people who first helped the Europeans explore the Canadian north. The river has been a long linear trip for me. It has wound to the left and to the right countless times, but it has all been a straight endless line of movement. I paddle across the short stretch of lake to the first island I see. The distance is perhaps greater than the distance down the entire river, but the river journey took me three hours and this lake crossing takes an hour. And it feels like half an hour because I can see the destination from the very beginning of my crossing. What if I were to draw a map of my canoe trip down the river and across the lake? If I used a compass and surveying equipment, or global-positioning electronics, I would end up with a map that looks a lot like the ones the fishermen were examining at the head of the river, a detailed Ministry of Natural Resources map. This type of map is often called accurate.

The map in my head as I headed across the lake was much different. In fact, it was not until I looked at an official map of the region later, after coming home, that I realized that the distances across the lake matched the length of my trip along the river. No, the map in my head was based on time and obstacles. The river, if I had drawn it for others to follow, would have been about ten times as long as the lake crossing to the island. The constant bends and the rocks and the beaver dams and the portages would have each added many virtual miles of river to *my* map.

82

There are a few scattered islands in my path. On one there is a group of fishermen setting up camp. I wonder if the pair I met on the river are with them. They are loudly discussing the next day's fishing: "See, here's the spur over to the east of that island. The map has it goin' pretty far out. That's why we go around the other end. The fish'll be there on the south side when it's first light. We won't see 'em, but they'll be there, all right."

That's "why" we go around the other end. The map provides the template for our behaviour. The map predicts the actions; it is why we do things. The question "why?" implies that final causes, events reached in the future, dictate the reasons for actions in the past. Essentially, the surveyor's map is a teleological tool. Because there is a map, the events of the next day's boat trip to the good fishing area in the lake are pre- scribed by a secondary reality, namely the map itself, and this map is laid over the water, obscuring the currents and the winds and the islands. The actions of the day to come are already "in the past" in the sense that the map determines the actions of the traveller. Carefully laid out as a plan and then followed, the map is a kind of prophecy waiting to be fulfilled. And furthermore, after a day's journeying using a map, the traveller feels compelled to examine the day's progress. The map has predicted the course and now confirms it.

What would their route be if they followed no map? The winds this time of the year are from the west. We are to the north of the island. The wind carries a boat or a canoe easily over to the east of the long spur. It makes the distance seem rather small, not as far as it appears on the map. You can duck to the south of the island at the most eastern ex- treme and escape into the shelter of the south side. Coming back, you continue along the sheltered southern shore of the island, and then go around the west side, using the westerly wind to carry you back to the campsite on the north shore of the lake.

If they only consider the distances as they appear on the map, my fishermen will start out going the "wrong way" toward the west before sunrise, when the winds will be low. As the sun rises, the wind and waves will stir up and they will be caught halfway there, battling the weather. It will be a much longer trip, even though the physical, mea- surable map distance is less.

83

Mappings with destinations carefully laid out for the reader can lead to preconceptions. I remember arguments I had with my fellow regeneration[11] scientists. The adult newt was our creature for study. If one of its limbs is cut off, a new limb bud appears, and eventually bones, elbow joints, and digits reform. To many workers in this decidedly medieval area of study, the limb bud is a model for the growth one sees during embryogenesis.[12] For them, the final form of the newt's limb is incipient in the seemingly undifferentiated, or unformed, early embryonic limb bud. The final map of the limb, with all its wrist bones and digits, in the opinion of these traditional regeneration scientists, can be seen to be "mapped" inside a small lump of presumptuous tissue. Effectively, the final form is considered to be acting as a morphogenetic magnet for embryonic growth. The final form, the adult limb, is seen as the "purpose" for all the earlier embryonic development, and the final form is thought to reach back from the future to control the trajectory of the growth of the embryonic limb bud. And furthermore, scientists I knew have claimed they can find the proof of this map by tracking tissue throughout the growth and differentiation of the limb. To me, discovering that tissue situated at the tip of the limb bud ends up at the tip of the fully formed limb is hardly surprising. Nor is it surprising that the transplant of a partially formed limb tip into an anomalous donor site leads to the formation of an unusually placed limb segment.

Tracing the origins of the final shape of a newt's limb, by going back in time to the uninspiring mound of a limb bud, is wishful thinking on the part of my fellow regenerationists. It is also teleological because it assumes that the final shape has an influence. There are very fancy cover-ups for this kind of thinking. There is the assumption that the shape must lie within the interactions of the dynamic growing elements. But no matter how the explanations are worded, the impetus for the model for embryogenesis is the belief that a final form lies within that which precedes it; the final end point is thought to be incipient in the organism. This is the expression of the desire of the investigator who, like Aristotle, attempts to find guidance from final causes. It is a desire for "purpose" in the universe. It clouds the thinking of many scientists today.

84

The winds are low now in the evening. I paddle against the pine smell coming from the diminishing heat of the island. I am looking for a campsite.

The strong sweet smell carries me back to a time thirty years before. The smell is a sign, telling us it is time to make our evening camp, our Ojibwa guide informs us. In a lake not far from Sioux Lookout in northern Ontario, we stop paddling only after the sun has gone down—up to now we have resisted the temptation to stop, but as the evening comes on, the pines and the cedars lure us ashore. We are tired from paddling and portaging since daybreak. "Here," our guide said earlier, pulling away moss and leaves at the head of the lake, "gimme some tobacco, one of you." And we lay tobacco on the hidden petroglyph, the keeper of the lake. Now, as we pull our canoes on to the shore, he teaches us how to build a camp from the forest. We make a small fire and eat quickly. Each of us has only one blanket, but we construct nests of young hemlock. Hemlock has flat needles that grow out from the sides of the twigs. And the boughs are bent with a natural spring in them. We pile them up to make mattresses. I sleep in the soft night air, floating.

85

The hierarchy described in Darwin's theory of evolution implies that there is a predisposition in ancient biological forms, a predictor of the animals and plants of today, a mapping of the future form right onto what you see in the fossil record. This is a kind of overlayer. There is, then, in the mind of the western scientist, a dual image present in all things. Rather than study the thing itself, the animal or plant in its environment, the scientist needs to wrap it in a covering, a map. Unfortunately, the map often shields us from the item in question. We see through the filter of our maps, and we can see nothing else. We see the filter only.

86

I pull up the canoe, remembering the dream I had sleeping on the hemlock boughs thirty years ago. The day of canoeing is passing before my eyes. As I drift into sleep, I remember every single tree and bulrush and rock and wave. The river shoreline and the variegated coast of the large lakes are like photographs in my mind. Their realness is mapped onto my consciousness. I know where I have been, and I can see the shape of the landscape. But it is no surveyor's map; it is a personal journey. I remember the impressions of this personal map, and the images begin to fill my head again. And then I realize that I am remembering today's journey along with my journey of thirty years ago. The efforts of canoeing are rocking my body as I unload myself and my gear onto the dry land.

87

I was once at a lecture where a palaeontologist wrote down an astoundingly large number, something in the trillions. He said it was the estimate for the number of fossils of animals, plants, algae, and bacteria that were thought to be embedded in the rocks of the earth. And that was the proof against the dubious theory of creationism. "That is the evidence! Right there!" He glared at the crowd assembled, not one of us ever having harboured even a secret belief in the creation myth. Creationists believe in a strict interpretation of the Christian Bible, with no room for the development of creatures over evolutionary time. Did the palaeontologist need to worry so much about foolish ideas of

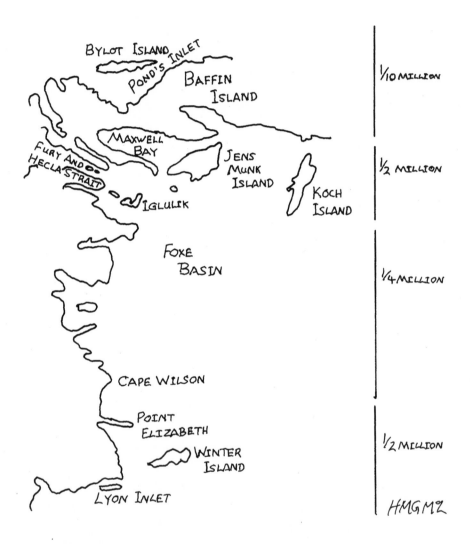

Ivaluardjuk's map of Melville Peninsula and Baffin Island, ca. 1900.[13] Areas of personal interest are drawn larger.

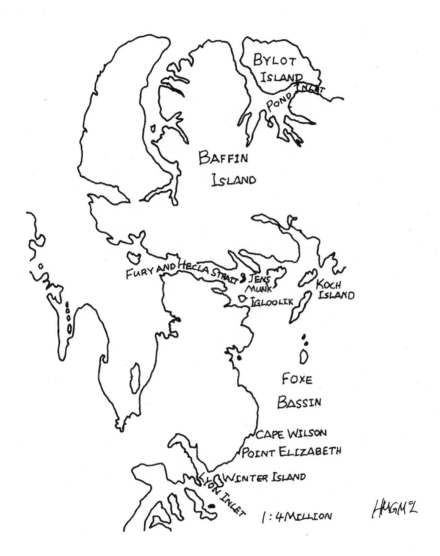

Survey map of Melville Peninsula and Baffin Island.[14]

the scientifically illiterate? And was he not ignoring the reality of the fossils for the sake of the evolutionary model? He could only see the filter, the overlayer, and not the life underneath it. There is surely a wealth of concepts yet undetected that can use those trillions of fossils to equal advantage.

88

Travellers to the Canadian Arctic relied on maps made by their Inuit guides. They are not aerial drawings or surveyors' layouts of exact distances and landforms. They are formed from the experiences themselves. As a result, there are idiosyncrasies. Rivers that are difficult to travel are drawn as being longer than they are; lakes that are easy to cross are disproportionately small. Areas that are close by and therefore

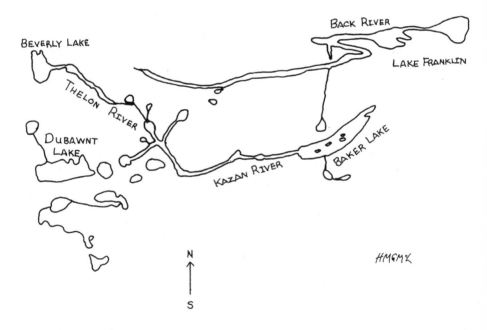

Igjugarjuk's map of the Kazan River, ca. 1900.[15] Caribou crossing points are exaggerated in size and in their east-to-west orientation.

familiar take up more than their share of room on the map, and distant
regions appear to be much smaller than they would be shown on a surveyor's map. How like to my own canoe journey these maps are. Were
they helpful? I suspect they were. The Inuit people have survived with
an intimate knowledge of their terrain mapped into their heads.

89

Ivaluardjuk lived near Lyon Inlet. When he drew a map, it is significant
that the region most familiar to him was drawn to a 1:2,000,000 scale,
whereas the region north of this was drawn at 1:4,000,000, and the
region at the top of the map, Baffin Island, the area least known to him,
was drawn at 1:10,000,000. The area around Igloolik and Jens Munk
Island were also drawn at the 1:2,000,000 scale, even though they are

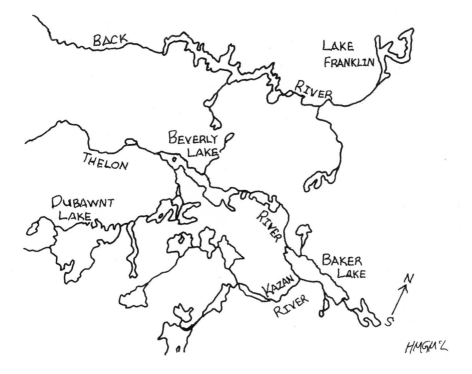

Surveyor's map of the Kazan River region.[16]

relatively far away. This probably indicates that this was a region well known to the mapmaker, perhaps a common destination point. The surveyor's map of the same region shows how much Ivaluardjuk's layout is distorted. However, the Inuit rendering of the region is not incorrect. It is based on experience and is not dominated by geographical measurements that have no immediate bearing on his life.

90

Igjugarjuk lived in caribou-hunting territory in northeastern Canada. His maps emphasized the hunting concerns of this region—the rivers are lengthened and widened and are drawn with an exaggerated west-to-east orientation compared with the surveyor's map of the same area. The relative size and orientation of the rivers shows their importance in the consciousness of the mapmaker. Like the reindeer in Siberia, the caribou migrate northward in the spring. West-to-east-oriented rivers must be crossed during this migration and are very good places to hunt the caribou as they congregate on the banks. The rivers are therefore important elements on the maps, representing barriers that are perpendicular to the south-to-north movement of the caribou.

91

The maps of the Inuit are not layers over reality dictated from a teleological perspective. They are mapped after the fact, representing the experiences of the mapmakers. They represent the interaction of the hunters and the landscape. They are dialectical.

92

I wake up to pain. When I bend down to cook over the small stove I have brought with me, I am stuck in that position. I cannot use my back muscles. Too much strain the day before. I crawl back into the tent and find the painkillers I craved yesterday. Then I wait as the frosty morning crackles around me.

Later, my small gas stove gives out and I must find wood. This island is too small to supply very much. I decide to make a special trip to the north shore of the lake to load up on dry branches that have collected over the past winter. The wind has picked up and is blowing from the west. With any luck, it will be in my favour. I can paddle crossways into the waves going northwest, and that way, if the wind stays constant, coming back will be easier. I reason that if I do the hard part of the journey going out, I am assured of being able to make it back.

93

When I looked into the lobby of the Savoia Hotel I couldn't believe my eyes. A marble Greek-styled sculpture of a naked maiden poured water into a pool of water surrounded by live plants. I had walked from Red Square in the freezing night. I was dressed badly, but my Canadian passport got me shelter. I showed it through the hotel lobby window, and with a quick opening of the door I was ushered inside. Radio Moscow had advertised the place, rooms starting at US$900 a night. In 1991, the ruble was trading at almost 100 to the dollar, a devaluation of over tenfold in a year. One night's stay at the Savoia would set the average Russian back seven years' pay.

94

The trip to the hotel was calculated in the same way that I contemplated the trip to the north shore of the lake to look for dry wood to burn in my campfire. The canoe paddle to the far shore would be difficult, but if I managed it, it would prove that I could get back to home safely: the hardest part of the trip was necessarily the journey to the destination to prevent disaster coming back. And the circumstances were similar; the water in the northern Ontario lake in late May of 1992 was close to freezing—it would kill anyone who fell in within a few minutes. Moscow in January 1991 was very cold too. People did die there, standing exposed outside with nowhere to get warm. In a way, both the canoe excursion looking for wood and the trip to the Savoia hotel looking for food and drink were challenges to the environment, a cold landscape that would find out if I could adapt, a landscape lying in wait to mould me to its final purpose. But my dialectical approach predicts that the traveller can have an effect on the surrounding landscape; there is a reciprocal relationship, and the cold wind and water of the lake can be transformed to an extent; the bleak night of Moscow can be changed. I was relying on my Canadian passport and on my money to effect this change, to allow me to control the elements. So far it was working; I was inside the lobby of an expensive, and warm, hotel.

I wanted to use the international phone they had for foreigners. And I wanted to eat. The cafeteria in my Communist Party–run residence on Leningradski Prospekt had closed before I returned earlier that night. The hours were strict. And I had nothing to drink. The thought of lining up for beer again was not appetizing, so I had come out to Red Square looking for the Savoia or any other refuge for foreigners. I had come by Metro, tiring of constantly having to bribe the guy at the gate of my residence to phone for a taxi. The underground train system in Moscow is extensive—I could go anywhere quickly.

I cannot afford the prices at their restaurant. I stay only to make my phone call, the phone card eating up the time as the international communication clicks and buzzes and rings go through. I have almost no time to speak to my family in Canada. "Yes, I'm eating well. How is everyone? I can't talk long . . . the phone card is running out . . . no, there are no phones where I'm staying . . . my love to every—" It clicks off. I have no more American money to buy another phone card. I've left the rest of my American cash and credit cards in my residence, and anyway phone cards cost US$24 a minute. This call has cost me US$60. I go back into the freezing streets to look for the Metro station, this time determined to find a western hotel where I can afford the food, and where they'll take rubles.

95

The canoe is full of sticks and branches now. But my plan has not worked out. The wind has picked up a lot while I have been on shore, and it has shifted. It is now coming from the southwest. I will have to paddle directly into the wind and waves to get back to my island. The size of the waves worries me, and it is starting to rain icy pellets. Settling into the canoe, I realize that I have another problem. When I was battling the waves at the beginning of my trip, I had a fully loaded canoe that was set low in the water. The branches I have picked up will not hold the front of the now empty canoe deeply enough in the water. I cannot go into these choppy waves with an underloaded canoe. I have to find a way of changing the relationship I have with the environment or I'll be staying here all day. I find myself asking, Am I being adaptively shaped by the template of the environment, or is this a confrontation, a meeting of the organism and the landscape in a dialectical debate? I don't know and I sure don't care at this point. I have no food or shelter here—it is all back on my island.

96

I am lost. The streets around Red Square radiate in spokes and circles, and it is easy to become lost. But it is also late at night and about 35 degrees below zero. I look for a taxi. Finally waving one down, I find that he will not take my rubles because I have only large denominations. Taxi drivers routinely charge huge rates, and until now they have taken American dollars or large ruble notes. Taxi drivers also know what is happening in all the criminal sectors, including the government. I am told what will only become common knowledge later the next day, leading to desperation and even deaths on the street. All currency bills larger than the 50-ruble note will be invalid. The next day I will hear from my Russian friends that twenty-four elderly people have died standing in the streets outside government offices waiting to change their money. They will be allowed only to exchange the equivalent of one month's government stipend. Many of them have kept their life savings in boxes hidden under floorboards in their apartments, not trusting banks. The stress and fear of having nothing leads to heart attacks, and the cold finishes them off. My friend Katya tells me she is illegally changing money for old people she knows. Katya has methods inside the bureaucracy, but she and the others can only save a few people from imminent destitution.

I tell the taxi driver to get lost. I continue to walk. I cannot find the Metro station, and I know I am in danger of losing the feeling in my feet. But I am luckier than the old people who will stand in the streets the next morning. I make it into a Metro station and go back to my residence. I have not found food or drink; I remain thirsty and hungry until the morning.

97

In Moscow that night I needed to use money, something that carried weight. I needed to transform the immovable elements around me, to bend them to my will, or at least to bring them halfway. I was counting on a dialectical exchange with the landscape, but it didn't work out. I came close to really suffering. The streets around Red Square were cold and bleak and deserted that winter. On the lake, I decide to transform the canoe-lake relationship. I find a large rock, a rock that I can barely lift, and place it carefully in the front of the canoe. It weighs the canoe down, transforming the relationship between me and the environment. Some would say I have adapted to the surrounding landscape; I prefer to think of the episode as an example of the intimate give and take an organism has with its environment, each one having an effect on and changing the other just a little bit.

I begin the hazardous paddle over the waves back to my island. When I finally land the canoe and unload branches for my fire, it is late afternoon. The journey for wood has taken most of the day. Looking at the map when I return home, I see that the distance to the shore is barely discernible. A short distance and a very long travelling time.

98

I think back to the frogs on the imaginary island. It is so easy to see the adaptationist's point of view: the frogs respond to the changing environment; they adapt. On an island that undergoes a drought, the small portion of the frog population with traits that allow them to live away from the pond manage to survive and eventually form a new population. The adaptationist viewpoint leads us to believe that the environment has *shaped* their appearance, their lifestyle—the believers in the natural selection theory see the frogs slowly adapting into an environment; they do not see that this is tantamount to believing in an unmoving landscape, a landscape that acts as the ultimate designer, a future goal that determines the natural history of the frog from a future vantage point.

To accept the concept of intimate dialectical exchange, where the traveller has an effect on the terrain as much as the terrain influences the traveller, we would have to see that the frogs can effect environmental change. It is easier with beavers, I think, as I travel down my river, jumping into cold water to pull the canoe over yet another beaver dam that has caused the natural flow of the river to be diverted into shallow swamps lining the banks. But frogs can have an effect, I am sure, especially in small spaces.

I remember my first time on this lake. It is 1970, and Danielle and I are camping, again in late May. We have avoided mainland camps because of the chance of meeting up with a bear. But one night we have no choice. We set up our tent on the shore of the lake, close to bear territory. Before we left the base camp two days earlier, we were told of one bear that had been breaking into cottages in a nearby village—not a comforting thought. In the middle of the night, we are wakened by a thumping against the tent. We are immediately terrified. "What if it's a bear?" Carefully, we move to the door of the tent, flashlight on, ready to run, shout, hit it on the nose. The door is unzipped, and there is nothing there, but slowly we realize that the tent is filling up with tiny, freshly metamorphosed toads, relatives of our frogs. The toads reveal their knowledge of the dialectical relationship they have with their landscape. They change our environment—they drive us out of the tent for hours. We turn it inside out, ridding our clothes and sleeping bags of hundreds of tiny pulpy toads bouncing over everything.

CHAPTER THREE

THE DARK WOOD

Nel mezzo del cammin di nostra vita
Mi ritrovai per una selva oscura.

In the middle of the road of our life
I found myself in a dark wood.

 – DANTE, *Divina Commedia: Inferno*, I

99

CONQUERING THE EARTH and naming it your own—what forms has this human endeavour taken? Conquest is followed by mapmaking. And then the map is superimposed on all older maps, on the hopes and aspirations of the conquered. Mapping is based on a dualistic way of thinking—the map is an interpretation of the reality beneath it, a superficial layer that presents itself as the true reality. But it carries with it the bias of its makers. And the map has a physical reality of its own. It is not merely theoretical. The physical manifestations of the map can eventually obscure almost all traces of the older civilizations beneath.

100

Gregor is pumping up the tire for the fourth time in half an hour. A car with a punctured tire in Siberia is bad enough, but this car only has three wheels, two in the back and one in the front. It is like a motorized tricycle. As the tire pressure drops, we swerve more and more recklessly over the ruts and the slippery mud. "It's been like this since March!" he complains in Russian "It's terrible, I can't go anywhere without stopping every two miles." Yes, we agree, it's terrible. Why did Gregor and his crippled vehicle have to be called in to take us to visit the Gulag[1] railroad? Why is car repair so foreign to people here?

"The trail is rough," Lyudmila said. "Your bus won't even attempt the trip." Besides, "nobody should know you are going there." She fidgets, not looking at us directly. Gregor is a friend.

101

The smell is solid. It seeps into everything we own—our clothes, our few pieces of furniture, and even into our food. Danielle and I are living in a small second-floor apartment on Lippincott Street in Toronto. It is 1970. Below us are our landlords. We walk through their front room every day. Every month I go down the stairs into their living quarters to pay the rent. "Yes, the weather is fine! Certainly, I would be very happy to have some of your homemade liqueur." I count out the $95, a fortune for us then. My formal speeches are what I think is necessary in this realm of foreignness. I sit drinking and the women cluster around me, attentive. Later Danielle asks me what I could possibly find to say— they don't speak English. "Well, the daughters do." I sit and absorb the formality. In their kitchen, I am also at the heart of the fish cooking. There is a special process for preserving cod, I am told by others. The Portuguese use something that smells like formaldehyde; it is a formidable smell that hides decay. To this day, I can still smell it if I think about the Lippincott house.

102

It is 1990. About two years before our visit, Lyudmila mounted the first display on the Gulag in the Soviet Union. It had taken more than thirty years since the death of Stalin for someone to be this bold. Her small museum on the Arctic Circle will not be noticed by many.

Josef Stalin tried to build a railroad across the north of Siberia. He was literally laying his map over the surface of the earth. The trail to the railroad symbolizes his frustration—nobody can conquer the permafrost. The road we are travelling with Gregor is really a ditch, banked on either side with wave-shaped hills of buckled earth. The damaged ground will not heal in these semi-frozen conditions; the ruts and pools of water will stay here for a century. I wait next to the car as Gregor uses the hand pump vigorously. We are going to the scene of so many deaths, the slave-built Siberian railroad. The water in the pools next to the car smells heavy, as if hiding the smell of hidden corpses. "Jeesh!" I shake off the image. I am not feeling well. The food is getting to me after a week in Siberia—too much fatty meat and no vegetables. I can't trust the water, and my lips are cracked from dehydration. No wonder I'm hallucinating corpses.

103

The Portuguese map of the world is an old one. In the house on Lippincott Street, I sat in a manifestation of the Age of Discovery. In the century before Columbus's famous voyage and for decades afterwards, the world was being drawn up into territories, as lands were being discovered in Africa, in Asia, and in what was to be the Americas.[2] The Portuguese were first on the seas, and the charts of the early Portuguese navigators were the basis for their first world map.

In 1502, a copy of the map was smuggled out of Lisbon by an Italian, Alberto Cantino, and delivered to the duke of Ferrara. The map influenced all later maps of that time, maps made for the most part by

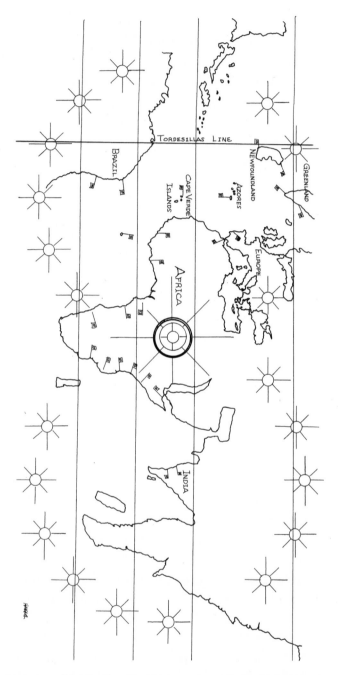

Author's version of the Cantino World Map, ca 1502.[3] The Portuguese have lined the
coast of Africa, and other regions of the world, with their flags.

Italian and German cartographers. The Cantino map is remarkable for its detail. In the fifteenth and sixteenth centuries, only confirmed geographical observations were included in the sea charts. This led to relatively accurate mappings of the known world. However, as accurate as the map may be, it has a distinct bias. The Cantino map is the map of Portugal, or the world turned into a Portugal spread thinly over the coastal surfaces of the known continents. It is a map in the true tradition of layering one reality over another, of one point of view obscuring any competing paradigms.

104

The Cantino world map was produced from a compilation of information from Portuguese navigators' sea charts—portolans. The map would have remained a secret for a considerable time had a copy not been smuggled into Italy.

The map is centred on a large compass rose in the middle of Africa. This central rose is at the intersection of two large circles, each consisting of sixteen smaller compass roses. In the original map, the lines coming from the compass roses form a criss-crossing grid that aided the cartographer in incorporating the information from the navigators' sea charts. The outlines of Europe and Africa are remarkably accurate, as are parts of Asia. However, the map departs from the strict empirical rules of the time in the Southeast Asia region. European traders did not reach that area until 1511, and it is thought that the shape of the area in the Cantino map is derived from the map by the astronomer Ptolemy from the year 150. The Ptolemy map had been re-examined by European cartographers after its rediscovery in the fifteenth century.

The new world as outlined in the Cantino map shows the West Indies, the east coast of South America, and hints of North America, Newfoundland, and Greenland. The heavy line drawn from north to south at the left side of the map represents the boundary drawn for the Treaty of Tordesillas, as decided by papal decree in 1482. By that treaty, all lands west of the line were granted to Spain. It is of interest to note that the Newfoundland region, with its rich Grand Banks fishing, is to the east of the Tordesillas line on the Cantino map, although it actually lies well to the west of the delineation cited in the treaty—960 nautical miles west of the Cape Verde Islands. (The Portuguese explorer Gaspar Corte-Real laid claim to what is now known as Greenland during his 1500 voyage, and to the Newfoundland region in a subsequent voyage, 1501. By that time, the Danes, who had settled in the region a few centuries before, were no longer present, although they did return later, as did members of northern Inuit groups.) The only place in the Americas actually granted to Portugal in the treaty was the eastern part of South America, modern-day Brazil.

The coasts of Africa and Asia, as well as parts of Newfoundland, Greenland, and South America are dotted with Portuguese flags, indicating their claim to new lands. Today, the world still lives with the heritage of this time of Portuguese discovery. It was the first step toward the European domination of the world.

105

I walk from the three-wheeled car over ground swelling with the tundra flowers of June. "I'll be back in about half an hour!" Gregor yells. His little car has one front seat for the driver and can carry two passengers in back. We are coming here in shifts. I am deposited with Sasha while Gregor goes back for Lyudmila and Jim and Fiona. My Canadian colleagues had wanted me to go first. The car looked so unlikely to make it, and now I wonder if they will really come in Gregor's next trip. It will take him longer than half an hour, I think, but then when I was in the car he had driven like a crazy person, trying to get as far as possible between flat tires. "Watch out! We're flipping over!" One of the waves of sopping earth embankment guided the car in a slow arc so that I could distinctly see sky below and dirt above us. "Fuck." Gregor gunned the engine and increased his already insane rate of speed. Airborne for only a second, we had continued unharmed.

At the embankment of the railroad, all is quiet. I stumble over something that has caught the toe of my shoe. It is a strand of old barbed wire. It appears to be part of a much longer piece buried under the tangled tundra plants. I can't pull it up. I almost cut myself, and then I see that it is connected to a piece of wire that obviously goes on for several feet or maybe several miles under the tundra.

106

Our landlords on Lippincott Street ate preserved fish. The fish came from Portuguese markets in Toronto, but it was imported from Portugal. The fish, mostly cod, was pulled out of the sea by Portuguese fishermen working off the coast of Newfoundland. Things hadn't changed much in almost five hundred years. The smell of fish on Lippincott Street connected us to the golden Age of Discovery, when Portugal shaped the map of the world from the sea.

107

Dualism dominates western thought—mind and matter, form and content, human and divine, and so on. Statements are made, descriptions are outlined, and the models used by scientists begin to have a reality of their own, despite often being only vaguely appropriate depictions of the phenomenon under observation. The map of science, its body of theory and tentative facts, obscures the reality underneath.

Dualism is a form of teleological thought. Mapping one layer of interpretation on another, or even one reality on top of another, is the creation of one's own destiny. In other words, if you don't like to risk the ending of the story, write it yourself. In teleological thinking, something occurs because it is meant to be. A railroad across Siberia is built because it has always been incipiently there, waiting to happen. From this point of view, Stalin was fulfilling his and the world's destiny. Similarly, the believers in pure adaptationist Darwinism consider the appearance of new life forms to be the culmination of a series of events that can be traced backward through time. The final form of the animal or plant acts as a magnet, attracting the evolutionary events from the future. Both Stalin's railroad and the evolutionary hierarchy described by adaptationist scientists are examples of maps that have been layered over the surface of the world.

108

"Let me out of here!" Jim is grumbling from Gregor's car. The second shipment has arrived more quickly than I predicted. Jim is large and Lyudmila is largish for someone so short. Despite the cramped quarters, Fiona had come with them too, and they all fall out of the tiny car like a circus act.

"Look at this barbed wire!" I try to interest them in the traces of a gruesome history.

"Oh yeah. Right." Fiona looks as overtired and unhealthy as I do. But Sasha has travelled with us for the whole journey and shows no signs of ill health. It is as if the generations of oppression we are about to investigate have hardened him in ways completely foreign to us.

109

Scientists and politicians create models of reality; they do not define absolute truth. The models are biased. The adaptationists look for likely explanations for how the environment may have shaped the evolution of an organism. An abundance of seed-producing plants led to the favouring of bird offspring with short curved beaks, perhaps. The conditions of the habitat drew the form out of the genetic background. The bias lies in the fact that almost any explanation can be thought of after the fact. If it is discovered that the seed-producing plants became abundant only after the short-beaked birds evolved, then one can go to another explanation: perhaps male-to-male fighting during mating season favoured short strong beaks. There is intrinsic bias in the approach because the adaptationist cannot lose in this game. This is not predictive science; it is explanation after the fact attempting to act as a description of actual, but unknown, events in remote evolutionary history.

Political leaders can create similar logical problems. Stalin was typical of megalomaniacs with power. He perceives the final form first and only then, while standing in the future and urging the rest of us to come there to meet him, he moulds the past leading up to the event. The railroad was always to be. The difficulties involved in making it would be overcome no matter what because, for him, it had a reality embedded in the future, acting as a magnet dragging the tundra, the sodden earth, the millions of slaves through their inevitable transfigurations. All manifestations were meant to be—they were meant to be in the past, they were meant to be in the present, and they were meant to be in the future.

110

Because dualism manifests itself at the very heart of our scientific mapping of existence, dualistic explanations may prove to be virtually unavoidable.

In 1997, an experiment[4] was conducted to reveal the existence of non-existence—the Casimir force, the pressure exerted by empty space. In other words, the experiment sought to prove the existence of something where there is supposed to be nothing—a vacuum with no matter and no energy. That is pure dualism, the simultaneous presence of nothing and something. In this case, it is nothing and an infinite something—true opposites. I consider this to be the ultimate map overlying the "reality" underneath.

In the 1920s, the theoretical physicists Max Planck and Werner Heisenberg predicted that the duality of quantum mechanical interpretations of reality would extend to the description of pure vacuums. They described a vacuum as consisting of infinite numbers of virtual particles winking in and out of existence. This condition was predicted even at absolute zero, theoretically the lowest possible temperature, at

which point the entropy change of a system should be zero and therefore there should be no energy—no motion, no time, and no way to
confirm existence. This "zero-point energy" was named the Casimir
force as a result of experiments done by Hendrick Casimir in the 1940s.
Casimir predicted that the existence of virtual photons in a vacuum, or
the existence of non-existence, would reveal itself through a weak
attraction of two objects separated by a very tiny space. If the space
between the objects is small enough, some of the virtual photons that
"exist" in the absolute vacuum surrounding the objects will have wave-
lengths that exclude them from the space between the objects. This
will result in the infinite zero-point energy on the outside being larger
in scale than the infinite zero-point energy on the inside, and the two
objects will be pushed together by the greater pressure outside the tiny
space. To prove this prediction, in 1997 Steven Lamoreaux of Los
Alamos National Laboratory placed two gold-coated quartz plates very
close together and measured the forces pushing the plates together. His
results showed that there is infinite "something" in a vacuum—which
by definition contains nothing. I consider the experiment to be the
literal demonstration of the inevitability of dualistic interpretations of
nature in western science.

   To counter that this experiment shows that the concept of dualism
approaches a kind of "truth," I will not dispute; I observe only that the
"truth" is confined within its own contextual constraints. The fact that
there is a consistency to the dualism of western scientific perspectives,
even down to the level of a vacuum at absolute zero, shows the rigour of
our scientific model of the world; for me, however, the results prove
that the thoroughness of our science also ensures that alternative models cannot make even an appearance. Western scientists pursue certainty, and they believe that their consistent results prove we are on the
road to truth. I think that consistent results are in themselves suspect—
how can we be so consistently right when investigating the universe,
after all? Consistency and certainty provide us insight into science's
tendency toward the provision of self-fulfilling prophecies, a tendency
that would not be nearly so obvious were it not for the fact that in
experiments such as this one, for example, western scientists have the

hubris to claim an understanding of existence itself. But what form has this understanding taken? Existence has been shown, empirically, to be and not to be.

111

Gulag

I scramble up the embankment to the railroad itself. It extends as far as I can see in either direction. The ties are laid in a crooked array. The rails curve and twist, but the railroad exists. The section where I stand was never in use; the permafrosted earth was unforgiving. The ground heaved and lurched throughout the seasons, and the railroad could not hold true. But in this region of Siberia alone, 340 kilometres of rail was built, and for years the slaves of Stalin came to struggle with the frozen earth, with the steel, with the horrendously heavy wooden ties, and with the weather.

112

I fell in love with the Cantino map the moment I saw it. The Age of Discovery thrills me. The world discovered with the breath of sea air and romance is drawn into the Portuguese map. Portuguese flags cover the coasts of Africa and Asia. Ancient civilizations are of little importance when compared with the science and the commerce of Europe, this map says. The map of the world is shown through the eyes of the conquerors. But it was not just bravado. Today the world map shows the influence of the Portuguese conquests of five hundred years ago, in Angola, Guinea, and Mozambique in Africa, in Goa on the coast of India, in East Timor in Indonesia, and in Brazil. We still live in the world drawn by the Europeans, starting with the Cantino map of 1502. And that world discovery was fuelled by the knowledge that we could uncover the mechanisms of nature using our science. Our skilled navigators were the technicians of an aristocracy of scientists and philosophers.

113

"Many millions of peoples die in here, right by your feets," Sasha is whispering to me as we walk. I don't want him near me; this time is too precious to me. I know it is true, but I didn't know only a few days before. I need time and solitude to figure it out.

"Look all around you," said the man who pulled me aside a few days earlier on the runway at Ukhta where we were fogged in. "There were ten camps around this airfield back then, and nobody talks about it. Where are you from? You're foreign, aren't you? Who let you come here? What are you here for? Do you want the truth? Do you care about what really happened here?" My mind is reeling as I try to tell him that I don't speak Russian, but I do understand enough to get this message. I push by him, gesturing foolishly that I don't understand and I must join my colleagues. I am trapped in my own ignorance of a world tragedy so big that the shame obscured it from people's minds. Later, Lyudmila will tell me that many of the residents of Salekhard were here at the time of the Gulag. Former prisoners and guards now live side by side, but almost nobody refers negatively to the past. Even the former prisoners think that the Gulag was a good thing. The prisoners must have been meant to be punished; otherwise, why did it happen? They were bad because they were punished. This is really teleological. All Stalin had to do was lay out his reality, and the lives of millions of people, with all their dreams and their aspirations, became as nothing. His railroad covered the earth and the people who slaved for it. From the time the Gulag camps started in 1928—along the northern railroad, in mining operations across Siberia, and in giant building complexes in many Soviet cities—until about 1956, when Stalin's influence ended three years after his death, it is conservatively estimated that ten million people died of cold, overwork, and starvation rations, with another ten million dying from mass dislocation and famine.

"I remember being a girl in Sverdlovsk," Lyudmila tells us. "We played in the forest near our home, but there was a place where we were not to go. Of course we went there. Sticking out of the ground we saw the hands and feet of people who had been buried in shallow graves. They were the inhabitants of an entire village not far from us. But we knew that they were monsters, men, women, and children, who had defied the state." They were in their graves because it was always meant for them to be there.

114

The Portuguese discovered lands to exploit them. This was most evident in West Africa. Portuguese Guinea on the west coast of Africa was discovered by Nuno Tristão in 1446. He was killed there in 1447 while negotiating for slaves to bring back to Portugal. Portugal went on to trade in slaves from Africa for centuries. Yet despite the tragic circumstances, there is something powerfully exciting about the Age of Discovery. *"Ayo vista lo mappamundi, e la carte de naviguari"*—I have seen the map of the world and the chart of the navigators, they sang at the time. Mappa Mundi, map of the world, is something that has to be felt inside to understand. I imagine the vastness of the seas falling behind under my vessel as I approach new lands.

115

On Lippincott Street, our landlords had plastic parrots perched on a trapeze suspended from the ceiling in their front room and plastic plants that looked like tropical flowers. Their decor echoed the Age of Discovery. They longed for the perfumes of the tropical rain forests and the colour and sound of a seaport.

116

I stand on the railroad. The ties are under my feet. I look to the east and I look to the west. The wind rushes against my nostrils, and I feel the prickling of a wave of delight that starts in my nose and ends in my testicles. I am delighted to be here, I realize. This is a vast region and I am standing on a monument of human endeavour, one that can probably be seen from the moon, it is so extensive. Suddenly my head is clear and I no longer feel fatigued. I have been caught by the thrill of the Age of Discovery and the conquering of the earth, as inappropriate as that may be.

117

Not all maps are layered onto the reality underneath. Not all of them depend on conquering the earth and all the creatures living there. Alternatives to natural selection and the survival of the fittest exist. In 1979, the palaeontologist Stephen J. Gould and the geneticist Richard Lewontin criticized the commonly held belief that natural selection is the mechanism behind all evolutionary change—a simplistic approach, they observed, that successively replaces one failed adaptive explanation with another, never pausing to question the basic underlying logical assumptions.[5] The history of adaptationist explanations is a seemingly unending series of *a posteriori* arguments that can be traced to the general interests and biases of the researcher involved. Thus, as Gould and Lewontin complain, the shape of the face of an Inuit person once depicted by researchers as "cold engineered,"[6] has more recently been described as an adaptation for "chewing tough meat and skins."[7] Horns and antlers once described by zoologists as "weapons against predators" are now more commonly seen as symbols of competition with other males of the same species. There is always a *purpose* behind the adaptationist explanations. Survival of the fittest harks to the teleological answering of the question "why?" Appropriately, Gould and Lewontin label the adaptationist viewpoint the "Panglossian paradigm," named after the character Dr. Pangloss, whose beliefs satirized those of the philosopher Leibniz, in Voltaire's *Candide*. Dr. Pangloss asserts that all things are in their rightful and most perfect place in the world, because that is how the world works.[8] The adaptationists believe that all things have settled into their current rightful place after continuous bouts of adjustment through natural selection.

118

We begin to walk along the ties, Sasha still talking continuously at my side.

Railroads always smell strongly. Even though there have been many years to soften the smell of creosote in the wood, I can still feel its tickle in the back of my throat. "Just follow the tracks back, if you want an easy route," my girlfriend of thirty years ago had told me. She lived in the country, and I had arrived for dinner with her family. Her parents were not about to help out a skinny teenager who was bothering their daughter on a school night. Now it was dark and I walked back toward my home in Belleville along the tracks, mainly to avoid the dogs who lurked by the road. They would wait for me, listening, and then launch themselves down the long driveways barking and snarling as I passed. The railway smelled, and in the dark that smell was frightening—something about its lonely pull to distant places, the constant fear of other travellers. A long linear trail must be attractive to others moving in the night, I reasoned, and such a trail would bring us all together eventually. I didn't want to meet them.

On the way back to Belleville, in Ontario, thirty years before, I had struck off into the gloomy and much blacker forest next to the tracks. Here in Siberia, I want to run off the tracks again. But the raised railway is surrounded by wet swamp-like terrain. I am trapped on the linear trail of the railroad. Who will I be forced to meet if I continue over its seemingly endless length across Siberia?

119

Natural selection still holds its place in science.

Every trail I take to uncover the current trends in scientific logic ends in a confrontation with the pervasive belief in *design*, the belief in ever-more-perfect refinements, the belief in the ascent of the ladder to perfection—the Great Chain of Being of creatures from the lowest to the highest.9 And every trail leads me to encounters with people I would rather not meet, but the road is narrow and I cannot avoid them. The philosopher Daniel Dennett is such a fellow traveller along this skinny railroad across Siberia. In a bald endorsement of Darwin's concept of natural selection through adaptation, Dennett traces Bach's writing of the *St. Matthew Passion* through "[b]illions of years of *irreplaceable* design work,*" everything from the refinement of the human species, to the context of the society in which Christianity was born, to the nurturing of Bach as a child, to the ten-year writing period of the music. After hundreds of pages of detailed arguments against detractors of the natural selection theories, including Gould and Lewontin, Dennett ends with his own Panglossian theme of the best of all possible worlds, a world whose ultimate perfect design has grown through ranks of lower forms to emerge as the emulation of the perfect supreme being above us all:

> We correctly intuit a kinship between the finest productions of art and science and the glories of the biosphere. William Paley was right about one thing: our need to explain how it can be that the universe contains many wonderful designed things. Darwin's dangerous idea is that they *all* exist as fruits of a single tree, the Tree of Life, and the processes that have produced each and every one of them are, at bottom, the same. The genius exhibited by Mother Nature can be disassembled into many acts of micro-genius—myopic or blind, purposeless[10] but capable of the most minimal sort of recognition of a good (a better) thing. . . . Is this Tree of Life a God one could worship? Pray to? Fear? Probably not. But it *did* make the ivy twine and the sky so blue, so perhaps the song[11] I love tells the truth after all. The Tree of Life is neither perfect nor infinite in space or time, but it is actual. . . . Is something sacred? Yes, say I with Nietzsche. I could not pray to it, but I can stand in affirmation of its magnificence. The world is sacred.[12]

I cannot agree with Dennett. At the heart of his ideas is a belief in the inevitable climb up the hierarchical ladder leading to perfection, in the ultimate designer. Despite his reference to the purposelessness of natural selection, Darwin's dangerous idea, there is a broad hint at a purpose nevertheless. The "good" or "better" thing is perceived evidence of the final purpose of all things. It is this belief that characterizes western science and that underlies its basic bias.

120

"How many camps were there along this section of track?" "Can we travel along the railroad right across the north?" "Did trains ever get this far?" On and on the questions come from my colleagues, and from me. The answers drone on with inept translations from Sasha. I don't want to hear them talking, and I don't want to hear myself talking. I have already decided that we will include the Gulag and Stalin's railroad in our exhibition on Siberia back in Toronto. But I can't stand making it into a simple business proposition.

"Here we are having many labels with name of Stalin." Pointing under our feet, Sasha shows us a rail with Stalin's name embossed on the steel.

"Can you bring that back to Toronto for us?" I listlessly ask the impossible.

"Of course" is the reply. Lyudmila's husband went out later and cut the section of rail off with a hacksaw, and we did have it in Toronto. How do they have the energy? After a week in Siberia, I am drained and I am grey with the effects of fatigue and bad food.

Stalin's railroad is in the Panglossian paradigm. For Stalin, it was there because it was always meant to be there in this best of all possible worlds. It is even possible to argue that the railroad was the result of natural selection. After all, Stalin would have had to select it from a list of any number of projects, but this one got the nod over many others. And the harsh environment certainly resulted in the deaths of countless slave workers. Only the strong made it through—natural selection at its best. A railroad across the north would rival the great achievements of world leaders through history. The sacrifice of a few million people could be justified in light of such a feat.

121

Not all attributes of an organism come about through natural selection. The great central dome of the Cathedral of San Marco in Venice is placed on four large arches set in a square. The conjunction of each arch forms a tapering triangular curved space called a spandrel. The spandrel is a form that falls out naturally from the joining together of arches. This is known as an epiphenomenon, an event that grows out of other established events, in this case a shape that comes about inevitably from the combining of arches. The spandrels are used as a metaphor for shapes that could come about naturally during the evolution of animals and plants,[13] shapes that would not be associated with any process of adaptation through natural selection—inevitable shapes, in other words.

122

How many shapes can a dictator take? Not very many. The interaction between a ruthless conqueror and the people he quells can be described as an epiphenomenon. There are only so many shapes that can occur at the conjunction of two civilizations, at the intersection of a people and the invader. Looking at the Cantino map, I see a linear Portuguese trail along the coastlines of Africa, Asia, and the Americas. At about the same time as the Portuguese adventures, voyages were launched from Venice, no doubt watched over by the spandrels of San Marco, those "inevitable" architectural shapes overseeing the birth of our modern European world conquerors, as they drew their maps across the images of older civilizations.

Conquerors do not live within the bosom of the conquered; they follow coastlines, they follow rivers, they follow trade routes, they follow supply lines. They draw long skinny lines over the discovered and defeated territories. These lines are enough to transform the world, because they cut across the fabric of a civilization like a tailor's shears. Stalin drew a line across the north, and he cut through the civilizations of the northern peoples. To do so he transported whole villages of people from the south, tore them from their homes, and strung them out in a line, a long line along the length of his railroad. Stretched out in this line, they could not see each other, they could only see his railroad. Communication along the road was limited to immediate neighbours—to the east and to the west. And travel, too, was limited to the east and west. North and south did not exist for the prisoner along Stalin's railroad.

123

I lag behind the others. I am conscious of doing this deliberately. Their talk disappears into the distance ahead of me. I can see the tundra plants beyond the wet boggy muck on either side of the raised railway. There are tall grasses growing in the wet pools. I stare at the wet and scramble down the embankment to touch the muck. I feel the strange urge to touch something more sinister than mud. "They are buried all around you," Sasha had told me. Every year, bodies are found. In Moscow, while we are staying there, the newspapers relate the discovery of a mass grave near one of the wedding-cake-shaped buildings known as the Seven Sisters—hideous huge places built under Stalin by slave labour. Why not here on the railroad? Why not especially here, where in the late 1940s, in winter, ten to twenty people died every night, in each one of the forty-seven camps along the short distance of railroad being built near Salekhard. The permafrost causes the ground to heave and shift, bringing bodies up every year. I hear they float down the Ob at times. Swimming there, had we shared the water with these others?

124

Stalin was a conqueror who could assign inferiority and make it stick. Even the slaves themselves ended up believing in their lack of worth. This is the secret to slavery—changing the world view of everyone so that we all believe in superiority and inferiority, master and slave alike. The Hereford Mappa Mundi, ca. 1300, traces for us the roots of slavery in the modern European mind. These roots are connected to the concept of race and the superiority of the European, but they can be applied even to Stalin's Gulag prisoners, because in becoming prisoners they became an inferior race in the minds of all those who lived in Soviet society. "We knew that the people buried there . . . with their hands and feet sticking out of the earth . . . we knew they were not even truly human," Lyudmila told me of her childhood in Sverdlovsk.

The Hereford Mappa Mundi is divided into three sections, Asia on top, Europe on the bottom left, and Africa on the bottom right. In the southern part of Africa, there are depicted races with monstrous attributes. There are people with only one leg and one eye, people with no mouths, and people who have no heads and whose faces are on their chests. These monsters come from long traditions of fearing and detesting all things foreign, but in the Hereford map we see laid out for us the consolidation of the idea of the three major sectors of the earth. From this division we have developed the more sophisticated concept of the three major races. More important, we see the roots of the belief that large portions of the earth are inhabited by beings who are less than human.

125

The Hereford Mappa Mundi is the most completely preserved medieval map of the world. It has been kept in Hereford Cathedral, in the west of England, since it was created. The circular map is divided roughly with a central T shape, formed by the Mediterranean Sea, the Nile River, and the

Aegean and Black Seas. Jerusalem is at the centre of the map. In the original map, there are many scenes depicting life and the earth's peoples in all the then known areas of the world. Important historical events are placed on a map that also depicts modern cities and cultures. So the Garden of Eden is shown at the top, and the crucifixion, and even the future apocalypse, alongside London, Paris, Egypt, and India. The Hereford Mappa Mundi was typical of the maps of the time.

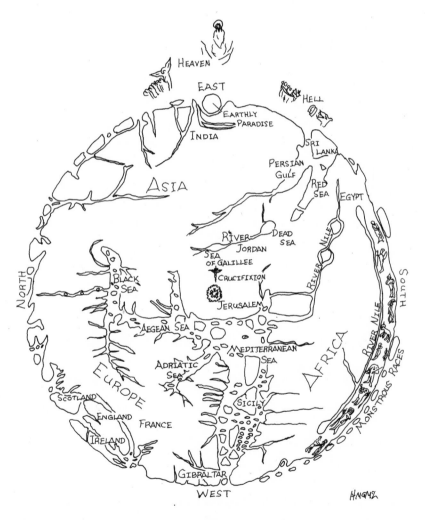

Author's version of the Hereford Mappa Mundi, ca. 1300.[14] The world is neatly divided into the major regions, with monsters depicted in the southern regions of Africa.

126

Animals are not made from Plasticine. Natural selection cannot mould them into just any shape. Frogs do not grow wings, even if they keep falling off cliffs for generations. Even if one could suggest that unusual flyers, such as squirrels, developed the trait owing to natural selection in environments that favoured flying, that selection would have to have occurred within the constraints of squirrelness. Thus we have "gliding" squirrels at best; they do not soar with the eagles.

But adaptationist theory would have it that anything is possible in the living world, given enough time. This is unlikely. Soaring eagle-squirrels will never come to be. And people will never dispense with their heads and grow their faces in their chests. Not all things are possible in this best of all possible worlds. But since the Middle Ages we have believed that there are niches in the world for everything and that everything is possible. A world of infinite variety, but with everything in its place. The eagle-squirrels will be found, or could develop at any rate, so we say, and the monster races do exist and will stay in southern Africa.

127 .

I touch the mud. The Siberian north is peculiarly quiet, so I sense at the same time some kind of sound coming from my own head. Are these sounds always there, usually drowned out by the commotion of everyday life around me? The sound is a thumping of my blood, a ringing in my ears; it feels like a warning not to tamper with these sacred things. But the mud is banal. It does nothing for me—it is just mud. There are no dead hands sticking up out of the semi-frozen dirt.

Why do I want to touch the dead? This place pulls me in. As I get back up to the top of the railroad embankment, I continue along the tracks. All is quiet now. I cannot hear the others at all. They could be miles away. I let the emotions of the railroad take over. The world is divided between the powerful and the slaves. The slaves are monsters who are less than human, but they have learned to love their place in the hierarchy of things. They work submissively until they die of cold and starvation and overwork. The powerful stand upon the work of these slaves and survey the railroad cutting across the texture and the history of the north. The power of the railroad is evident, even with its bent and twisted rails, its broken bridges, and its misplaced ties going off infinitely to the horizon. Those rails and ties never carried a single railcar across the northern wasteland of Siberia, yet the power is tangible. And I discover another feeling—the railroad is erotic. The railroad is death and sex. I cannot help it—it acts on me like an aphrodisiac. Somehow the reality of standing on this mound of death is turning me on. I feel heat and congestion in my loins. Why can't I feel the proper emotions, the sadness, the despair? Where is my sense of justice, where are my ethics? But maybe I have discovered something. The drive behind these megalomaniac projects is deeper than logic; it lives in the groin.

128

On the outskirts of Belleville those many years ago I did get off the railroad. I was not trapped. I went into the forest, the dark wood that would frighten most people, but to me it was a relief after the ominous fear I felt on the tracks. In the forest I would not meet anyone. The chances were too slim. The forest was vast, it went off in many directions. The railroad was a long narrow trail, and all creatures on it would eventually have to confront one another, but the forest had all the directions at its disposal; it was not a linear trail where all travellers must eventually meet.

Was I also avoiding a deeper emotion on the tracks? Was there an erotic element to the tracks even on the outskirts of Belleville, perhaps foreshadowing my walk in Siberia almost three decades later? I don't know the answer. I do know that the forest was a wild-looking place on that black night. The weather was foggy, and there was no moonlight or starlight. Eventually I realized that I had to find some marker to guide me home. I was lost and I had no feeling of being in control of the earth under my feet. I had none of that erotic charge that I felt on the railroad in Siberia.

Civilizations are forged by conquerors who move along linear paths. The conquerors are followed by the settlers who stake out their territory beside the length of the trails. If you go off the beaten track, you enter the wide forest. The forest has no definition; there are no lines to lead you from one end to the other.

129

Species of animals and plants are thought by some to follow a Bauplan,[15] a basic pattern of growth and structure that cannot be ignored, no matter how strong the pressures of natural selection. Human beings may walk on two legs, but our Bauplan is quadrupedal, and we continue to suffer for fighting against this immutable fact. We have back problems, birthing problems. The Bauplan proponents feel that they have moved away from the *a posteriori* arguments of the strict followers of Darwin's theory of natural selection. A basic underlying pattern creates constraints against which the forces of natural selection can only be realized as non-consequential refinements, they say. Thus one cannot use the after-the-fact approach and ask, What environmentally influenced adaptation events must have resulted in these traits? Aspects of the underlying pattern may indeed have been developed through interactions with local environments over the eons of time, but the Bauplan cannot be easily pried apart in order to study its causes, especially since the conditions of its formation may be untraceable.

Despite its attempts at defeating the teleology inherent in adaptationism, however, the concept of the Bauplan is still essentially based on an ideal pattern to which an organism aspires. This is still teleological. The pattern is the magnet that draws the organism throughout its embryonic development. Furthermore, the concept is dualistic. The Bauplan is placed over the terrain of the organism like a map. It is a surface reality covering the tangled undecipherable wildness that is the actual creature underneath, a wildness that is intractable for the very human scientist.

What do I gain from this analysis? It is mainly this: even the critics of Darwin's selectionist, adaptation paradigm cannot rid themselves of the teleological underpinnings of western thought. An "ideal" plan, a design for the ultimate perfect organism, always appears to be the preferred interpretation. And laid on top of the actual is a plan, a map, that substitutes for any real thing we may have the opportunity to encounter. And always the map has a familiar human aspect to it. A Bauplan is an architectural concept, an ideal that, even in the abstract, is reflective of human interests in structures and in contiguous frameworks. If there is to be an ultimate map for the cosmos, why must it be so human in character, I wonder.

130

The wildness of the forest was not readable. I needed to overlay a map that had the human linear touch, something with lines and borders that would help to orient me and guide me home. If I could have seen the stars, I could have created my own line through the wildness, but it was dark and foggy. After walking through the trees and across boggy clearings for about fifteen minutes, I began to regret my rash behaviour. Why had I left the track? And why had I decided to make the trek home shorter by moving away from the track at a 45-degree angle? I could have at least followed in the direction of the railroad even if I didn't want to be on it, I chided myself. The forests around Belleville were large enough to swallow me up at least until morning, and it was getting colder. I definitely needed a human pathway in this wilderness. I could go back to the track, I thought, but I wasn't sure of the direction.

131

Both the Cantino Map of 1502 and the Hereford Map of 1300 were maps that revealed the preconceived Bauplan of their creators. The Cantino Map was Portugal stretched over the coastal surfaces of the world. The Hereford Mappa Mundi was the literal physical geographical affirmation of the centrality of Christian Europe. The reality underneath the maps was a wild place, totally undecipherable to the Portuguese or to the medieval Christians. The maps placed on top made sense out of the world, never mind that they radically altered the terrain. And the overlaid maps became a new reality. This is the true meaning of duality; both manifestations are real. The Portuguese coastal tracks across the outer surfaces of Africa, Asia, and the Americas resulted in real civilizations. The fishy smell of our Lippincott home was the result of the Portuguese invasion, the first of many from Europe into the wider world.

132

The railroad of Stalin was another skinny trail of a conqueror. It did not end up as a successful enterprise, or did it? The railroad was laid over a wilderness that Stalin did not understand—the cultures of the reindeer people, the vast taiga forests and the northern tundra of furry animals and bleak winters. The railroad, though, became its own reality, just as the Portuguese coastal markers became Angola and Mozambique and Brazil. The railroad heralded the establishment of northern cities and industry across Siberia. Even though rail travel is non-existent in most northern regions today, and certainly not possible on Stalin's railroad, travel to the north and working in the north are accepted as commonplace. The imposed map has earned its place by fashioning reality.

133

Up to this century, a scientific model was seen to be useful in its own context and for a particular purpose. New facts introduced to the model would alter it. But lately cosmological models have increasingly been seen as code-breakers to ascertain the ultimate truth of the universe. Philosophers of science discussing these issues are aware of the overlaying of human rationality on nature. But even as they acknowledge the religious roots of the western dogma,[16] there are those who still end up as fervent supporters of a "designed" universe, one with all things in their rightful place. Exemplifying this marriage between religion and science, Paul Davies, a theoretical physicist and now professor of natural philosophy, writes:

> Gottfried Leibniz suggested that we live in the best of all possible worlds. . . . It may be that rapid scientific progress is just a quirk of twentieth-century history, and that we are as far as ever from knowing "the mind of God." Yet I feel compelled to believe that, through science, we really are being allowed to glimpse the rational foundations of physical existence. . . . Freeman Dyson once wrote . . . "I do not feel like an alien in this universe. The more I examine the universe and study the details of its architecture, the more evidence I find that the universe in some sense must have known we were coming." I feel the same way too. In some strange and perhaps unfathomable manner, it begins to look as if we are meant to be here.[17]

134

Through the fog, I saw something that startled me. It was a fencepost, at the corner of a farmer's field, at the edge of the trees. Why, after I'd encountered deep darkness in the night forest, would anything alarm me, especially since it wasn't moving? Then I realized that human thinking had imposed human form over the underlying wild nature, and this had made me jump unconsciously to the conclusion that it was a person out there, after all the trouble I had taken to leave the railroad tracks to avoid other people.

It was human civilization and I knew I was safe. Like all people, deep down I craved the rational, even while seeking the wildness of the forest. I walked along the fence until I hit an inside corner, and then, by keeping to the edge of the fence, I eventually made my way, zigzagging back toward the outskirts of town. I could see the lights of houses in the distance. An hour later, I was home. The map of human reason had guided me home, through this dark irrational wood.

135

At last I understand the railroad. I know what Stalin felt when he laid this track of destruction. But I had to come here to stand on it to understand it. The railroad superimposed reason on the wildness, rationality on primitive Siberian tribes, and ultimately control over the lives of the slaves. And the feelings of power conceal a sexual urge that defies the politics of even those who would be ethical.

I walk along the tracks wondering how we will ever translate this railroad into an exhibit in a museum. We will need a sense of the people who died here and the power that held them in place. The pieces of rail will come to Toronto in the Siberia exhibition. Along with them we will bring a few of the cards filed in Salekhard in the 1940s by the NKVD and the MGB, the organizations that later, in 1954, became the KGB—one card for every person, adult or child, who was transported to work on the railroad. "You can't take these cards back with you—we brought them out only for your information!" Lyudmila's face was white, as we stood arguing in the freezing Moscow night outside our hotel the next winter.

"All right, then let me talk to the local KGB representative," I said rashly, not caring that Lyudmila was starting to shake. She really did fear them. After she'd lived so many years in a police state, who would blame her? But was there really any danger in taking back to Toronto some old records, small cards like the report cards we used to get when I was in public school? I wanted them. They were fascinating; each one summed up the entire life of someone who lived and may have died in the work camps. One of them was a record of a boy only thirteen years old, and another was his mother's. But I was collecting again. In the same way as I had collected Hartegenov, the sculptor, I was now collecting the dead slaves of the Gulag. To Lyudmila, these were real people, real for the little girl who had played among the shallow graves of "monsters." I did not have her history.

I did try to reach the head of the KGB office in Moscow the next day. It is remarkable how little I cared about the warnings of my Russian friends. I couldn't relate to their stories of foreigners going to prison for minor acts of espionage. I think now that I should have cared about what might have happened to them if I had succeeded in having a detailed conversation about the records held by Lyudmila. But the Soviet bureaucracy defeated my attempts. I could not rouse the KGB officials. In the end, Lyudmila sent the cards to us, after I don't know what coercion from Sasha or what nightmares she might have endured about the KGB.

136

"Can we walk back?" Jim complained. We had to return from the railroad the same way we had come—in the little three-wheeled car. We were getting cranky by now. I think the Gulag stories were causing us a lot of stress. Also, we knew that we had to do something about the Gulag in the exhibition, but we had never intended to have such stuff in an exhibition about science. What was the connection to science anyway, we were wondering.

"Let's get it over with." Fiona inserted herself into the back seat. Lyudmila squeezed in beside her, and then Jim wanted to get in. So they all got out and tried again to fit themselves into the tiny back seat in the most economical way. When they finally did manage to position themselves so that they could survive the trip, Gregor had to tell them to get out so that he could pump up the leaking tire, which by this time was flat again.

CHAPTER FOUR

PARIS AND AMERICA

Licence my roving hands, and let them goe
Behind, before, above, between, below.
O my America, my new found lande,
My kingdome, safeliest when one man man'd,
My myne of precious stones, my Empiree,
How blest am I in this discovering thee.
To enter in these bonds is to be free,
Then where my hand is set my seal shall be.

    – JOHN DONNE, "Elegie: To His Mistris Going to Bed"

137

I HAVE UNDERESTIMATED my stamina. Even though I'm hungry and my feet hurt, and I need new shoes—the heels are worn down and I keep twisting my ankle—I keep going on, hoping to see just one more avenue, one more five-storey building with intricate fronts and iron gratings and elaborate doors. I am wading through the crowds of evening commuters, going upstream as they hurry toward Métro stations carrying baguettes and packages under their arms. The colours, especially, are getting to me. After the Soviet Union, I am startled by the reds and stark yellows of the plastic bags dispensed by stores and shops. Packaging in Moscow was drab, faded brownish tones. And the women here are dressed in colours too. Paris is like an alcoholic drink to me—I have arrived for one night on my way home to Canada and I am determined to drink it all.

138

Paris is a series of concentric circles that appear to radiate from a central rectangle, the Jardin des Tuileries. The city hangs on a river, the Seine, like a nest woven by silkworms on a branch of a tree. The Moscow I had just left is also built in circles, is centred on Red Square, and hangs on a loop of the Moskva River.

Paris and Moscow have an overwhelming quality about them. And as I walk through some of the grander streets of Paris, I am reminded of a journey I had taken the year before in Washington D.C. The American civilization has a capital that reflects the imperialism of the west. Gracious boulevards radiate from a central cultural park, the Mall.[1] Meadow-sized lawns separate monumental Greek-styled buildings from one another. Like Moscow, Washington strives to emulate Paris, the great French centre of our western cultural heritage.

It was 1989 when I went to Washington, D.C., where I visited Richard, an investigator at the National Institute of Mental Health, who assisted me in developing an understanding of the workings of the human brain. "Our labs are in the St. Elizabeth's Hospital," he had said, but I hadn't known that this was in Anacostia, the southeast sector of the city of Washington. We had been told to avoid this area because of a recent rash of shootings. But, excited by what was happening in his lab, I was determined to go anyway. Richard was working with a team of medical researchers; his task was to measure the brain *as it thinks* by hooking patients up to PET scanners.[2] In giving the subjects a specific mental task to perform, the scientists were tracking the physical manifestations of thought, watching for patterns that show up on their instruments. Their experiments were a window into parts of the brain that are implicated in various mental activities. This was a first glance into the inner workings of consciousness.

I make arrangements for the trip to St. Elizabeth's. "That's where the really crazy people are kept," I am told. Gretchen and Baiba, my Washington colleagues, will come with me. We meet each other in front of the Smithsonian's Natural History Museum. The traffic is dense near the Mall area downtown, and we stand on the street waving down taxis that never stop. Finally, after twenty minutes, one does. "I can't take you right there; I might have some more to pick up" is our greeting from the first driver to stop. The taxi system is bizarre in Washington. We are sitting three abreast in the back seat, and the driver wants to fill his front passenger seat. Unlike most places on earth, in Washington the taxi is not yours when you get in. The driver will pick up other people and even drop you off within a few streets of your destination if it is more convenient for him. Anacostia is definitely not convenient because the driver wouldn't get a fare back to the centre of town. Almost everyone in Anacostia is black and poor.

139

When I look at the map of Paris, I see it is not really laid out in a circular pattern; it is more like a snail shell or a spiderweb. The central part of Paris is separated into twenty districts called arrondissements. The arrangement of the arrondissements is what gives the impression of a web or a snail shell—they are stacked up from the Louvre in the first arrondissement to the graves of Balzac, Jim Morrison, and Colette in the twentieth, in a spiral, around the Seine. All the arrondissements belong to Paris, and yet each is separate, with its own atmosphere. Each has its own council and town hall. Each neighbourhood has a distinctive history and culture. Each is like a crystal, holding its own inner light and yet reflecting the image of all the Paris arrondissements around it. The crystals are held by the strings that form the structure of the web or the net.

140

A few places are marked on my map of Paris. They include the Quartier Latin, Place de la Concorde, and Place Pigalle, all districts that I visited during my walk through the city one evening. As I travelled from one arrondissement to the next, I discovered that although each district has its own unique style, there are reflections of all the other districts to be found in any one of them.

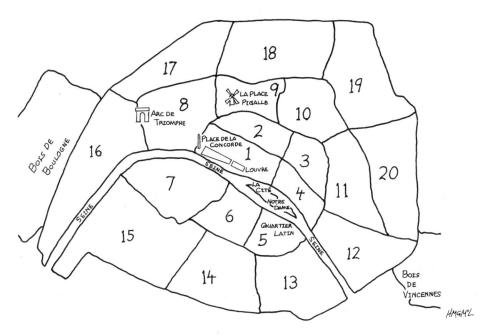

Map of the arrondissements of Paris. Each district is unique and yet represents Paris as a whole and is a reflection of all other districts.

141

As we drive into Anacostia I am struck by a singular activity. It is midmorning and no one is walking on the streets. But the place is crowded. The streets are lined with people sitting on the curbs, their feet stretching into the roadway. There have been a lot of killings, gang and drug related, and as I look from our taxi I think maybe this is why the people are all outside—they can see each other better. They can keep an eye on one another. Or maybe this is simply a manifestation of a different cultural experience?

Our taxi is one of very few cars. Even so, I am afraid we will run over somebody's feet every time we turn a tight corner. The people on the curb look at us as if we are the beginning of a parade coming down the street. They sit and talk to one another—the atmosphere is at once festive and wary. Our taxi driver didn't find anyone to fill the front seat, which means that we are being taken directly to our destination and not simply dropped off in the general vicinity. I am grateful for that. As we slow down, approaching the entrance to St. Elizabeth's Hospital, the people on the curb stare at us as we stare at them. I am uncomfortable and a little nervous about being here. Our driver is more nervous than we are. He is black, and I suspect he has more to fear if he decides to stay around here for any length of time. "I won't be waiting for you. Here's the number of the company if you need a cab back to town." He hands us a card once we are inside the gates of the hospital grounds. St. Elizabeth's is an ugly old brick institution. And it is vast. Buildings are laid out over expanses of grass, hemmed in by huge trees. The windows are small, and through each one I imagine the eyes of homicidal maniacs. "Hinckley is in here,"[3] I am told, and I look up expectantly at the windows above me. I tell myself I'm paranoid.

142

It was late afternoon when I arrived at my hotel in Paris, coming from the airport. I watched the taxi meter add up to a hopeless cost. One way from de Gaulle airport was equivalent to a week's expenses in Moscow. But I had to see Paris, especially after the greyness of Soviet Russia, even if I only had one night before returning to Canada.

My hotel was in the Latin Quarter, the fifth arrondissement. I can't remember the street now, but I was happy because it was short and narrow. The bed was short and narrow too, like the ones we had in

Moscow, in Leningrad, and in Arkhangelsk. I had to walk up four floors, but the experience was authentic, I told myself.

I set out to see Paris in one evening. I remember walking along rue Soufflot, crossing St-Jacques and then turning up Victor-Cousin to look at the Église de la Sorbonne. I am enchanted by the history I am passing. It is like the civilization of the west laid out before me. I make my way to the boulevard St-Germain, and then, determined to keep to little streets, I slip down rue Boutebrie, then la Parcheminerie, the rue de la Harpe, then St-Séverin, past St-Séverin church along rue des Prêtres St-Séverin, and then back to where I had been on rue de la Parcheminerie! I did not make this circle deliberately. The blocks are short, and other streets intersect them at surprising angles; continuations of little streets have new names once they cross another. I might have been clued in if rue Boutebrie and rue des Prêtres St-Séverin had the same name, since they are effectively one street with a name for each block. At this rate, I will be lost forever in the maddening maze of Paris. Cafés are everywhere. Little shops sell baguettes and pâté and cheese. In this area, the people in the cafés are young, students, smoking Gauloises and talking animatedly, about philosophy, about other people not arrived yet or people who are not coming at all. I feel completely out of place. There are no lone strangers at tables, and even if there were, they would know how to behave and they would be accepted. I decide to continue on to more likely tourist areas, somewhere less intimidating. At the riverside nearby, I stare across at the Île de la Cité. The lights are going on around Notre Dame. It is getting dark and a little chilly.

143

Wignarajah came to me at the time that I was going back and forth between Canada and the Soviet Union. I was asked if I could give him some work; he had received a Ph.D. in India in biology, come to Canada, and was interested in a museum career. Wignarajah had a different cultural viewpoint, and would eventually provide proof for me that a scientist's perspective on science is related to his culture.

I put him on our new project; we were exploring the cultural nature of science and the inherent bias of the scientists of the west. But he had trouble working with us. He would set appointments to interview staff members to discuss their viewpoints on the objectivity of scientists or on discrimination in our social setting, and invariably I would be called up the next day, or the person involved would "accidentally" find me on my way through the museum. "Please don't send Dr. Wignarajah to see me again. I don't appreciate the unspoken suggestion that I am biased." Eventually, Wignarajah complained that he would have to change his project because no one would talk with him.

As revealing as the personal interrelationships between Wignarajah and the rest of the team were for me, however, I was most affected by the challenging dichotomy of his *intellectual* viewpoints. Despite his superior knowledge of cultural variations in the interpersonal relationships that characterize our society in Canada, he still believed that there were *no* cultural differences when it came to observable facts, or basic processes of science. For him, any apparent differences between his approach to studying the natural world and those of his colleagues were all on the surface. Yet despite *his* belief in the universality of science, my work with Wignarajah was bringing *me* to the conclusion that there are cultural differences in the practice of science that reach down into the very basics, the very foundations of our thought processes.

144

Richard is a high-level researcher. He works with a large team of students, technicians, and post-doctoral fellows who use his sophisticated brain-imaging equipment to perform state-of-the-art experiments. He is on to something, he knows, something quite profound. He is among the first to produce accurate images of the conscious human mind.

Unlike Wignarajah, Richard comes from a world that I know very well. He is a man who speaks with authority. He is friendly, but gives the impression of being very busy, with little time to spare. "Yes, I understand this will be displayed in the travelling psychology exhibit," he says, indicating that he will therefore spend some time with us, but we will need to be accommodating. "We're doing a procedure this morning. You'll have to put on gowns. As long as you're participating in the experiment, you'll be dressed like the technicians."

Baiba and Gretchen don't complain, not even by rolling their eyes at me. They're used to this condescending treatment, working as they do with so many professors and psychology researchers. I don't care— I only want to get his PET scans for the museum exhibit. The technicians start setting up the equipment. Surgically gowned, they are white all over. They wheel in carts with syringes and bottles and gas cylinders. One of the cylinders contains the radioactive Xenon gas that will be inhaled by the volunteer patient during the experiment. The PET scan device is readied. It looks like a giant metal halo with tubes coming out like spokes. The experimental subject will sit in a high dentist's chair, his head placed in the PET scanner halo. He will breathe the Xenon gas through a snorkel. The experimental subject and the scanner are to be set up behind a window that is a mirror on the subject's side, but permits us to observe through our side. Computers are turned on, and test scans appear on screen as demonstrations for our benefit. A PET scan looks like a head sliced across the top, with brightly coloured blobs indicating sections of the brain. Red means high positron emission, high activity, and blue low activity. Shades in between indicate various intermediate levels of brain activity. "We're looking for high activity in the dorsolateral prefrontal cortex,"[4] Richard tells us. We will be watching for the functioning brain to reveal itself before our very eyes, lighting up the lateral portion of the prefrontal region as a particular kind of thinking takes place. The experimental room gleams with stainless steel surfaces, and it glows with colourful computer screens. We are ready for the experimental subject. We are ready for the brain to reveal itself.

145

Partly to get away from the cold wind coming off the Seine, I walk back to the boulevard St-Germain, and I continue in a direction where I sense there is action. In the distance, I can see spotlights on beautiful buildings. I need to cross the river. I see a Métro station, Cluny La Sorbonne. Inside the station, I study the map. It is bewildering. In Moscow a few days before, Jim and Fiona and I were lost for hours. The subway system in Moscow is complex. When a station serves as a junction with another line, the train on the other track is not simply one that will take you back where you came from, but one that will take you farther into or out of town, depending on your destination. It will not allow you to backtrack, as Toronto's subway does. The train to make a return journey will be in another part of the station. We had overshot the station we needed and decided to try to go back. Not realizing the complexities of the Moscow system, we ended up in another part of town entirely. By midnight we had left the subway trains and had been walking for a couple of hours, still looking for our hotel. Luckily it was summer and not too cold. "That's it! That's the statue of Gagarin!" Fiona finally yelled. "That's where we live!"

"Oh, Gagarin! Thank you for being so fucking big!" Every monument in Moscow seems to be an oversize figure of some famous person. Gagarin, the cosmonaut, stood many storeys high. We could see him for about a mile, and he guided us back to the hotel.

In Paris I am looking at the possibility of being lost again on the Métro. I decide to go somewhere where I will be able to see a big monument, like Gagarin. I head for the Champs-Elysées stop, which means changing lines twice. Not wanting to repeat the mistakes made in Moscow, I read the signs very carefully. My French is better than my Russian; I manage to get there. I step out to see the Champs-Elysées, the Arc de Triomphe in the distance and the Place de la Concorde in the other direction. The avenue is glittering with lights. Traffic screams by. As I walk toward Place de la Concorde, I am conscious of the people around me. There are young people here, just as there were around the Sorbonne. Here, a couple are wrapped around each other, not lost in philosophical discussion, but there is a flavour of the Latin Quarter nevertheless. What is it? I sense the smell hasn't changed. It's the Gauloises. Something of the fifth arrondissement is found in the eighth and vice versa. The dark little cafés of the Latin Quarter had not been without a rather surprising sense of style, a style that I now see emanating from every foot of the avenue des Champs-Elysées.

146

In the minds of western scientists, honeybee hives have a queen that is the centre of the bee culture, with pollen and nectar gatherers and guards and nurses and baby bees all playing roles, but all in subservience to the queen. This beehive model is a typical western hierarchy. Wignarajah, combining his biology background with his interest in public museum displays, developed a new model for studying beehives. He came up with a beehive organization that puts the queen bee into just one of many "bubbles," or spheres of influence, within an array of bubbles. There is no hierarchy, just overlapping bubbles, interconnected and all equally important. The queen bee's bubble overlaps or reflects the worker-bee bubble and so forth—the arrondissements of a Paris of honeybees. "Indra's net," Professor Priestley said to us nearly thirty years ago, as Danielle and I sat in his class on Hindu and Buddhist philosophy. East Asian studies had drawn me because of the Chinese politics of the time. The Cultural Revolution was an event to be studied in detail, but the study carried us in much deeper, into an examination of the logic of existence. Indra's net was an image from Hinduism that I remembered when Wignarajah arranged his bees. In Hinduism, there is imagined a fisherman's net that has a crystal at every knot. I didn't think of Paris when Wignarajah told me about his model for beehive organization. I should have. His beehive ideas were worthy of the great city of Paris, where the arrondissements are like crystals in a net. Each has its own essence but also reflects the images of the other crystals all around it. And the reflections reflect infinitely.

The whole net of Paris is like a living organism. Each crystal reflects its neighbours and its own reflection in its neighbours'. The reflections of reflections reverberate across the net into infinity. This is a model of the way things work, and it is an alternative to the hierarchical system of the west. I saw in Wignarajah's model the beginning of a museum exhibition on the nature of science itself, of cultural variants that would question whether we can ever approach a universal truth. If reality could be seen from one perspective as being measurable within a hierarchy and from another as infinite reciprocal reflections, then how many other ways of modelling nature could there be? And, maybe most important, do we ever acknowledge that there are models other than the one we use so frequently in the west, our hierarchical ladder to perfection, the model that pervades our thinking?

147

I believe that the acceptance of the hierarchical model is so dominant that we cannot even detect its influence. Today, we live in the shadow of hundreds of years of prejudice, a prejudice with roots in our intellectual history. These roots could not reveal themselves more obviously than in the descriptions, made by the founders of the European sciences, of people of African and Asian descent. It is in these descriptions that the hierarchical model of the world is accepted as a given. The ranking of the so-called races of humanity is not even questioned. The hierarchy of all things, from the lowest to the highest, is taken to be gospel, and is not understood as a model only. Alternative models, such as Wignarajah's network, are taken to be subsidiaries, useful for particular applications only,[5] and not as substitutes for the entire schema of the scientific organization of nature. The possibility that the many cultures of the world could offer equal contributions to our future science is laughed at even today, especially today, by those of us who pursue scientific explanations of the world.

148

In the early 1800s, Georges Cuvier, considered by many to be the founder of comparative anatomy, wrote about the races of humankind. He considered them to be a continuation of the hierarchy he perceived in the animal species of the world:

> The Caucasian, to which we belong, is distinguished by the beauty of the oval which forms the head; and it is this one which has given rise to the most civilized nations—to those which have generally held the rest in subjection: it varies in complexion, and in the colour of the hair.
>
> The Mongolian is known by his projecting cheek-bones, flat visage, narrow and oblique eyebrows, scanty beard and olive complexion. Great empires have been established by this race in China and Japan, and its conquests have sometimes extended to this side of the Great Desert; but its civilization has always remained stationary.
>
> The Negro race is confined to the southward of the Atlas chain of mountains: its colour is black, its hair crisped, the cranium compressed, and nose flattened. The projecting muzzle and thick lips evidently approximate it to the Apes: the hordes of which it is composed have always continued barbarous.[6]

Charles Lyell, Darwin's contemporary and supporter, wrote extensively about the animal species of the world, putting them into hierarchies as a matter of course. Human beings were fitted into this hierarchy as well:

> The great fact, that the brain of the Bushman, as [Dieterich] Tiedemann [child psychologist (1748–1803)] shows, leads towards the brain of the Simiadae [monkeys], implies a connexion between want of intelligence and structural assimilation, so does the prognathous tendency of the Australian & Negro race. Each race of Man has its place, like the inferior animals.[7]

Today, we are not so unsubtle as to describe the peoples of the world as being closely akin to apes. Nor do we describe their civilizations as meaningless. But we do continue to accept the apparent superiority of European logic and science as an excuse for the continued ranking of the peoples of the earth in a hierarchy of existence.

149

Wignarajah came to me from a Hindu tradition. He could not see that there were cultural variants possible in the pursuit of scientific knowledge. His blindness to his own unique contribution in his Indra's net of a honeybee hive revealed to me that people generally are unaware of their own prejudice and bias in approaching the study of nature.

The essence of the Hindu study of nature was made even more clear to me when I commissioned the development of a Hindu calendar. It was in 1995 when I approached colleagues of mine who had connections to the Hindu community in Toronto. I asked for something I thought would be easy. I wanted a Hindu calendar that would correspond to our Gregorian year 2000. This was to be a part of a collection of calendars from a number of cultures.

The process took more than a year. I began by contacting friends, and then friends of friends, and then their relatives in India, who eventually found for me a calendar maker in Naupade, a town near Bombay. The chain of human connections needed to find the calendar maker foreshadowed the process of calendar making itself. The Hindu calendar is not established far in advance. Each year has to be calculated by hand, with reference to numerous charts of the moon's position, its phases, the sun's position, and the planets. In effect, a calendar maker is also forecasting the future. The interrelationship of astronomical observations and human earthly actions creates a calendar that is truly a network. Wignarajah's model of nature is in evidence here. There is no authoritative hierarchical model, prescribing the details of the calendar. The process of divination and mathematical calculation are intertwined with human activities over the time span of a year. Yes, I

know it could be argued that all this could be put into a computer program and we would have had a calendar in a few hours, not several
months. However, the fact is that it did take months, because the process of thinking through the calendar, of thinking through the network
of interlacing activities, both celestial and human, was intrinsic to the
calendar itself. What's more, the calendar maker had to begin where he
had last left off, so I was presented with several years' worth of Hindu
calendar. The usual course of action is to set up a calendar one year in
advance. He had the 1996 time period ready, but I had asked for the
year 2000. This necessitated creating ones for 1997, '98, and '99, as
well. The process of calendar making was a discovery. It took my expert in Naupade through an endeavour that was like forging a pathway
into an unknown country. This is a non-teleological way to think; the
outcome is not assured, and sights are not set on an end point that will
dictate the shape of events and places in between. In the mind of the
European, the year 2000 is accessible. We can leap into that time frame
in an instant. In the mind of my Hindu calendar maker, I believe, the
process had to be developed painstakingly, one day at a time, laying out
the moon's phases and its position in the constellations and the religious holidays that correspond both to the sky and to the activities of
the people on earth. At the end of the process, I received several note-
books, with each day of the future carefully written out by hand.

150

The small portion of the Hindu year, which corresponds approximately to the Gregorian year 2000, is typical of the calculations of
the calendar maker D. K. Soman. The words are written, for the most
part, in the Roman alphabet rather than in Sanskrit, because this particular calendar was calculated especially at my request. In the first
column, the *Tithis* are listed. These have to be calculated one by one
using charts that have been the mathematical source for Hindu calendar makers for centuries. Each *Tithi* represents the approximate time
it takes the moon to go ahead of the sun by 12 degrees (as measured

on the great circle arc of the sky). A *Tithi* can take between twenty and twenty-four hours. Sometimes a *Tithi* is slow, lying over two calendar days (as is shown on January 11 and 12 on the example page). If a *Tithi* is fast, two *Tithis* can occur on the same day (as is shown for January 14). The third column shows the *Nakshatra*—the star constellations where the moon resides each night. Soman also calculated the festivals for a number of calendars corresponding with the Hindu days. The Hindu festival of *Pongal*, for example, is indicated on this sample page. *Pongal* is significant as it occurs shortly after the winter solstice, during the time of the "return of the sun," as it begins to rise again in the sky. *Pongal* is a significant human event in the agricultural society of southern India and Sri Lanka.

All the calculations were done by hand by the calendar maker, in a linear fashion, one day following the next. The lives of the Hindu people are related to the calendar, and it, in turn, is related to the movements of the moon, the sun, and the stars. The laying-out of a calendar is a journey whose outcome is not assured. Therefore, the painstaking effort seen in this example (but multiplied many times over) is absolutely necessary in the mind of the Hindu calendar maker.

The calculations can be drawn onto a graphical calendar, corresponding to the celestial movements of the sun and the moon. The moon's position in the sky is charted through a series of constellations. Over the course of a 27.3 day period, the moon moves from its highest position in the sky (the constellation "Ardra") to its lowest part of the sky (the constellation "Mula"). The moon is also charted with respect to the Bright phase (Krishna), starting with the full moon, and the Dark phase (Shukla), starting with the new moon. In addition to the constellation positions and the Krishna and Shukla phases of the month, there are other arbitrary month delineations that have developed with the calendar over thousands of years; these are the months with names like Pausha, Magha, Falguna, and Chaitra.

All religious holidays depend on the movement of the moon through the sky and on the position of the sun in its cycle. The Hindu calendar is an interweaving of human activities and celestial observations. It is a map that is a coming together of activities on earth and in the heavens— reflecting each other in an infinite network of interrelationships.

151

As I have said, Paris should have been on my mind when I encountered Wignarajah's network model of honeybee hives. My trip through Paris that night in 1990 was one of constant discovery; I bounced from one district to the next, often coming upon novel sights but still seeing Paris as a whole, a network of communities. Each community was a distinct unit, but could not be defined in isolation from the rest of Paris. So I see the conflict between western science and the science of the Hindu calendar—the science of Wignarajah's honeybee hive organization. In western science, we are very eager to define an object in isolation and to examine its actions as a singular unit in nature. The moon's phases and movements through the sky can be understood in isolation from human endeavour, we say. But the moon is a part of an interconnected world when we seek to achieve understanding within the Hindu network model.

Paris was a revelation in another way. Though it provides evidence of a vibrant network, the city also represents the height of western civilization, occupying a place at the top of the hierarchy. All human activities are seen as a reflection, to a lesser or greater degree of achievement, of the Paris model, the gold standard for civilization. People from other civilizations are seen as artifacts in Paris, examined for their attributes, for their proper position in the hierarchy. Understanding this, it is not surprising that, in 1815, after the death of Saartjie Baartman, the famous "Hottentot Venus," a Khoi woman who while still alive had been put on display in England and France out of curiosity about her African physique, Georges Cuvier dissected her genitalia and put them on display in Paris's Musée de l'Homme.

I have no map to guide me through Paris, so I rely on my instincts. The shops are all closing and people are escaping to the suburbs.

Hindu calendar, showing the sky—the moon's phases and its position, the elevation of the sun, and the religious holidays, for a part of the Hindu year 1921–22 (approximately Gregorian year 2000).

PRAMATHI NAM SAMVATSARE 1921 ; PAUSH SHUKLA पूर्णिमाको पौष पूर्णिमा PAKSHA, VIKRAM SAMVAT 2056 ; ... JANUARY 2000 AD
SHALIWAHAN SAKA 1420 ; PARSI 1369 JAIN SAMVAT 2526
ISLAMIC (HEGIRA)

TITHI तिथि	DAY वार	NAKSHATRA नक्षत्र	INDIAN DATE भारतीय तारीख दिनांक	PARSI DATE पारसी दिनांक	ISLAMIC DATE मुसलमानी दिनांक	GREGORIAN DATE ईस्वी दिनांक January	FESTIVALS त्यौहार
SHUKLA 1 PRATIPADA	FRI	PURVASHADHA	PAUSH 17	AMARDAD 19	RAMADAN 29	8	
2 DWITIYA	SAT	UTTARASHADHA	18	20	30	9	
3 TRITIYA	SUN	SHRAVAN	19	21	SHAWWAL 1	10	SHAWWAL BEGINS / Idul Fitr
4 CHATURTHI	MON	DHANISHTA	20	22	2	11	
5 PANCHAMI	TUE	SHATATARAKA	21	23	3	12	
6 SHASHTHI	WED	PURVA BHADRAPADA	22	24	4	13	
7/8 SAPTAMI ASTAMI	THU	UTTARA BHADRAPADA	23	25	5	14	MAKAR SANKRANTI / PONGAL
9 NAVAMI	FRI	REVATI	24	26	6	15	
10 DOSHAMI	SAT	ASHWINI	25	27	7	16	
11 EKADASHI	SUN	BHARANI	26	28	8	17	
12 DWADASHI	MON	KRITIKA	27	29	9	18	
13 TRAYODASHI	TUE	ROHINI	28	30	10	19	PARSI SHAHRIWAR BEGINS
14 CHATURDASHI	WED	MRIG	29	SHAHEVAHAR 1	11	19	
15/1 PURNIMA/1 PRATIPADA	THU	ARDRA PUNARVASU	30	2	12	20	SOLAR MAGH BEGINS / TOTAL LUNAR ECLIPSE (NOT VISIBLE FROM INDIA)
	FRI	PUSHYA	MAGH 1	3	13	21	PAUSH PURNIMA BEGINS / PAUSH PURNIMA

A Hindu mapmaker's calculations.

Other action looks expensive—fancy restaurants and private clubs. Eventually, I follow the routes of the tourist buses. They are all headed in the same direction, it seems. They guide me away from the everyday activities of the Parisiens and toward the racier nightlife that all great western centres boast and that is the mark of a true civilization. On rue d'Amsterdam, I find a small restaurant that looks vaguely inviting. It is still early, and I feel I can fit into the crowd. "Please come in! Come in!" The waitress is a transsexual wearing revealing clothing; she recommends a red wine with my meal of duck. I am cold and tired and hungry. I accept. Bring me a good meal and a bottle of wine. I have entered the ranks of those who count for something, no longer a stray cat wandering through the streets of Paris. The decadence is almost palpable. This is the height of the civilized world, Paris, and it can only be experienced if I relax in this luxurious restaurant, become intoxicated on wine, and fill myself with French cuisine.

152

The preparations for the PET scanning experiment are almost complete. The experimental subject is brought in. Two technicians enter, gowned in white surgical attire. Each holds an arm of the thirty-year-old black man who has agreed to inhale radioactive isotope and have his mind read by the scanner. He can barely walk on his own. He is slouched over, his face is collapsed into itself, the muscles around his mouth are slack. His dull eyes look at us without acknowledging our presence. Or maybe he is hiding his embarrassment by putting up a shield. They sit him down on a chair, pull up the sleeve of his hospital gown, swab his arm with disinfectant and prepare to inject him intravenously with his daily neuroleptic medication that will control the hallucinations associated with his chronic schizophrenia. The man's head is down during the whole procedure.

He has given his consent to take part in the experiment. How such a man could have been aware of the implications of such an experiment is beyond me. He is a patient suffering from a serious form of schizophrenia. He has very little ability to relate to people or to plan ahead. The experiment is testing the activity in the prefrontal region of his brain—the section of his brain where he makes "plans for the future." Using such a patient is important in an experiment that is monitoring the activity of the frontal regions of the brain. It is predicted that a schizophrenic patient will display less activity when given mental tasks designed to activate planning for the future, we are told. However, patients given drugs that limit the hallucinations and mental agitation normally seen in schizophrenia are predicted to do better—to have PET scans more like those of normal people. While under the PET scanner, the subject will concentrate on a specific task, a computer game based on the Wisconsin card-sorting task.[8] This will keep the brain function focused long enough for an accurate reading of the brain's activities on the scanner.

The man being prepared for the PET scan reminds me of the people lining up on the curbs of Anacostia just outside the hospital. He has no real choice in his destiny. He does not understand the science and the history that have led up to his participation in these groundbreaking experiments. But I guess, for this man, the job is as good as it gets.

153

From 1932 to 1972, an experiment was conducted by high-level medical researchers in the United States. During those years, reports of this experiment were reported to the U.S. Congress and were published in leading journals. The experiment became infamous, known as the Tuskegee syphilis project. For forty years a group of men in Tuskegee, Alabama, were watched as their illness progressed. The researchers wanted to see what happens to people without treatment. No treatment for syphilis was given because the men were the "controls" in the experiment. Experimental controls are watched for natural occurrences, and no intervention and no treatment is given so that they can be compared to others who have been given treatments of various kinds. The men involved in the Tuskegee experiments were not informed that they were being denied treatment that existed for the disease. They were paid a small amount of money for helping the investigators. Many of them died of the disease. The remainder all suffered terrible health problems. They were all poor and black.

Although I know the investigators I met at the National Institute of Mental Health laboratories in Washington would not in any way support the inappropriate blindness to the ethics of experimentation exhibited by those involved in the Tuskegee experiment, I nevertheless find myself asking where we scientists draw the line. I would suggest that the decision to use the poor, the uneducated, and the essentially unaware underclass is a natural outcome of a kind of blindness, a blindness to the power wielded by all of us who are in charge of our science-based society.

154

I am finished my meal, and slightly drunk. I launch out onto the streets to find more of Paris. Just down the street from the famous Moulin Rouge, a mixed group of Japanese tourists is being ordered back into the bus by a young man with a heavy French accent. I am amused by the guttural sounds of his Japanese, a style usually reserved for men-only conversations in Japan. The elderly Japanese women in the group seem intimidated by his masculinity. They are coming out of a club decorated with pictures of nude women and proclaiming a spectacle inside. There is a man at the door to the establishment. "Really good stuff upstairs, *monsieur*," he says to me in French, "Come on in, please." I struggle by the old Japanese men who are straggling down the stairs. Why, I ask myself, am I going into such a place? It's not even authentic Place Pigalle fare—tourists are filling it up. But something tells me that the Place Pigalle has always been like this. The tourists are what make it authentic. I go in.

Inside, the air is heavy with a kind of unwashed-flesh smell. Women line the booths, wearing lace and velvet reminiscent of the last century, but chintzy. There is a woman on a stage. I can barely make her out in the dim light. She is taking off her clothes to the sound of lugubrious music. She is staggering on the stage, her eyes are dull, her expression indifferent. "You like her? I think she is beautiful, no?" One of the women of the booths insinuates her arm into mine and guides me onto a bench seat near the stage.

"I am a little worried about her," I reply.

"Oh, so you disapprove?" I think she is maybe a little misinformed about the lives of the average visitor. Paris so far is not nearly as decadent as its reputation proclaims.

"I mean I think she is going to fall off the stage."

"Buy me a drink?" she asks, looking put out and insulted by my lack of sexual excitement, and I think, fine, a drink to make up for a rather difficult conversation. "A bottle," she demands, and again I say, fine, still intoxicated from my duck and wine dinner and feeling expansive, flattered that someone could be having a conversation with me in this cold city. A waiter in a tuxedo, who looks dangerous, it seems to me, brings a bottle of Champagne for my inspection.

"Fine." Her conversation is boring to the extreme. I don't care for her descriptions of film stars and her hopes of becoming a dancer. What could she have talked about with the Japanese tourists? I am here to see and understand, and, yes, to study Paris, to study the centre of our western civilization. I am a scientist, I tell myself, and I am not interested in drug-taking strippers boring me with their personal hopes and dreams.

155

We isolate the object in western science. The item to be tested is seen in as pure a setting as possible so as to be without influence from the bias and culture of the experimenter. In the case of human experimentation, when we are looking at the workings of the human mind, for example, the experimental subject must also be isolated from bias and any cultural setting. With isolation of the subject, we begin to have confidence in the results of an experiment. So when we consider the measurement of intelligence, we hope to find tests that have no connection to cultural settings. When we measure the workings of the conscious brain, we do so using as pure and boring a mental test as possible. The Wisconsin card-sorting task consists of sorting cards into categories. By demanding that the experimental subject concentrate on this mental task, Richard ensured that he would collect an accurate reading of the human mind in action. Thoughts about friends, about what happened last night, about what was going to be served for lunch, about sex—these would result in confusing patterns on our computer screens. Mind reading is only in its infancy, and we can only understand a few of the patterns. Consistency and isolation of the subject—that is the very basis of western science.

156

Later in 1989, I went on another journey to the United States, this time accompanied by my friend and associate Mark. Mark is a designer. We were off to Atlanta to see Kanzi, a bonobo chimpanzee who had been taught to communicate using a language board. Kanzi can understand spoken English, and by pressing keys on this computerized keyboard, Kanzi can tell people what he wants. Kanzi is another experimental subject.

"Come in here, Kanzi, I want you to meet some people." Sue Savage-Rumbaugh holds Kanzi by the hand, and he comes in to greet us from behind the iron bars of the room he sometimes shares with Panbenisha, a younger female bonobo. He is slouching in, his head down and his eyes looking rather dull. He does not look at us directly. He appears to me to be uncertain and a little embarrassed by our presence.

"Talk to him," Sue suggests. "If you want to come in here with him, you'll have to strip off your clothes. He's kind of aggressive with men, and he has to see that you're not challenging his sexual role as chief male." By this I guess she means that if he can see I don't have an erection, things will be okay. It seems to me that this is the permanent state of Kanzi's anatomy. Later I learn that he usually gets this way around women. I am already beginning to feel inadequate around this chimpanzee.

"No, I'll just meet him through the bars, thanks." I also notice that Sue is missing one of her fingers. Bonobos bite.

"Panbenisha! Hello, sweetheart!" Kanzi and Panbenisha are jumping all over the room now. Panbenisha is so excited by our visit that she shits on the floor in about four places. But it's hard to tell if they really know we're looking at them; they never look at us, at least not for very long. It's as if they don't really want to admit that we are here. "Kanzi, go over to the toybox and bring me the big blue ball. No, it's in the toy box. You put it in there last night, remember? I know it's supposed to be on the shelf, but just look in the toy box." Kanzi can respond to endless novel commands. He truly does understand. But he doesn't look at Sue when she talks to him. He listens, and he moves correctly from the shelf to the toy box. There is no eye contact.

157

The technicians are preparing the experimental subject. They are showing him how to respond to the shapes and colours that will appear on the computer monitor in front of him. They look like the hearts, diamonds, clubs, and spades of playing cards. "Do you know how to sort the shapes now? You have to figure out the puzzle to plan your next move, do you remember? But we've been through all this before, right?" The subject is now seated in the dentist's chair. His nose is clamped shut and a breathing tube is inserted into his mouth. The PET scanner is about to be lowered over his head. The technician is asking again if he understands his task? For the first time since he came in, the man speaks.

"Yessir," he says dully, looking down, his eyes never making contact.

Richard is exuberant in his preparations, now that the experiment is about to begin. "I hope he concentrates. This could be a good one," he says to us as he closes the door to the little isolation room where the subject will work on the sorting puzzle while his brain is read by the team assembled around the PET scan monitors. "Once we turn on the Xenon gas, we have to take about ten minutes' worth of scans to establish a baseline for comparison. The trouble is, you can't be sure that his attention will last long enough for a good reading." The computer screen lights up with a scan taken from the man's brain. I am actually seeing the thinking patterns of a human being at the same moment as he is thinking. Baiba, Gretchen, and I are becoming excited.

"Wow! This is incredible!" I can't stop myself. It is amazing, and the power of this knowledge is truly intoxicating.

158

"Why can't you buy me just another little drink?" she whines at me.

"We've had a whole bottle of Champagne!" But I'm conscious of the fact that the Champagne seemed to go rather quickly for a whole bottle and that she seems to be feigning drunkenness. I am more drunk after the wine I had with my duck dinner, and I am not talking like an idiot. My "observation" experiment is beginning to backfire on me. I cannot see that I am being objective here. The place has a disturbing quality about it. Waiters hover over us all the time, giving me nasty looks. Most of the other tourists seem to have left for more lively places. The other women in the room are sad little shadows with the same dull look that I get from my new friend. None of them look me in the eye. They are all completely bored with me and everything else in this place. But I should be grateful—they are perfect experimental subjects.

159

"Jesus!" I hang on to the dashboard. Mark screeches the rental car around a complete 180-degree turn. The back end of the car flies in front of a truck.

"Don't try this at home," he laughs. Looking for the one sleazy bar we know about in Atlanta, we've missed our turn, so we are spinning around in the middle of traffic. "I don't care, I don't want to miss this, I want to see one of those places that you keep saying are filled with *ennui*." They *are* filled with ennui, I say to myself. They're filled with men with sad looks in their eyes, men who would rather be someplace else.

"Look, Mark, I study these things."

"Yeah, right." Mark grins as he scoots us into the driveway of a weird little establishment on the outskirts of town. The loud music coming from inside doesn't sound like ennui, I have to admit.

Getting here was disturbing. Atlanta is still unofficially segregated. Coming over an invisible barrier in town, we were stopped by a virtual parade of black people dressed in suits and fancy dresses going to a special evening church service. There was not a single white person among them.

But this place is black and white, completely mixed. We order beers. "Not much ennui here," Mark observes. The black woman standing on the stage right in front of us smiles from between her legs as she bends over to inspect us. She is joined by another equally naked white woman. They look us right in the eye.

"Let's see if we can meet Kanzi again tomorrow."

"Yeah. Right."

160

I want out of here, I say to myself. The man in the PET scanner is dutifully completing the computerized card-sorting task. His brain scans are working out very well but the session seems endless.

"Look at this. These are the dorsolateral prefrontal cortex areas. You can see the activity. His thinking is being directed toward forward planning, something we call a memory of the future." A memory of the future, I think—how powerful. The man's future has been isolated into a few moments of fame in an experimental apparatus. The measurements are crisp and clean.

161

Kanzi shakes hands with me through the bars of the room. "Talk to him!" demands Sue.

"Hello, Kanzi." I am struck by his gaze as he looks at me for a moment. I am hooked. I sink into his dark eyes. There is somebody in there. But his hands are the length of my forearm.

"He is very strong. Be a little careful. He likes your ring!"

"Oh great. It doesn't come off, at least not without the finger," I jest uneasily.

"No, no, Kanzi, leave the nice man alone. It's *his* ring." Kanzi has given up looking at me and I am again nervous. There was a moment of contact, and then he disappeared into the role of experimental subject once again. His powerful fingers stroke my ring. I carefully draw my hand away as his long nails rake the back of my hand.

"Eeee!" he screams.

162

"I want to go now. Please get me my bill."

"What? Oh all right," my surly companion responds grumpily. What kind of a place is this, I think. I now suspect that it is they who have been studying me. I am no longer the student of sociology, so proudly aloof. The bill is staggering.

"What!" I exclaim. "There must be some mistake!"

"*Monsieur?*"

"Eleven hundred francs?"

"Yes, *monsieur*? For the bottle of Champagne."

The waiter looks ominous. I decide not to argue. This is the highest level of civilization and I am being taught my place in the hierarchy. But leaving is difficult. "I paid my bill, and now I am leaving!"

"Not so fast, *monsieur*. We have things to discuss." I push past a man guarding the stairs just as a new customer comes in. I should warn him, but he offers an escape route. I hear yelling and swearing behind me, but I keep on going. I can just imagine what else they wanted to sell to me.

163

Sue Savage-Rumbaugh and her husband, Duane Rumbaugh, have been teaching bonobos and other chimpanzees to "talk" using language symbols. Kanzi can point to hundreds of symbols, and he can understand hundreds of English sentences. They are challenging the more popular hypothesis, championed by researchers such as Noam Chomsky, that human speech is a special human development, wired into the brain, separating people from animals. As I write this I am reading a review by Philip Lieberman,[9] who has been studying the relationship between talking and thinking for many years. He concludes that we are not wired with a special speech apparatus. Rather, he believes, for speech production and comprehension in the brain we use old mental machinery, developed early in the evolutionary passage toward being human, machinery once used for complicated hand movements. But, like Chomsky, he does think there is a special development that separates humans from animals. Talking and thinking appear to be linked.

An experiment was conducted in which climbers ascending Mount Everest were tested for a diminution of both their speech and their cognitive capacities. The lack of oxygen did result in a reduction in their speech capacity. Along with this lack of control over talking, the climbers also lost control of their ability to understand simple questions and commands. Lieberman concludes that talking and thinking go together. And for Lieberman, it is actual "verbal" talking that is the key. Chimpanzees cannot talk. They can point to pictograms and they can use sign language, but they cannot verbalize. Speech is a new development because it is linked with thinking. It is not simply a reworking of old evolutionary mechanisms. People communicate, thinking and talking their way to conscious interaction.

My encounter with Kanzi makes me wonder whether Chomsky and Lieberman aren't correct. Although there were moments when I felt I was really communicating with the chimpanzee, I was mostly aware of a distance, a separation, between human and animal, that could never be bridged. But how can I reconcile a belief in the hierarchy of animals with my search for a non-hierarchical, non-teleological understanding? There are always moments when my own biases, trained into me by my culture, reveal themselves. I was disturbed by the lack of eye contact with Kanzi, and I was willing at that moment to believe in the hierarchy, to believe that we are a part of a ladder of evolution, humans at the top. Was I confused by the lack of connection I had with the world of Kanzi, and did I perhaps misconstrue my lack of understanding as proof for my own superiority? After all, I was equally disturbed by the lack of eye contact with the experimental subject in the PET scanning laboratory. Does that experience confirm an unacknowledged belief in my superiority over people like him, as well?

164

"All right!" Richard is beaming at our experimental subject. "That wasn't so bad, was it? They'll take you back to your room now."

"Yessir," the man replies, "yessir." Is he thinking while he is talking?

Later I say to myself, how can I do nothing about this? I ask a few discreet questions; my psychology colleagues in Washington are surprised. How can we ask questions about such eminent researchers? It is not these people I am questioning, but all of us, I say. Do we ever stop to consider our approach to studying human subjects? Yes, but the experiments are done with the greatest degree of integrity and the protocols have been passed by the National Institute for Mental Health review boards. The subjects are fully briefed and act on their own volition. There is no danger to them during the experimental procedure. And the results are of the utmost importance to our understanding of the workings of the human mind.

The schizophrenic black man shuffles out, attendants holding him by both his arms. He is leaning down almost to the floor. He doesn't look up to see us as he passes. He is not participating in the animated conversation that is all about him, his brain activity, his thoughts shown on the computer screen. My observations at the St. Elizabeth's laboratories are the stimulus for another museum display—just another human being collected and exhibited for the public. And down the way from the human brain scans, Kanzi's language board is on view for our general education.

165

Wignarajah's model of nature demands the inclusion of all the parts, acting as a system. There is no method for differentiating hierarchical levels. What could be the meaning of one member of a beehive being more important than another? The queen cannot get along without the worker bee. The levels we see in our western hierarchy are reflections of our own political structures, but we have come to believe that these are intrinsically embedded in the natural world around us. Cuvier dissected pieces of Saartjie Baartman for display in a museum. Her labia were of particular importance to him. What about her life, her interests, her friends, her children? No, she was properly dismembered, her pertinent parts isolated and displayed in a scientific fashion.[10] Kanzi is an experimental subject in the study of language. His life and interests are not considered when the development of human language ability in the brain of a chimpanzee is debated among primatologists. And the mental patient who volunteered to have his brain read is a product of a human hierarchy, a small unimportant person in the history of the west. Our order is intrinsically hierarchical, and it prescribes the place we occupy in the world. Our gifts to the system as a whole are not considered as equal contributions.

166

Paris has taught me important lessons. I saw in her arrondissements the reflections of Indra's net, an arrangement showing that every part of a system reflects all the others and that no one part is more important than another. But Paris has also revealed for me the more common model of the western hierarchy. I have been put in my place, a lower rung on the ladder than I would have hoped. At the heart of western civilization I have seen the hierarchy in action. I am, for a short time, an experimental subject, suitable for study and for display.

Slowly I make my way back to my hotel. The interconnected communities of Paris no longer appear to reflect each other like the jewels in Indra's net. They are all one huge maze now, interconnecting streets going on seemingly forever, disappearing in the distance. None of them go directly to my destination. But I walk along them anyway—I cannot afford a taxi after that huge Champagne bill. And all my cues are gone. I can no longer follow the smell of tourist buses.

CHAPTER FIVE

SOUTHERN AFRICA AND LENINGRAD

The offing was barred by a black bank of clouds, and the tranquil waterway leading to the uttermost ends of the earth flowed sombre under an overcast sky—seemed to lead into the heart of an immense darkness.

– JOSEPH CONRAD, *Heart of Darkness*

167

WRITING IN 1739, David Hume described the basis for empirical science: experience comes first, and only then can we formulate the hypothesis or the *idea*: "all our simple ideas in their first appearance are deriv'd from simple impressions, which correspond to them, and which they exactly represent."[1] Hume enunciated the belief that there is a real world, a very stable natural world, that is waiting to be discovered by means of our observation and reasoned deliberations. Ideas, or theories about the world, are then derived from these real experiences. The theories thus correspond directly to the real world.

He further believed that we can approach the "truth" embedded in nature by forming hypotheses and asking questions about these hypotheses. Hypotheses will be proposed, tested, and if found wanting, replaced by new theories, but the truth will be the inevitable goal.

> We must, therefore, in every reasoning form a new judgment, as a check or controul on our first judgment or belief; and must enlarge our view to comprehend a kind of history of all the instances, wherein our understanding has deceiv'd us, compar'd with those, wherein its testimony was just and true. Our reason must be considered as a kind of cause, of which truth is the natural effect . . .[2]

> Let our first belief be never so strong, it must infallibly perish by passing thro' so many new examinations, of which each diminishes somewhat of its force and vigour. [3]

Hume describes the essence of western scientific method: there is a reality out there, and through the formation of hypotheses, or theories, and the subsequent rigorous testing of these theories, one will approach an understanding of this reality. This is the basis for Stephen Hawking's claim that someday we may even know "the mind of God," the implication being that there must be a mind to know.

168

"Braamfontein train station," Monty is telling us as we drive by the Oriental Market area. Shops are fronted by iron grilles and messy piles of goods are displayed behind dirty windows covered in razor wire. Sunday is not a big market day in downtown Johannesburg. "It's very close to our site in Newtown. It could be a major entry point for visitors to the new science museum." We are on our way to Soweto, in the southwest of Johannesburg. Commuters from Soweto and other black townships around Johannesburg don't use the trains any more, not since a few years ago when there were a number of cold-blooded murders on the trains, perpetrated by people unhappy with the demise of the apartheid system in South Africa. Now, black residents from Soweto use a fleet of minibus taxi cabs. Braamfontein station looks neglected.

The road is suddenly covered in smoke billowing from behind the buildings along Bree Street. And it stinks. "Garbage fire?" I hypothesize.

"Yes."

"But it's kind of big—I mean, we can't even breathe here."

Monty increases the speed and we manoeuvre uneasily through the empty streets. His BMW station wagon is stuffy. The mechanism for my passenger-side window is broken and I can't open it. It's very hot today. Smoke is filling the car. "Regular cleanup, I suspect." Monty is not concerned. His driving is erratic—no stopping for red lights, turning over sidewalks. At least there's nobody on the sidewalks. Between the buildings, I can make out a few people standing, unmoving in the smoke, watching the burning. How can they just stand there? Some garbage cleanup, I think to myself.

169

Karl Popper, continuing in the line of Hume and others such as Ludwig Wittgenstein, sought to further define the process of science.

> A scientist, whether theorist or experimenter, puts forward statements, or systems of statements, and tests them step by step. In the field of empirical sciences, more particularly, he constructs hypotheses, or systems of theories, and tests them against experience by observation and experiment.[4]

For Popper, no universals can be inferred or derived from inductive logic. No singular experience, and its immediate interpretation, can be taken as absolute truth. There must be imagined observations that, if found, would prove the first theory to be false, depending on the answer. No theory can ever be taken to be absolutely true, according to Popper, as a good scientist will always be thinking up new tests for the hypothesis to withstand. His approach, and it is the approach of most scientists today, reminds me of a test for a knight in medieval times. The knight had always to be tested, driving his lance through his opponent on the battlefield, even the mock battlefields of the pageants in peaceful times. Experiments are like pageants; they attempt to overthrow the champion theories. But the underlying view is that there will be eventually extremely robust theories or models that will withstand the most serious challenges. Popper considers the imagining of new challenges to be key to good science. This is the heart of his concept of *falsifiability*: an experiment must be imagined to be falsifiable so that there can be constant challenges. And, although there can be imagined no ultimate truth, Popper considers the process of constant testing and challenge to lead *closer and closer* to "truth."

I had theorized that I was seeing a garbage fire in Braamfontein. To be a good scientist, I would have had to test that assumption. A simple statement from the eyewitnesses standing in the smoke would have been a good start. We did not stop to ask them. My hypothesis thus stood untested. I let my host drive us away through the smoke and I stopped asking questions.

170

Journeys are hard. You end up in a place that has no familiar landmarks, or at least those landmarks that appear familiar turn out to be something else, something you could never have imagined or put into any of your hypotheses.

The winter of 1991 is cold. I am in Moscow on my own for a while before Jim and Fiona can come to join me. Sasha wants to take me to Leningrad to meet Savily Lapitsky and to visit the Arctic and Antarctic Institute. Lapitsky is a painter who was a prisoner working on the Gulag railroad in Siberia. "We will take a night train. It has sleeping in it." The train station is smoking with dense train exhaust. I walk along the snow-covered platform, smelling the oily tarry smell of travel to exotic places. But the flavour of excitement is fleeting. The night is freezing, I'm exhausted, I haven't eaten very much over the past several days, I can't talk very well because my lips are cracked and bleeding. "How long is the trip? Can we buy food here? Who are these people in uniforms?" I attempt a few questions.

"Soldiers," replies Sasha.

"Yes, but where are they from and where are they going?"

"You don't ask out here. I will tell many things when we are inside." Sasha explains nothing to me. Gradually I become more and more quiet. I decide to submit to whatever he has in store for me. The lack of control is making me feel physically sick, but I do not complain. I am unaware of how Russian I have become.

"What's the matter with you three?" Jürgen had said the summer before when he flew from Toronto to Moscow to meet Fiona and Jim and me after our Siberia trip. "You're so passive. You don't complain. You take everything they give you. You've turned into Russians!" He glowered at us accusingly. We knew there was something wrong, but we laughed, brushing his accusations off.

"We're like husky dogs," Fiona had joked as we rode the train together from Leningrad to Moscow that summer. It was earlier in the trip, before Jürgen had come to meet us. She lolled her tongue out of her mouth, as she hung out of her sleeping berth. "Just beat us and we come back for more. Work? Oh goody, yes. Please beat me and make me work. No food? Oh good, I like it that way!"

Now I could say, "Freezing snow and ice? Oh good." But I'm really submissive this time around. The joking is all out of me.

171

I have been called away on assignment to South Africa during the time I am writing this book. I am in Johannesburg because there are people interested in building a science museum, and interested in my work on the nature of prejudice in the history of science.

It is November 1997, three and a half years since the election of the African National Congress government in April 1994, almost eight years since the ending of apartheid in February 1990, and since our trip to Siberia in the summer of 1990. From the Soviet Union to South Africa, this is for Jim and me just another repressive regime undergoing a facelift. "Should be just like old times, eh?" Jim says as we land in Johannesburg. Fiona isn't with us this time. She is having a baby, due the day after we arrive in South Africa. Too bad—she kept the peace between Jim and me in the Soviet Union, kept us from being too wild.

Danielle agrees with the concern. "Don't swim in any rivers this time," she said before I left. "There are parasites in the water. Actually, I think there were probably parasites in the Ob River when you and Jim swam there."

"No, I don't think there could have been any parasites in Siberia—it was too cold."

"You just believe whatever you want to believe, don't you?"

Jürgen will join me and Jim in a day. "Jürgen isn't coming until tomorrow anyway, let's sleep." Jim is whining. I am feeling very groggy from the trip, but I want to get out there and explore. Monty is oblivious to our semi-comatose state.

"Maps." Monty is an architect who has been helping to build and plan Johannesburg for decades. "Study them—they'll tell you that Johannesburg is at the very *centre* of activity in South Africa, and that the *centre* of Johannesburg is the *centre* of all of that."

"When will we be going into the *centre*, anyway? The *centre* of town." I am a little insulting. My emphasis is awkward. I'm tired but I want to get out of this hotel. It doesn't feel like the centre of anything. In Johannesburg, white people stay in safe enclaves, away from any "centre."

"Uh, soon . . . today . . . we'll drive through briefly."

172

Henricus Martellus's map is the last major map of the world made before the discovery of the New World and Africa is the centre of attention, as Portuguese explorers were mapping its coast. Bartolomeu Dias made the first rounding of the Cape of Good Hope (called by him the "Cape of Storms") on his 1487-88 voyage. Martellus's map is

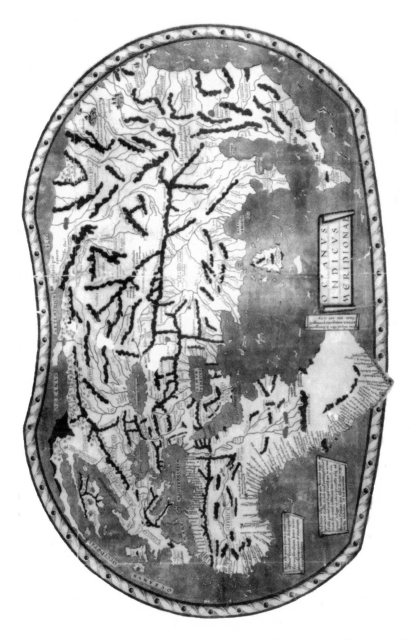

Map of the world, drawn by the German mapmaker Henricus Martellus, ca. 1489.
The west coast of Africa (shown on the left side of the map), reads like a ledger docu-
menting the discoveries of the Portuguese. (This map, ref. no. MAPS*920(38), is
reproduced with permission from the British Library.)

important for the detail it gives to the coastline of Africa. Africa appears like a ledger, the coastline carefully registered in print. Effectively, as the Portuguese travelled down the coast, the African continent became a *document* of discovery and European conquest. The "ledger" ends at the Great Fish River, which is just past the Cape, the last site visited by Dias before his return to Europe. The interior of Africa is not important. Details of the interior still show mythical landmarks such as the Mountains of the Moon as the source of the Nile, a place noted on Ptolemy's map of the year 150.[5]

The Portuguese did not become well established in the Cape region of southern Africa. They battled extensively with the Xhosa people of the area. As the European settlement of Africa progressed, the Portuguese preferred the Mozambique region farther north, on the east coast. Dutch and English became interested in the Cape early on. By the early 1600s, the Portuguese were giving way to the English and then the Dutch. Eventually, the Dutch set up in Table Bay at the Cape, and the English maintained a port of refuge (for their voyages to the east) in St. Helena. The Dutch maintained a colonial government until the English conquest of the Cape area in 1795, and the subsequent peace settlement in 1814. That situation did not significantly shift until the National Party's election in 1949 and the establishment of apartheid. At that point, the Dutch-based Afrikaner culture was re-established as the central influence on South African culture. During these four centuries of colonial struggle, the interior regions were constant battlegrounds between the Afrikaners, the English, and the many black African cultures. All through this history, black African–based cultures were not supported by any centralized government until the election of the African National Congress Party in 1994.

173

The map of the world became an object of science during the time that Africa was being discovered by the Portuguese. No longer were monsters seen on the drawings of distant lands. Verifying the exact shape and position of continents took precedence. It was the Age of Discovery and the beginning of the Age of Reason. Philosophers such as David Hume and Immanuel Kant would define the nature of human thought, the delineation of knowledge, and the process of scientific discovery in great detail over the next three centuries. But the modern Age of Reason started with Africa, with the ledger of place names down the coast of Africa, with the detailing of the conquest of Africa.

In his *Treatise*, Hume demanded that rigour be expected in scientific theoretical thought. He believed in observation first, followed by the theory. He believed in testing the theory, or hypothesis, with a series of questions, so as to hone his judgment. This is the belief of scientists today. We feel that this will weed out personal viewpoints.

At the time of Hume, it was very important to develop a critical scientific, empirical method that would form the basis for scholarly work that would, in turn, lead us toward an understanding of the natural world. I should not be surprised at Hume's interest in all manner of topics in this regard. Since Africa and its people were such a vital part of the Age of Discovery, I would expect the subject of Africa to come up. However, there is a lack of judgment in the following statement that leads me to believe that scientific judgment can be clouded by personal beliefs even in those who write the rule books. Hume wrote this is in his *Essays* in 1748:

> I am apt to suspect the negroes, and in general all the other species of men (for there are four or five different kinds) to be naturally inferior to the whites. There never was a civilized nation of any other complexion than white, nor even any individual eminent either in action or speculation. No ingenious manufactures amongst them, no arts, no sciences. On the other hand, the most rude and barbarous of the whites, such as ancient GERMANS, the present TARTARS, have still something eminent about them, in their valour, form of government, or some other particular. Such a uniform and constant difference could not happen in so many countries and ages, if nature had not made an original distinction betwixt these breeds of men. Not to mention our colonies, there

are NEGROE slaves dispersed all over EUROPE, of which none ever discovered any symptoms of ingenuity; tho' low people without education, will start up amongst us, and distinguish themselves in every profession. In JAMAICA indeed they talk of one negroe as a man of parts and learning; but 'tis likely he is admired for very slender accomplishments, like a parrot, who speaks a few words plainly.[6]

Hume was supported by other philosophers of his time. Immanuel Kant wrote the following:

The Negroes of Africa have by nature no feeling that rises above the trifling. Mr. Hume challenges anyone to cite a single example in which a Negro has shown talents, and asserts that among the hundreds of thousands of blacks who are transported elsewhere from their countries, although many of them have been set free, still not a single one was ever found who presented anything great in art or science or any other praiseworthy quality, even though among the whites some continually rise aloft from the lowest rabble, and through superior gifts earn respect in the world. So fundamental is the difference between these two races of man, and it appears to be as great in regard to mental capacities as in color.[7]

If such judgments were made so easily about the African peoples, what clouds could there be covering the lofty goal of understanding the natural world of the biologist, the chemist, or the physicist?

174

Before driving past the fire near Braamfontein station, Monty takes us into Sandton. "All the downtown businesses are moving out here. They feel safer, but I really don't know why they think it's safer." We are eating in a very chic restaurant at the giant shopping mall that forms the heart of Sandton, the new white Johannesburg. "I'll show you some quite remarkable buildings, just eyesores, terrible places, tearing the fabric of the neighbourhoods." We drive past computer firms, banking establishments, small manufacturers, all hidden behind the walls and electric fences that characterize the homes of wealthy whites. The homes and the businesses are next door to one another. Razor wire is strung over Sandton like a fine network of gauze. Home-invasion crimes and car hijackings are so numerous that everyone talks about them, all the time.

Later, it is with a friend of mine, driving in the suburbs of Johannesburg, that I will feel afraid, the one and only time I really feel that way during my visit to South Africa. "We are lost," my friend Hemant will tell me. His fear is contagious. I look nervously out of the car as he rings the bell of the house that we thought was the destination of his young daughter Smita, who is sitting behind me in the back seat with Jürgen. I feel that Jürgen and I are responsible for her while Hemant disappears behind the house to check further. What will I do if we are attacked? I don't know the rules of this strange society. I look around at the bivouacked homes, the walls, the razor wire, the deserted streets. Being lost is not good in Johannesburg. Knowing where you are going sets up a signal to those around you. You are not vulnerable if you know where you are and where you are going. Showing weakness can lead to attack, even death. Every day people are murdered here. Some people have hired armed guards who stand at their gateways, but others argue that this is an invitation to criminal rings. I glance at the armed guard standing down the street holding an assault rifle. Hemant comes back to the car. Nothing has happened, but my heart is racing.

"Monty, slow down so I can take a photo of these barbed-wired walls." We do not slow down; we race through Sandton. Monty is preoccupied with anyone who appears on the street. But the streets are almost deserted. I cannot understand his fear. It is still early in our South Africa trip; I haven't yet been lost in the suburbs with Hemant and Smita.

175

Karl Popper lays down the rules for scientific inquiry. To Popper, writing in my century, and to many of my fellow scientists, there is really no chance of achieving ultimate truth, since there is always a further test for a hypothesis. Popper lays out methodological rules:

(1) The game of science is, in principle, without end. He who decides one day that scientific statements do not call for any further test, and that they can be regarded as finally verified, retires from the game.

(2) Once a hypothesis has been proposed and tested, and has proved its mettle, it may not be allowed to drop out without "good reason." A "good reason" may be, for instance: replacement of the hypothesis by another which is better testable; or the falsification of one of the consequences of the hypothesis.[8]

For Popper, a hypothesis can only be accepted if it is testable, and it must remain until it has been shown wanting. And a scientist who no longer takes part in the challenge of the pageant "retires from the game." The implication is that those who are successful are there because of merit, they have won many challenges in "the game." I look around the rich suburb of Sandton in Johannesburg, and I see rich whites who feel they have wealth because of their merit. They have striven through challenge after challenge.

176

Before my trip to Leningrad with Sasha, when I had been staying at the Communist Party residences on Leningradski Prospekt in Moscow, and when I was desperate for English-speaking companions and good food, I travelled by taxi one evening to a western hotel that sold drinks and food I could afford.[9] CNN was playing live coverage of the Gulf

War over a barful of Americans. Saddam was in retreat, all his forces strained to their utmost. To the customers at the bar, the Iraqis were committing heinous crimes in Kuwait and needed to be punished. "Damn them fuckin' Iraqis," my new-found drinking partner exploded. "They're gonna get theirs, all right. They're never gonna start that again." Did I have any doubts about the truth of the CNN news? My Radio Moscow news reports back in my room were much more circumspect. The allies were marshalling overwhelming forces against Saddam—that was all they said.

On the train, Sasha and I listen to the soldiers sing and giggle and drink. They race up and down the train, chasing each other and anyone else who seems like fun. They are young and small and dark. I don't recognize any Russian in their conversations. Sasha and I are sharing a small sleeping compartment with two teenage girls. They are English, daughters of diplomatic families, on their way for an excursion to Leningrad. Sasha and I politely refuse their offer to share the bottle of vodka they are quickly finishing off. "I have to pee!" one of them announces and tears off into the corridor. Coming back, she is complaining, "Damn loo is filthy. Those Iraqi boys are peeing on the seats." The two of them laugh, and they are off to play in the corridor with the soldiers.

"Iraq?" I look at Sasha. Instead of answering, Sasha tells me about Stalin. All the time he was making deals with the British and the Americans, he was feeling out the possibilities with Hitler. But vacations? Just how routed is Saddam Hussein anyway, if his troops are having a recreational training holiday on the Moscow-to-Leningrad train? Sasha loves intrigue. I can't tell how much of what he is telling me is the truth and how much is just a good story. But I am aware that I have no way, sitting on this train full of Iraqi boys, to test his theories or those of my western refuge, the television screen showing the American hypothesis as revealed by CNN.

All night the soldiers run up and down the corridors of the train. I cannot sleep. The girls come in and go out, only stopping to drink more vodka. The noise, the interruptions, and lack of food and sleep are adding to my philosophical disorientation.

177

The champion must be challenged in the pageant of science. The scientist must be able to imagine the favoured theory finishing up in the dust, defeated, or it is not a theory at all. *No* real theory can ever be given support simply by bringing forward observations that support it, that verify it. There must always be the *possibility* for an idea to be falsified. Popper lays this down as the most sacred aspect of scientific thought:

> Theories are . . . never empirically verifiable. . . . [N]ot the *verifia-bility* but the *falsifiability* of a system is to be taken as a criterion of demarcation. In other words: I shall not require of a scientific system that it shall be capable of being singled out, once and for all, in a positive sense; but I shall require that its logical form shall be such that it can be singled out, by means of empirical tests, in a negative sense: *it must be possible for an empirical scientific system to be refuted by experience.*[10]

The emphasis here is on the fact that a system that "can" be imagined to be falsifiable is one that can be taken as a proper theory. This is the basis for empirical science, science that experiments with the world. But what is the basis for experimentation? To experiment, we scientists must first visualize the world in which we work. We must feel quite confident that we know all its components in at least a good general way. We must be able to imagine the end point of a test. We must visualize the falsification of a theory. Popper is quite explicit about this. For a scientific system, experiments must be imagined that can discredit it through falsification. Therefore, the *landscape* of the experiment and all its elements must be imagined before the experiment is undertaken.

Also, experiments require scientists to take pieces of the world apart, to isolate items for examination. These items are taken out of the landscape, or others are substituted. Sometimes pieces of the world— insects, molecules, nation-states—are taken out of their usual environments and are placed into novel situations. In these experiments, we imagine that the rest of the natural world is unaffected and that we have controlled for just this one little change. We then examine the results of our hypothesis. The beetles will control the aphids in the gardens, aphids that have never before met up with these particularly voracious beetles. Or, as in the case of apartheid South Africa, we will separate the black people from the white people and we will give both groups the freedom to pursue their very different cultural goals.

178

"On second thought, I really would rather you didn't stop here to take photographs." Monty is moving us through the downtown streets of Johannesburg. The anti-hijacking device in his car forces him to turn off the ignition before our doors can be unlocked and we can step into the street.

"What do you think these people think about you when you take their picture?" Jim had said at the last intersection.

"I don't really care, Jim."

"Well, I'm not going to let you out here on your own. You're too reckless." Dingy clothes typify the street sellers. Colourful rows of peaches line the sidewalks, chickens in cages, and everywhere razor wire guards the storefronts and buildings behind the street hawkers. Car hijackings are common at some of these intersections. And robberies. Young boys come up on either side of you and ask for something, try to sell something, and then they grab or stab. Sometimes they use guns. Murder is common too, we are told. Monty doesn't want to stop near the taxi areas. Thousands of people come by taxi from the Townships during the weekdays. Even today, a Sunday, there are some taxis. Shootings have occurred at this intersection during the past week. So I take no photos. Every single person we see in downtown Johannesburg today is black. We are the only white people. This is the great apartheid experiment, still being acted out, years after its abolition. An element of the world has been separated out from downtown Johannesburg. The white people do not walk on the streets.

White people we meet in other parts of Johannesburg all say the same thing, to a person: "I haven't been to downtown Johannesburg in five years. What are you doing there?" Messing up the experiment, I guess. The continuing apartheid experiment.

But what is this experiment telling us? Taking out an element, white people, from the society of downtown Johannesburg has not led to a simple result. Johannesburg cannot pretend to its former stature as a world-class city, with all its business and cultural links intact. And Johannesburg is a mirror of South Africa. Apartheid did not simply separate cultures, and its announced illegality cannot result in a simple restoration of a whole, intact, integrated society.

179

Experimental science is limited. On the whole, it does not work. Yes, Popper did eliminate some of the problems found in Hume. Falsification is better than verification. Falsification is much more rigorous and puts a theory to a very severe level of testing. It takes only one episode of falsification to eliminate a theory and an infinite number of verifications to satisfy the sceptics using the verification approach. But hypothesis testing is intrinsically *teleological*, no matter if it is falsification testing or verification testing that is taking place. In either case, it is necessary to imagine the landscape of the experiment. The natural world must be accepted in terms of the personal image held by the experimenter. Otherwise, no imagined test of falsification would be possible. And imagining the landscape is de facto allowing for the final result, even though imagined, to dictate the hypothesis. Therefore, the theoretical thinking is not one of discovery but rather one of reverse engineering. The end point dictates the nature of the model.

When I worked as a biological researcher studying regeneration in adult newts, we held to the usual scientist's image of the natural world. The biological system of an animal could be seen as a collection of components. If you take one component away, the resulting changes in the organism will indicate the effect, the job, so to speak, of that particular component. So, for example, I did experiments that involved removing the thyroid glands of newts and then watching the effect of this operation on regrowing limbs. The limbs grow back completely in newts that have intact thyroid glands, and not very well at all in newts that are lacking them. For regeneration investigators, this indicates that thyroid hormone is a significant factor in the regeneration process. Similarly, removing nerves from the regrowing limb results in no regeneration. For over a century, researchers have been looking for regeneration factors present in nerve endings in limbs. The search for magical factors has kept many scientists in business. But the scientists are missing a certain philosophical distance in their deliberations; they lack perspective, and they cannot see their mistake. Their hypotheses are testable and even falsifiable, but only in a very *narrow* range. They are self-consistent in the experimental domain of factor (hormone) removal and substitution. What the scientists don't see is the possibility that the entire system, the entire growing limb environment, has changed profoundly on the removal of even one of its components. Taking away the thyroid hormone very likely did more than remove one hormone, one component. Its removal shifted the whole regenerating system into new and unexplored territory.

180

We arrive in Leningrad at 6:30 a.m. It is about thirty degrees below zero Celsius. Sasha and I start to walk through the streets. We don't know where we can go exactly, but Sasha thinks we can find a coffee shop. There is nothing open in the train station, and besides, the building is not heated. We are not due at the Arctic and Antarctic Institute until about eleven o'clock, and we will see Lapitsky after lunch. Our return train leaves at 11:30 p.m. There is nothing to do for four hours but walk and see the sights. All of the other passengers have people meeting them to take them someplace. Our two teenage girl companions are sitting on the floor of the station holding their heads. We ask if they are going to be all right. "Our friend said he'd be here. He'll come soon, I'm sure. God, I wish we hadn't drunk the whole bottle."

The soldiers are being herded away to waiting trucks. We step out into the snow, the only people leaving the train station on foot.

I am carrying a bag over my shoulder, not heavy, but it weighs me down more and more as we walk through the streets. After Moscow, I thought I was immune to the cold, but I find that my feet are beginning to freeze. Sasha talks to me about his walks over miles of Arctic ice, treks lasting months at times. This is a spring outing for him. We walk on and on. I can no longer talk. There are no coffee shops, and for that matter no buildings are open at all. Absolutely nothing is familiar to me here. The landscape is ice, the buildings are mountains and rock faces hemming us in, there are no people out except the two of us, there is no place to shelter us, and we must not stop to rest or we will freeze. The cold has changed everything for me. One element of change, and the entire system has shifted under my feet. This is no experiment to test the effects of cold on my constitution. It has transformed everything, my very sense of who I am.

181

I entered the study of scientific subjects through the back door. I had not taken the usual prerequisite subjects. My undergraduate degree was in Chinese language, philosophy, and literature. I switched into the sciences because I wanted to study the natural world, with a view to exploring the philosophy of science in the west. But I wanted first to learn the techniques and the methods of a real scientist. I didn't realize at the time that it would take me decades to come close to learning much about either the philosophy or the techniques.

To prepare myself for my first term of science subjects, I set out in the summer of 1971 to memorize and to learn all I could about the periodic table. The periodic table is a map. It is a layout of all the known elements, the atoms, the basic units that make up the matter in our universe. Each element is unique, with established qualities, experimental reactions, appearances, bonding strengths, and potential for linking up with other elements. Our material universe, including ourselves, can be discussed in large part through our discovery of the various elements.

All the elements are also linked with each other. Each is only different from its partner because of the tiniest of changes. Slight shifts in electron, proton, and neutron numbers carry us through from element to element as we cruise through the table. And other relationships appear. Elements with similar electron configurations will act similarly. So we get families of metals, for example, elements that are quite far from each other when you count the number of electrons or protons, but that act similarly because they have the same kind of "electron edge" to them. The point is this: as I studied the periodic table, I began to see more and more that it was the perfect map of the sciences. The elements were laid out discretely, just the way scientists like them, components of a system, nicely separable. But they are also so entirely interlinked that they can never be understood in separation one from another. They are a system.

The elements reveal the very essence of what I learned first in Leningrad and then in Johannesburg. If you change one small item in a system, the entire system shifts. One proton change yields an entirely new element, an entirely new mini-universe, as it were. So the whole table is a system, and each element is a system unto itself. At both levels I could not escape from the intrinsic interaction that is inherent in the very atoms of western science.

182

When I entered the chemistry class that fall, after the summer I'd spent studying the periodic table, I felt prepared. But I was never asked anything about the mutually interrelated elements of the table. And since then I have never found such things to be a topic of interest or study in all my years as a scientist.

183

When I learned the details of the periodic table, I was trying to find the keys to the temple. I wanted in to the temple of science. And like most outsiders, I learned the theoretical material, hoping that the real scientists would see me as a fellow member. But science is a narrow little world where the rules include actually doing science, touching the elements of the natural world.

The streets of downtown Johannesburg are filled with black people who come from the Townships. Soweto is one of those Township communities on the outskirts of Johannesburg. Monty is taking Jim and me to the edge of Soweto. "It is a bedroom community. Very little distinguishes it as a real community. The residents come into Johannesburg to work and to shop."

Later in the week, we return to visit a school and teacher training centre. In a classroom, a group of black teenagers look dully at an overhead projector image of a molecular shape. A young white teacher is lecturing them. As I look at her, I suddenly feel her hostile eyes meet mine. "That is the 'System' class," Sipho Dlamini, a local science curriculum co-ordinator, tells us. "System" is a project that hopes to bring candidates up to a standard that will allow them entrance into university.

"We have no experimental equipment in our schools," a young black teacher tells us. She teaches science from a purely theoretical perspective. Black students have to imagine everything. Soweto is completely black except for a few of the teachers in this centre and a few other professionals who come in to work during the day. Black science in South Africa is completely theoretical.

The absence of whites is a defining quality in Soweto. The absence of science is also a defining quality. This is a foreign culture for me.

184

Coming back from South Africa, I read the editorial in *The Sciences* by Rodney Nichols,[11] president of the New York Academy of Sciences. For Nichols the "scent" of science is everywhere. He sees no theoretical distance to separate the average member of our society from the fruits and the understanding of all things scientific. North America and Europe are not Soweto. The world of science is a part of our world of opportunity and freedom. In keeping with this business approach, he is suggesting that ideas actually "compete," challenge each other, like animals in a jungle: "Discovery demands openness, debate and the *challenge* of competing ideas."

185

We have found a café. Along a dirty little street not too far from the Arctic and Antarctic Institute where we will be having our 11:00 a.m. meeting, we see a doorway that is open. And we have only been walking for an hour and a half. We go inside. There is no heat. And there is no coffee. The people inside are waiting for deliveries. They insist that I hang up my coat. It is the responsibility of one of them to hang up coats, so we must comply. Sasha convinces them to leave me alone—I am a foreigner and not used to their ways, he tells them. It is colder inside the café than outside. We sit for ten minutes waiting for their delivery of coffee and buns. It doesn't come and Sasha thinks our continued refusal to let them hang up our coats will cause trouble. We leave, back into the cold and back to the endless walk. My back is aching, but the pain is almost warming.

186

There are sciences studied today that do not fit easily into the realm of hypothesis testing. There are sciences that have almost been ostracized for their inability to fit into the experimental mode. But through their study we see the weaknesses of hypotheses.

When I studied in the regeneration laboratory, my supervisor, Richard Liversage, insisted that we not socialize with the students from the ecology labs. "That is not science," he would say. And he was right, in the sense that science, as defined by the great philosophers of the west, demands empirical questioning. Ecology is a very broad observational study that does not easily allow for true experiments. Perturbation experiments, procedures that require cutting, removing elements, substitutions, or the addition of foreign substances, cannot easily be performed without utterly damaging the original life forms. When something is changed in an environmental system, the whole system changes, usually forever. Ecology is not a testable kind of science. It takes a different mindset. It takes patience and observation.

"We take 'em out in the morning, eh? Early, real early. I mean, around five in the morning, right? Some of 'em want us to take 'em out around four." The Native guides are taking a group of us by motorboat through the marshes of Walpole Island Reserve,[12] near Sarnia, Ontario. We're stopping for a smoke break. The guides like a smoke break every fifteen minutes or so, it seems. We passengers are at a conference of people studying Canadian Native people and their interaction with the local ecosystem.

"Yes, but why do the duck hunters want to get up so early, really? They're here for a vacation and the lodges are practically resorts. You'd think they'd welcome a little luxury and not get up so early."

One of the guides spits and laughs. "Yeah, well, we just do what we're told to do, right?"

"I guess that's when the ducks are there to shoot, though?" I offer an explanation. "Do you see more ducks early in the morning?"

Another guide grins. "The ducks are there all day, eh? I mean, they don't have nowhere to go after the morning. Where d'ya think they go? They're here now, aren't they? The only thing is, they like to go where there aren't any hunters. Doesn't matter what time of day it is." I laugh too. Nobody ever asks these guys for their opinion. But they watch the habits and the movements of the ducks, and the visiting duck hunters, their whole lives.

Native science does not easily admit the concept of experimentation. The environment is seen as a whole system, every part playing its role, but in a network and not in a hierarchy. It is a systems approach to understanding nature. Popper's need for falsification tests could not be imagined in this ecological system, because the elements cannot be separated out one from the other. For that matter, to the Native guides, the hunters who visit the duck-hunting lodges are as much a part of the ecosystem of Walpole Island as the ducks.

187

We have found another coffee shop. It is now almost 9:30 a.m., and we have been walking for almost three hours, trying to keep warm. This one has coffee. A woman comes out from the back kitchen area carrying a very large bucket of it. She is swinging the bucket with two hands. It is milky coloured. The milk and sugar have already been added. She is swearing as the hem of her filthy white lab-style smock dips into the bucket. The last time I saw a lab coat as dirty as that was on one of the animal-care technicians in my old zoology lab. Animal blood and guts, it reminds me of. She wrings the smock out into the bucket, not wanting to waste any of the coffee. There are three of us lined up to buy coffee and buns. I don't even care that I will be drinking coffee that is already cool, and that has just been flavoured with the woman's filthy clothing. I am starving and cold. Sasha lets the old woman who is waiting with us step in front. She is shaking, and she is very thin. Sasha asks if we may have our coffee with her at one of the high tables. There are no seats, so we must stand to drink the coffee.

The story she tells us convinces me that the world has been turned inside out. There is nothing here that is a part of my ecosystem. I believe that one little change, the cold, has changed the entire universe. The old woman lives in a one-room apartment allotted to her by the state. She has no food at home and only enough money to buy a bun and coffee once a day at this coffee shop. Her hands are shaking as crumbs escape her grasp and fall to the floor. I look down mournfully at those lost crumbs. She tells us that the winter of 1991 is as bad as the winter of 1941–42, when Leningrad was under siege in the war and there was no food and the cold was killing people on the street. "People ate the bodies of their own dead children," she remembers.

188

Apartheid is a powerful concept. It is not possible for such a concept to die easily, because the idea itself has a form. It forges its way through the landscape, in the same way as a river forms its bed by driving relentlessly against the rocks and soil over millennia. Theories of humankind, ideas like apartheid, are theories of science. Scientific theories develop through interaction with the world—they delve deep and become part of the fabric. They are *not* laid onto the world as a thin gossamer covering only.

189

I read the newspaper that has been pushed under my hotel-room door. On page three there is a photo of people standing in a smoking field near Braamfontein station. A squatters' camp, of homes made of corrugated tin cardboard and paper, has been deliberately burnt down by the city. The squatters were given a day's notice that they were being transported to a new location on the outskirts of Johannesburg.[13] I read that many will not leave. Their homes are in downtown Johannesburg, they have their children enrolled in schools, they have work downtown, they have no money to commute to the downtown from the outskirts of the city. They are being moved to an area that has fewer facilities than their squatters' field near Braamfontein Station. This was my garbage fire whose smoke filled Monty's car as we drove through Johannesburg on our first day here.

The separation of people by class and colour has grown into the very fabric of the place. The *idea* of apartheid is too deeply set to leave. It forms its own comfortable berth, establishes itself more easily than any new squatters in the area.

190

Popper's approach is teleological at the experimental level. The testing of hypotheses is teleological, because scientists must visualize the "landscape," the environment within which they are working. Effectively, they must see the end point, the final goal of their experiments, in order to imagine a potential situation that could falsify their results. However, Popper's approach is also teleological at a much deeper level. Popper, like Hume before him, imagines that theories are shaped by experience, by the natural world and its impact on us. Ideas come after impressions, after the experience, according to Hume and Popper. That is equivalent to saying that the world acts as a template for the ideas. That is to say, the world is out there waiting for the ideas to be formed as a result of the impressions made by the world onto the ideas themselves—a kind of evolutionary model for the emergence of theories. The natural world, and by extension the intellectual natural world within which ideas naturally reside, is seen as static, waiting for ideas to "adapt."

This is an intellectual trap. It is very similar to the teleological problems encountered with the adaptationists offering pure Darwinism as the answer to understanding animal and plant evolution. For the adaptationist, the landscape acts in a teleological fashion—the results are foretold in the environment before the encounter with the animals and plants. An alternative intellectual approach, the mutual interaction of all the elements—animals, plants, and the landscape—yielding a totally new and not easily retraceable trajectory, is rejected by most evolutionary theorists.

Popper is an adaptationist. For Popper, "ideas" themselves also have to test their strength against the forces of a waiting hostile environment. He speaks of the "survival of the fittest" theories:

> According to to my proposal, what characterizes the empirical method is its manner of exposing to falsification, in every conceivable way, the system to be tested. Its aim is not to save the lives of untenable systems but, on the contrary, to select the one which is by comparison the fittest, by exposing them all to the fiercest struggle for survival.[14]

This is an adaptationist concept. The theories have to struggle within the natural and intellectual environment as defined and understood by a particular scientist, or school of scientists. The environment determines the ideas. The ideas are formed, therefore, in a teleological fashion.

What if we apply a dialectical approach to the formulation of ideas? Instead of struggling for survival, pitted against one another to see which is the fittest, the ideas are like beavers living along a streambed in a marsh. Or they are like the first oxygen-producing plants that appeared on earth. The oxygen was a waste product, but it changed the environment and soon became a necessary ingredient for most of the earth's life forms. Ideas dam the streams and rivers, divert the watercourse, cut down trees—in short, they change the landscape; ideas change the very atmosphere we breathe and render it hostile to the "anaerobic" organisms of their world. It is being found more and more that living organisms inhabit the earth in even the most extreme regions—in the vents of undersea volcanoes and the ice of the poles, and even deep under the ground, to a depth of several hundred feet at least. There is no real "non-living landscape," it seems—it is all a living exchange of thriving, mutually interactive beings. So ideas thrive in a living mass, defining each other as they seek to survive. They effect change on, and they are in turn affected by, the landscape. The juxtaposition of ideas with the environment of intellectuals, and their observations of the natural world, leads to novel and entirely new conformations. How do we find Popper's fittest theory in this approach? Well, there may not be a fittest theory. *Any* theory holds forth, with considerable intellectual vigour, when it has a role in its own niche development. I propose that this is closer to what actually happens when ideas are being tested. Those ideas and theories that form a comfortable berth hang on longer and spawn offspring that are, in turn, viable. Thus we have a constantly changing intellectual landscape, and one that has a variety of appearances, depending from which viewpoint it is seen.

191

I search for the antithesis of apartheid. Later in the week, we go into Johannesburg at night, a domain that has a new idea, a new theory, flowing through the streets like a river reshaping its banks after a flood. Whites do not go there.

"I'm a Rastaman—I don't belong in Joh'burg. I'm a songwriter—no, I'm a poet, and I'm so depressed, I'm depressed because I should be happy, you know what I mean?" We are being accosted outside Kippies, a jazz bar.

"Yeah, sure." Monty's son Nicholas is irritated. Nicholas's wife, Monica, gets up to dance with the Rasta poet, who stinks of beer and dirty clothes.

"Tell me if you want me to go," the Rastaman simpers at us.

"Go," I say, but too quietly.

Monica is enjoying herself too much. She turns to us. "Do you want to go where there are only black people, no whites? A club?" Monica is wild.

It is really late, and Jim has been waiting outside, ready to go back to the hotel. "No, no. It isn't safe." He looks at us.

"Come on, Jim, this is going to be the real night-life scene."

"I can't. We have to go back to the hotel. I feel sick, I'm so tired."

Monica is coming up to the minivan, the Rasta poet trailing behind her, holding her hand. He climbs into the minivan with us. "We have to go at least as far as Yeoville. We're giving him a lift."

"Monica," Nicholas warns, but he starts the engine.

192

The night in winter in Leningrad covers most of the twenty-four-hour day. Our visits to the Arctic and Antarctic Institute and to the home of the painter, Savily Lapitsky, take up the few hours of daylight. By five in the afternoon, we are back to walking the streets of Leningrad. It has been dark for almost two hours. Here there is an idea that has forged the shape of the people, that has interacted with them to form a firm bond of mutual support. That idea has a shape of its own and can only be described as fear, and hunger, and cold. What a way to learn about the Soviet Union, I am telling myself. I am numb with cold and fatigue. We have not eaten well all day. The hoped-for meals with our hosts turned out to be old pastries and weak tea.

We take a bus from Lapitsky's apartment complex, passing mile after mile of identical buildings. In the downtown canal district, we look into bookstores for an hour, then we walk. We go back to the train station and wait in the cold. I am too tired to go any farther.

193

Rockey Street in Yeoville is like the wild west. Bottles are strewn along the street. People come reeling out of bars, drunk or stoned. I am walking behind the others, and I bump into a coal-burning brazier. Chicken is cooking on sticks, and they jiggle as I nearly knock them over. Three men mutter at one another in Zulu, looking at me. So what if this is dangerous, I'm thinking—it's interesting. I am trying to convince myself that Jim's concerns had been unwarranted. "You can't stay here by yourself," Jim had said, standing in the door of the minivan. "I'm sick to my stomach, but I'll stay here with you if you won't come back to the hotel. We have to all stay together, it isn't safe here."

"Yeah, yeah." We had put him into a taxi, and Jürgen and I had gone out on foot into Rockey Street with Monica and Nicholas.

The crowd in the club spreads open to make room for break-dancers, but we can't move back. We are crushed almost on top of them by everyone who wants to see. I watch a young woman. Writhing to the music, she is coming in my direction, holding her crotch provocatively. The thumbs and forefingers of both hands frame her pubic mound, and then she dips down to rub her hips against the man who is spinning across the floor on his hands. A little girl is smoking a joint next to me. She looks about fifteen. The air is thick with smoke. There are no apparent rules here. But everyone is making room for everyone else. They make room for me, but do they even see me?

194

I remember 1985, in the summer. I am in New York City, in Manhattan, in the Village. I decide to walk back alone to where I am staying with my friends Elsa and Sydney at their home on West Ninetieth. It takes hours. "Where were you all night?" Elsa says the next morning. "I didn't think you were staying here any more."

During the first part of my walk uptown, I feel relaxed; it is a pleasant evening and there are a lot of people around me. But then I enter a zone that feels abandoned and somehow lawless; it is foreign territory for me. "Where's the money, bitch?" A young black woman is pushed up against a wall by a man. She knows him, I can tell. She is arguing back. The two of them do not register my presence. I walk on, and I come to a group of women. They are fighting with the men in the alley as I pass, screaming, then swearing, then running away, then running back swinging their handbags. They are all black or Hispanic, all wearing short skirts and flimsy tops and high-heeled shoes. Two of them are on the street waiting for cars. One of them lifts her skirt as a car passes and does not stop. I note that I am in the Twenties, streets I was told to avoid, especially at night, and I am walking alone. But I do not fit the theoretical model of the people who walk these streets. I am not a part of the idea that is formed almost as a covenant between the environment and the idea itself, between the people and their self-defining hypothesis. Therefore I am not even seen. I continue my walk until four in the morning—through the Twenties, the Thirties, the Forties and on up to Ninetieth. And during the entire trek, no one speaks to me and no one notices me.

Hume has it backward, I am thinking. Hume believed that ideas must always follow from impressions or experience. Hume's concepts helped define the modern-day scientific method. But I am learning that the idea comes first, and only then can the impression or the experience be realized. I am not seen because I do not fit the idea of the place. I cannot be "realized" because the idea or theory of the people around me cannot encompass my existence.

195

It is the end of a long day in Leningrad. "There is food for sale now." Sasha guides me over to the kiosks in the train station. I want bottled water. The tap water in Leningrad contains parasites. But they have only tea, and I decide to risk it, since it's been boiled. Sasha recommends we buy only bread and eggs to eat. They are safer, he tells me. We eat at the tall tables at one end of the crowded platform.

I remember the little sand crabs who chased over the beach in North Carolina when Danielle and I took our children there one summer. The crabs came out at dusk. They looked like little hands scurrying across the sand. Little hands come up over the table as I am eating in Leningrad train station. First one little hand crawls from the table edge, feeling its way, then grabbing the pieces of egg and eggshell that are adhering to the pieces of waxed paper they've been packaged in. I drop all my food, the bread and the rest of the eggs. The little crab hands are coming up over the tabletop again. There are three of them, and they take everything away. I cannot see the owners of the hands, and I don't want to bend down to look under the table.

Sasha is watching me. I could not survive long in this environment, he must be thinking. I do not fit in, I am not a part of the theoretical pact, I have not made a covenant with cold and hunger. They do not define me, but they may literally kill me. Sasha never says a word to me, but he watches as I decide not to eat.

196

There is a haze of smoke on the dance floor, but I look up above it. We are on a rooftop and the stars are out on Rockey Street. The constellation Orion is visible above the horizon, just as it is when I look at the Toronto sky. It travels back and forth between the north and the south. But there is something about it that makes me shiver. It is upside down. The sword that hangs from Orion the Hunter's belt, that little line of stars and nebulae, is pointing up and not down. I am in the Southern Hemisphere, where even the stars do not read the same. Orion's position in the sky makes me feel utterly lost.

I think about the sailors who travelled down the coast of Africa with Bartholomeu Dias more than five hundred years ago. They wrote their inscriptions over the map of Africa because everything was foreign to them. Just like me, standing on the dance floor but remaining unseen, they were not a part of the theoretical base that makes up Africa. Henricus Martellus's map was their attempt to forge a new idea over the coast of Africa. What must it have been like for them as they sailed slowly down the coast? The very stars that gave them their maps slowly inverted before their eyes. It must have been frightening. No wonder the people who live in the rich white suburbs feel so alone and unprotected.

CHAPTER SIX

LENINGRAD AND WHITE RIVER

A blue so blue that only blood is redder.

— SOURCE UNKNOWN

Lasciate ogni speranza voi ch'entrate!
Abandon all hope, ye who enter here!

— DANTE, *Divina Commedia: Inferno*, III

197

WHAT IS WRONG with teleological thinking?

When Aristotle laid out his four causes, he gave particular emphasis to the fourth, the one that explains the existence of a thing in relation to "what it is for." This is called the *final* cause because it refers to the final end of the history of a thing or process. The "end," or τέλος,[1] is thought of as the final purpose or goal of something. For Aristotle, the τέλος of a thing, its final cause, is crucially important; it is a question that can be asked of anything in the natural world.

Aristotle accepts the teleological process as a logical development.

Rather than questioning teleology, he argues against the opposite condition. With a view to discrediting the non-teleological notion, he asks: "What is wrong with the idea that nature does not act purposively and does not do things because they are better?"[2] Using a slightly disparaging style, Aristotle continues with a description that would probably satisfy the *non-teleological* believer, the citizen or scientist who imagines a world that has *no* designer to watch over it:

> [It] might be that Zeus does not send rain so *that* the crops will grow; it is just a matter of necessity. The vapour drawn up from the earth is bound to cool down; once it has cooled down it is bound to turn to rain and fall back to earth; and it is sheer coincidence that crops grow when this happens. . . . Take teeth, for instance: what is wrong with the idea that the front teeth necessarily come through sharp and suitable for biting, and the back teeth flat and good for crushing food? Why should there be purpose behind this? Why should it not be an accident? . . . So where every part turned out to be just as it would have been if it had had some purpose, the creatures survived because, spontaneously, they happened to be put together in a useful way.[3]

But Aristotle cannot entertain this non-teleological possibility:

> [T]his kind of argument might be used to pose the problem. But it is impossible for this to be the way things are. The point is that the things mentioned turn out as they do either always or usually, and so does every other natural object, whereas no chance or spontaneous event does. . . . [T]he things I have mentioned and everything else which is like them are natural things, as even exponents of the view I have outlined would admit. It follows that purposes are to be found in natural events and natural objects.
>
> Moreover, whenever there is an end [τέλος], the whole prior sequence of actions is performed with this end as its purpose. . . .
>
> Anyway, it is clear that a thing's nature is a cause, and that it is the kind of cause I have been saying—namely, purpose.[4]

So Aristotle does not ask what is wrong with teleology. He accepts it as a natural part of the order of things. And he further prejudices the reader by asking what is wrong with thinking non-teleologically and then proceeds to show that manner of approach as being without merit.

In light of Aristotle's uncritical support of the final cause, what is it that I find wrong with teleology?

The main concern I have concerning teleological arguments is the easy acceptance it has in the minds of modern thinkers. It is a hidden menace to careful thought. The belief in design and purpose pervades our thinking. Even today, those who apparently seek to rid their philosophies of teleology, such as the supporters of Darwinist adaptationism, end up maintaining the final landscape, the ultimate unchanging world into which everything must adapt. Students of evolution and philosophers of science draw for us a natural world where animals, plants, even ideas must compete to "fit in" to the template laid out for them. Their model of the world would have the end point dictating the form and the trajectories of the destinies of all things. This is the hidden τέλος even in the midst of modern science.

198

Changing the paradigm, changing the map—I don't want to face it. John and I have been travelling for over a week. It is 1967, the centennial year, and I want to see Canada. We have the summer off. The summer hasn't been given to us, though. I said no to a job offer from a friend of my father's, and it means that I now have no money and no support from my family. "So that's it, then?" My father's face had turned red as we sat on the cement porch.

"But you knew I was planning this trip since March." He went inside abruptly and I sat, my face on my knees, wondering when I should go inside too.

The next day he looked at me blankly. "You can have the money your grandfather sent me to give to you last Christmas. It was for a watch, but you have a watch." He gave me $40. "There won't be any more." I wasn't worried. I had a book about edible wild plants.

But now I feel real hunger as I wake up to cars soaring by me in the morning. They are only a couple of feet away from me; I can smell the exhaust like fresh waste from an animal. John and I can't leave the side of the highway to look for edible plants. The highway is the only touch we have with civilization. Besides, I ditched my frying pan and soup pot several miles back. They were too heavy. And the forest around us is very wild. We are south of Wawa on the east side of Lake Superior. We've been here for three days. No one is going to give us a lift. There are eight pairs of hitchhikers stranded on this one bend in the highway, thrown up like debris on the side of a fast stream. It's time to change the formula, change the paradigm. We have to get out of here.

The road is a paradigm, a special world that keeps us tied to the cars and to the route. We will hitchhike across Canada. The map is laid out and our travel is predestined, literally drawn out for us. But it's not working. We have to revolutionize our thinking. "All right"—I'm looking at the map we have of Ontario—"there's nothing for miles. We hafta stay on this road. There's no other way, and I'm not goin' back home, not now." John is staring gloomily at the cars going by. There have been hundreds of them all filled with families on vacation. We're sitting with another pair of hitchhikers, two guys from Ottawa. "Look," I say, "there's another kind of road, but it doesn't come near the Trans-Canada until we get to White River, and that's seventy miles north." My finger traces the rail lines that cut across our path from the east.

"You're crazy." But they haven't been sitting in the same spot for three days yet. John just looks at me, eyes wide and waiting.

199

In a world where the map is laid out and where everything adapts to its shape, the map is the paradigm for all things. Moving into a new map, a new paradigm, cannot be recognized because such an action confronts the very definition of the original map. Moreover, those who are living under the regime of the old map *will not even see* those who have chosen to be guided by the new.

200

We spend another night sleeping on the bank of the highway. John won't leave it. His thumb is out even while he is asleep standing up. A car slows and runs off the road onto the gravel about a hundred yards ahead. He runs, yelling at me to wake up and bring the bags. I can't think straight. I fumble around, leaving half the unpacked clothes and I don't see what is happening. John is standing and sobbing as I come up to him. There's no car. "He thought I was a girl, then he took off."

"No more nighttime hitchhiking, okay?"

We have blankets, no sleeping bags—they are too bulky and didn't fit into our plans. But now it's cold and I'm exhausted from hunger and boredom. John is sitting up biting his knuckles. Freezing under my blanket, I sleep as he heads off to find the others. I am wakened by snuffling sounds. Three full-grown black bears are walking down the road edge. They turn toward me for a moment, vacantly. I look directly at one of them; she is inches away. I close my eyes and go back to sleep.

201

Ideas form their own environment. A newly emerging way of thinking, or paradigm, will be the basis for entirely new endeavours. The idea, then, nestles into the intellectual landscape and creates conditions conducive to its survival. The American philosopher and historian of science Thomas Kuhn talks in *The Structure of Scientific Revolutions* about the effect a new way of thinking can have on the practitioners of science and philosophy:

> [T]he emergence of a paradigm affects the structure of the group that practices the field. When, in the development of a natural

science, an individual or group first produces a synthesis able to attract most of the next generation's practitioners, the older schools gradually disappear. . . . [I]t is sometimes just its reception of a paradigm that transforms a group previously interested merely in the study of nature into a profession or, at least, a discipline. In the sciences . . . the formation of specialized journals, the foundation of specialists' societies, and the claim for a special place in the curriculum have usually been associated with a group's first reception of a single paradigm.[5]

202

Sasha isn't concerned.

"But how are we going to get to Lapitsky's apartment?" We have been walking through Leningrad for half the day now. We had a couple of hours in the Arctic and Antarctic Institute, but it didn't extend to lunch. It's warmer, about minus twenty. But there are no taxis that will stop for us. We're due to meet with Savily Lapitsky at two o'clock. Lapitsky wants to show us his paintings of the Gulag. They are all in his apartment, in one of the endless suburbs of Leningrad, far from the downtown that I know by heart now after walking through it for a day.

"There is special way we know here." Sasha stands in the road and waves down a little car. It's not a taxi. The car stops, and Sasha sticks his head into the driver's window. The driver looks grimly at me and then turns to his wife. "Get in now, quickly." Sasha shoves me into the back seat. "They will take us there."

203

Animals and plants do not merely adapt to the natural world; they are a vital part of the changing living system. In the same way as animals and plants affect the natural world where they are living, developing, and evolving, ideas behave like the living things they are. And I believe it is not an unchanging intellectual landscape that demands the adaptation of "the fittest" ideas, but a malleable interactive countryside that lives and changes with the actions of all of its parts. Ideas are a vital part of the whole living intellectual system.

204

White River. We saunter from the bus station out onto the dusty street. "Which way to the railyards?" we ask. The woman in the shop just stares at us. It has cost us $8.25 each to travel by bus from the restaurant on the highway south of Wawa to White River. I now have just under $35 left from the $10 of my own and the original $40 my father gave me. But the expense was worth it—we are headed for the freight yards to travel by rail. We have broken the paradigm, and the world feels open to our new idea.

"I want cheese and bread." I'm worrying about our lack of nourishment over the past several days and I'm tired of peanut butter.

"My mom says fruit is important." John is standing on his toes, looking argumentative, but happy.

"Okay, okay." I'm adding up our resources. John and I agreed to make the trip on the same amount of money, even though his parents would have given him any amount. So John and I together have only about $70 left and there is a long way to go, roughly another five thousand miles out to Vancouver and back home again to Ontario.

"Why don't we get jobs?"

"Let's keep to the railroad idea. I don't want to hang around here watching our money disappear." I'm not happy with yet another new direction.

205

"I don't get it. Can you just ask anybody to drive you someplace? Why didn't we do this before?"

Sasha is looking ahead; he doesn't answer me. "No, no, I think he is in the next region." He and the driver are arguing over the directions to Lapitsky's place. We have been driving for over an hour through the suburbs of Leningrad. The driver is bickering with his wife, who won't even look at us. I am sure we have passed more than ten thousand identical buildings, tall concrete monoliths, rusty stains over their fronts, rags for curtains, children huddled in nasty little groups around the iron doors. They look as if they're standing at service entrances or garbage disposal zones, but there are no other doors to the buildings.

Snow is greyish here, soiled by something that hangs in the air. My whole stay in Moscow and Leningrad is a smell that stops my breath, an exhaust smell. There are no shops and no restaurants and no public buildings here. This is the residential section. And the numbers on the buildings are on small white boards that cannot be read from the road. Sasha gets out of the car every few hundred yards now to check the numbers. He is asking a small group of children. They just nod dully.

206

White River hasn't got much happening. We are noticeable additions to the town. We were the only ones to get off the bus, and the bus didn't linger—it took off down the road. I feel small and skinny, and I don't want a job in this town. I'm not sauntering any more, but I can smell the rail yards, and we slip expectantly down the main street. John is still arguing with me about food. I'm not listening. He feels like some kind of rabbit, bouncing next to me and jabbering. Suddenly, he takes off down a sidestreet. "Fuck off, I'm goin' back to the highway!"

"Wha' th'!" I chase down the little street and pull him down by his knapsack, and I use the heel of my hand to smash his head on the gravel. Two guys in plaid shirts start to come our way. "This is private!"

"Yeah, well, you better be making it private somewheres else, you fucking little assholes!" I suddenly realize we are not anonymous here, the way we were on the highway—we are trespassing on someone else's territory.

"John, Jesus Christ, let's get out of here." I try to pull him up. He is bleeding and he's crying again. John pushes back from me, walking backwards on his hands.

"We aren't at Wawa any more. We can go back to the highway." He is shaking.

Suddenly, I am crying too. "I spent a quarter of my money to get off the highway. This is the only spot where we can hop a freight car. We are fucking stranded in the north woods. Don't you understand that, you asshole!" I can't believe the language I am using with John. I never talk this way—I am upset and frightened.

The two guys are backing off now, looking embarrassed at watching the two of us bawling our eyes out. John is still pushing himself backwards along the gravel. "I don't need to worry, you bastard. You think I'm as much of a jerk as you. Here, look, I've got money, and I've got food too, and I'm going back up to the store to find out about the next bus." He is pulling a wad of bills out of his knapsack and a sandwich that must have been waiting there since we started out. He is eating it, ripping it with his front teeth. I watch him go.

207

New paradigms, or new theoretical models, force out old questions and bring in new. Often, the proponents of the new way of thinking cannot even communicate with members of the old regime. Kuhn feels that this is inevitable:

> We have . . . seen several reasons why the proponents of competing paradigms must fail to make complete contact with each other's viewpoints. Collectively these reasons have been described as the incommensurability of the pre- and postrevolutionary normal-scientific traditions.[6]

The map that guides the believers in a particular theoretical model can be laid on top of an old map and its presence never be noticed by the followers of the older tradition. The questions are not the same and the answers do not jibe. It reminds me again of the gas drillers and reindeer herders—the two civilizations are barely aware of each other. So it is for scientists. Each way of thinking is the only way, from time in the distant past to the inconceivable future, the only and the true way of thinking.

208

Savily Lapitsky's railroad is not the one I travelled on in 1967. My railroad, my dream of hopping a freight car, was a pass to freedom, a way out. I am looking for Lapitsky in the Leningrad winter of 1991 to find his railroad. He has been painting it since 1953, since he stopped working on it as a slave labourer, transported to Salekhard in the Yamal by Stalin's security police. Our paradigms, Lapitsky's and mine, don't match. "Look around you," the man had said to me the summer before when I stood on the airfield in Ukhta. "Ten labour camps were all around the edges of this airport. Why are you here anyway? Don't you know where you are?"

The suburbs of Leningrad are just urban slave quarters, I am thinking, and the air is still filled with the smell of violence. Sasha has stopped talking. He is shivering from his last encounter with unfriendly people at a doorway of one of the apartment buildings. We are driving around one unrecognizable block of concrete monsters for the third time, I think. The few raggedly dressed children look familiar. The driver's wife is saying we will have to get out now; they are late in getting to their own destination somewhere else in this maze of concrete. "We are close—I know that," Sasha reassures me. The driver pulls up alongside a snowbank behind a large panel truck and motions for us to leave. But first there is a transaction. Sasha brings out his wallet and is counting out 20 rubles, a lot of money in January 1991. The driver's wife looks at me and tells her husband he is a fool—there are American dollars. At that moment, the truck in front suddenly backs into us. The hood of our car melts into a flattened piece of tin, and we are pushed back a foot. The driver has leapt out and is screaming at the truck. His wife has gone pale, her face is white. Sasha thrusts another 10-ruble note

into her unmoving hand and shouts at me to get out. We run away
down the snowbanked street.

209

The map you use, or the theoretical model you follow, will change
the nature of the questions you ask. A scientist will see the world as
a different place depending on which ideas are used for guidance.
Kuhn describes the pursuit for an understanding of oxygen. In its first
manifestation in European science, oxygen was "discovered" as a substance, fitting into the prevailing theories of the time. It the second
encounter, it was "invented," forming the basis for a new theory or
paradigm, a new map for chemistry: the "idea" of oxygen would create
fertile intellectual terrain amenable to the cultivation of other like ideas:

> The impossible suggestion that Priestley first discovered oxygen
> and Lavoisier then invented it has its attractions.[7]

> Grant now that discovery involves an extended, though not neces-
> sarily long, process of conceptual assimilation. Can we also say
> it involves a change in paradigm? To that question, no general an-
> swer can yet be given, but in this case at least, the answer must be
> yes. What [the French chemist Antoine] Lavoisier announced in
> his papers from 1777 on was not so much the discovery of oxygen as
> the oxygen theory of combustion. That theory was the keystone for
> a reformulation of chemistry so vast that it is usually called the
> chemical revolution.[8]

New theories have the power to change the entire intellectual landscape. The chemical revolution following Lavoisier did not occur as a
result of simple observations of the natural world, succeeded by a theoretical adjustment, as would be the historical perspective of David
Hume, for example. No, a revolution occurs because of an idea, an idea
that alters the way we see things and the way we map our progress

through the world. As Kuhn points out, even the very objects we see around us appear to change under the introduction of a new paradigm. Before Lavoisier, chemistry theorists believed that phlogiston, a substance supposed to exist in all combustible bodies, was lost during the burning process. But since earlier times, in the work of Islamic scholars, for example, it was noticed that metals gain weight when roasted. Under the phlogiston theory, it would be expected that weight would be lost, since phlogiston was thought to depart from burning bodies of matter. The power of the phlogiston paradigm was so great as to lead scientists at the time to suggest that perhaps phlogiston had a negative weight![9] With Lavoisier, a new paradigm was emerging, but it required more than just a simple adjustment of perspective—the entire scientific world view was under siege. The map was being challenged. In effect, the imaginary perfect world to which science was headed, the end point, the τέλος, was being challenged.

210

Antonia is Savily Lapitsky's daughter. She and her mother hover behind us as Sasha and I sit and talk with Lapitsky in the main room of the apartment. There are two other rooms, all filled with the large wooden boards that Lapitsky uses as surfaces for his paintings. These are piled against the walls and the furniture ten-deep. In an adjoining room, among the paintings, Antonia has an upright piano. She is sent out to the room to play for us several times. "Go and play, please, Antonia. She is so good. She needs a career but it is impossible—we are poor, and I am hounded by the KGB. They will not let us emigrate together. In America, or better in Canada, she would have a chance."

The conversation is all in Russian. Sasha seems to have given up as a translator. I think he expects the paintings to speak for themselves. But Lapitsky is not talking about his paintings. "Every day he leaves us and I look out the window for his return," his wife says, telling Lapitsky's story over again. We have heard it a few times since we have arrived, several versions. The family revolves around this man who has not left the Gulag work camps of his youth. He is living there still. The modern world means nothing to him.

211

Kuhn asks how scientists are brought to make a transition into a new paradigm, and answers that they are often not able. They die out literally, taking their way of thinking with them, while younger scientists with new ideas prevail.

> Copernicanism made few converts for almost a century after Copernicus' death. Newton's work was not accepted, particularly on the Continent, for more than half a century after the *Principia* appeared. Priestley [the British chemist] never accepted the oxygen theory, nor Lord Kelvin [the Scottish physicist] the electromagnetic theory, and so on. . . . And Max Planck [the German theoretical physicist], surveying his own career in his *Scientific Autobiography*, sadly remarked that "a new scientific truth does not triumph by convincing its opponents and making them see the light, but rather because its opponents eventually die, and a new generation grows up that is familiar with it."[10]

Now I "sadly" realize that I have not found a fellow traveller in Thomas Kuhn. In the body of his text, Kuhn's understanding of the power of the paradigm in the scientific process has lent weight to my image of the idea being an active participant in the formation of its place in the world, theories forging their way through the intellectual landscape, sculpting it and shaping it, and being changed in return, a reciprocal exchange. But hidden throughout Kuhn's *Structure of Scientific Revolutions* is a firm belief in the enterprise of the science of the west. The indication that he thinks there is an ultimate understanding to which science is headed is embodied in his use of the word *sadly* in the quote referring to Max Planck. Kuhn sympathizes with Planck, who bemoans the slow progress of science, a pursuit bogged down, it seems, by scientists who cling to their mistaken theories. I would ask what makes one theory superior to another. Kuhn's initial hypothesis would seem to indicate that there can be little value to crediting one theory over another, as they are all products of a particular viewpoint or paradigm in fashion at any given time. But he indicates a belief in the slow progress of ideas over time, a concept that does give a higher value to the more recent developments of science. Kuhn believes in the progress of science. This latter concept takes us back to the hierarchy, the movement toward the guiding destiny of the perfect end point.

212

John has good reason to stick to his highway. He has money, so he can take a bus until he reaches a town where the road is filled with people willing to pick up hitchhikers. But he can't go alone. I chase him again. "John! Don't be a jerk, you can't go without me." He stops, trying to turn his head in a direction where there are no onlookers. He is shaking and crying. The little board houses on the gravel street look down on us. I back away, unable to think of anything else to say. He is trapped with me anyway, because I have no money and I can't take another bus.

"There's an old guy in the train yard—he'll tell youse what's what with jumping the train." One of the guys who were threatening us a few minutes before has come up to me. "It's gonna be tough for your friend, though, eh? He looks kinda out of it, eh?"

"Come on, leave them fucking bastards! Let's go!" the other guy is yelling, walking off.

213

Ideas for Kuhn are like animals, in the sense that he believes they can be studied in relationship to their environment. But he protests the relativist label. Even for a man who looked at science from the outside, who dissected scientists' smug tendency to couch theories from the perspective of one way of thinking, one paradigm, whatever is in fashion at the moment, even for a philosopher with such an insight into the problems of western science, it is uncomfortable being labelled as an outsider. And being a relativist, someone who believes that the individual perspective of a thinker or scientist is critical to the theories evolved, is a good way to become ostracized from the community of modern scholars. In his *Postscript* to *The Structure of Scientific Revolutions*, written in 1969, seven years after the book itself was published, Kuhn argues that he has never meant to detract from the success of modern science, and that he has always supported the idea that science paradigms "progress" over time. He argues that ideas live in an intellectual world that is undergoing an evolution, a progression from the lowest to the highest, just like the biological world as described by Darwin and others.

> Imagine an evolutionary tree representing the development of the modern scientific specialties from their common origins in, say, primitive natural philosophy and the crafts. A line drawn up that tree, never doubling back, from the trunk to the tip of some branch would trace a succession of theories related by descent. Considering any two such theories, chosen from points not too near their origin, it should be easy to design a list of criteria that would enable an uncommitted observer to distinguish the earlier from the more recent theory time after time. Among the most useful would be: accuracy of prediction, particularly of quantitative prediction; the balance between esoteric and everyday subject matter; and the number of different problems solved. . . . [S]cientific development is, like biological, a unidirectional and irreversible process. Later scientific theories are better than earlier ones for solving puzzles in the often quite different environments to which they are applied. That is not a relativist's position, and it displays the sense in which I am a convinced believer in scientific progress.[11]

Again we find the belief in the end toward which we are all headed. The final situation apparently guides us forward, for what else would define the ever-improving state of scientific theory? But doesn't Kuhn himself speak, even in this passage, of different environments, of different situations that yield different questions and different intentions and different ideas? Why does he choose to believe in the pursuit of the "truth," even when his ideas move the reader to a much different conclusion? I contend that he felt in danger of losing his membership in the scientific club of the western world. He is, by admission in the *Postscript*, responding to criticisms and trying to reassure his critics that he does believe in the progress of science. But in so doing he is also tacking his discussion of scientific revolution onto a belief that European-based science is headed in the "right" direction. Otherwise, he would not state that the scientific theories of today are "better than earlier ones."

214

"This is better than hanging out by the side of the road, eh?" I'm trying to encourage John a little. We are in the rail yards, leaning against a pile of hay bales in the barn next to the tracks.

The old guy was there when we got to the trains, and he told us what to do. "Wait till it's dusk, now, and don't go showing yourselves up by the station," he spits through his whiskers. "And choose a nice car, one that's not too used."

The rail yard is filled with empty cattle cars that are headed back west after delivering beef cattle to Ontario. They've been hosed down, but some of them still have lumps of sodden manure sticking to the floor. "This here train is headed out after dark tonight. It's got lots of good empty cars. You just throw a little hay into the car around dusk. But don't get in till after. Wait till the train starts to move away. It's real slow at first." We are hiding out in the barn, relaxing in the afternoon heat, but out of the sun, and John is smiling again. We have chosen a car, and every half hour or so we casually drag a bale of hay along the tracks and throw it in. John shimmied up into the car once to mess the bales around a little so they don't look too obvious. You can see into and through all the railcars because the walls are just slats of wood.

"I get claustrophobia, so this is the only kind of car I'm gettin' into, and we're not closing the door all the way, 'cause it might lock on us." John is taking charge now, and I'm secretly relieved. I'm getting a little nervous. The train guard patrols the grounds every hour. He and the old guy chat and smoke next to the switching shed most of the time.

"How does he not know we're here?" I'm asking John, but mostly myself.

"The guy said for us to stay out of sight, but he didn't say the guard didn't know we're here."

"Yeah, but Jeez! That's one weird way to handle things."

215

Seeing things as they are, or altering perceived existence with a theory—that dichotomy characterizes science. Scientists most often believe that they are seeing things as they are and are mapping out the universe with theories that match their observations. They have a vision of the world to which they are headed. At any given time, a predominant paradigm, or theoretical framework, will dominate the intellectual landscape, and the vision of the world that emanates from this paradigm will shape the things they see.

216

Stephen Toulmin giggled and joked a lot, and he scratched. As we talked, I became concerned for him—his shirt was soon bloody all across his shoulders. The more we talked, the more excited he became, and the more he bled. Gobs of blood ran from under his short sleeves and down his arms. He talked about reality. I was watching his white shirt turn red, and he talked about how what we see is not necessarily reality. I tried to focus on his reality and not on his blood.

Toulmin is a philosopher of science who preceded Kuhn in the examination of paradigm shifts throughout scientific history; he postulated that the point of view expressed by the scientists involved in any given experiment would have an effect on what we understand to be "true."[12] Furthermore, his acceptance of paradigmatic shifts does not appear to be predicated on a belief in an inevitable historical direction to the development of ideas over time. Toulmin questions the *progress* that defines the history of science for most scholars.[13] His arguments, unlike Kuhn's *Postscript* contentions, come closer to my proposal that ideas do not progress toward a greater and greater understanding of a fixed reality, but rather that they make their own environment—establish their own reality, as it were—a proposal that I believe is largely supported by Kuhn's arguments, if not his *Postscript* conclusion to them; in outlining the effect that a scientific paradigm can have on a group of scientists, Kuhn, in the main body of his text in *The Structure of Scientific Revolutions*, is effectively arguing that science is based on the intellectual survival of an idea, and that ideas, as championed by their carriers, the scientists, play a role in their own establishment within the intellectual environment. If you take this argument far enough, ideas make reality itself: since we can't see beyond our own perception of nature and since it is proposed that ideas form their own environment, then perceptions, which are in themselves ideas, must form the ultimate environment, namely, reality itself.

The key to this understanding goes back to my criticism of Hume in an earlier chapter. Hume stated that the idea is derived from the initial observation of the phenomenon, the approach favoured by most western scientists who believe in an external reality that must be observed and that will form the basis for theories about the world. My approach would have it the other way around: the idea is formed first, as a manifestation of a value system, and it establishes a niche for itself in the natural world, where the intellectual component is inseparable from the fabric of reality as a whole. The intellectual component, because thinking inherently imposes order, acts as the filter through which pass events, entities, and relationships from the world continuum. From this perspective, even the first perceptions one has of the world are formulated within an idea or through a filter, and since the idea forms a relationship and a niche for itself, and since this is tantamount to creating a dialectical relationship with the landscape, which relationship in turn develops into a state of reality, then it can be said that the perceptual ideas of the observer create reality itself.

217

Lapitsky's reality is definitely shaped by his one central idea. He is a former *zek*, a prisoner of the Gulag. This has not changed since he worked "on the horns" (he uses phrases like this all the time). "The horns" are the rails of the railroad, brutal, like horns. I want to hear his stories, and I want his paintings to come to Toronto for the exhibition. "We had no food—many people died from lack of food—and I am a Jew, so the guards hated me and they made sure that I missed the food rationing." Lapitsky tells Antonia to bring pastries for me and Sasha.

"No, no, please don't worry about us," I protest mildly. But I really want something to eat, anything. We haven't eaten since we stopped for coffee several hours ago. Lapitsky swoops into the main chair, magisterially waving me to sit too. "Why are so many of your paintings depicting the Nazi Holocaust?" I am looking at one particular work where he has incorporated a famous photograph of emaciated Auschwitz prisoners piled into filthy bunks.

"It is the same! Nazis, KGB, Stalin, Hitler, the same thing. Look, look, look at this one!" He drags a huge board out from behind a blanket. His wife rushes up to prevent five more paintings from falling over. Lapitsky doesn't acknowledge her actions. He shows us a very disturbing image of grotesque faces growing from a joined swastika and hammer and sickle. His wife is struggling to hold the paintings. She has cut herself on the edge of one of them.

218

In the early 1950s, while Lapitsky worked on the Gulag railroad, Toulmin wrote about the relationship between reality and scientific investigation; he was aware of the effects that language has on scientific models, but his writing indicates to me that, for him, there is always an immutable reality that cannot be affected by any theory that attempts to explain a particular phenomenon.[14] He states that "no experience that could be altered by a change in one's belief's alone would be acceptable to us as 'scientific observation.' " Yet he appears to waver from his thesis to a small degree when, in the same passage, he refers to a red sunset that "we know . . . is not *really* red," and points out that *physics* may "explain why a stick *looks* bent [when seen at the interface of air and water]." In either example, the implication is that the stick is indeed *not* bent, and the sun is *not* red. For Toulmin, it appears that if a theory can explain a red sunset, or a blue sky, as the refraction of light into colour bands as it streams through the atmosphere, then we at once accept that we are only sort of "seeing" a red sunset and the blue of the sky is not really so blue. Our experience of "bentness" or "redness" or "blueness" can be altered by reference to the intellectual explanation provided by the scientific discipline of physics. For me, this comes close to allowing a belief system, physics in this case, to affect our view of reality. This supports my arguments, in that it allows for the fact that *ideas* influence, and in fact formulate, our view of reality. But I am confused why Toulmin accepts it, since it is tantamount to accepting the actual alteration of our reality through the employment of "one's beliefs"—in this case, a belief system represented by the discipline of physics. In the final analysis, however, despite arguments that can be made regarding Toulmin's science filter on reality, it is quite clear that he, like nearly every other scholar of science philosophy and history in this century, draws the line at accepting any theoretical explanation that will lure us away from believing in the ultimate and absolute reality that is "out there." Science can explain perception, but the action of the observer, the scientist, cannot change the reality that does sit separately from the observer, unchanged, in his opinion.

I conclude that Toulmin and Kuhn—albeit from somewhat different perspectives, Toulmin not being quite so ready to accept a progressive definition of science—are desperate not to leave the safe confines of a teleological intellectual environment. For them, the different frameworks of theoretical thought are still the means to understand the universe that is passively waiting to be discovered. Their adherence to a fixed reality, external to the mind of the scientist, makes my point of view all the easier to explain. I am postulating that ideas *do* change their surroundings, both the intellectual and the physical, and that, in turn, this change effects a reciprocal change in the ideas, and on and on, back and forth, *ad infinitum*. This process extends even to the concrete reality we experience. I am suggesting that ideas can cause the very ground to shift beneath our feet.

219

Antonia brings us a package of meringues. They are still in their plastic cups, still in their original cardboard box. There are nine left out of twelve. She also brings a teapot. In the Soviet Union, tea is made very strong and is mixed with water to taste. Lapitsky sips the small portion of tea she pours for him, testing it like wine. He waves away the offer of water from the samovar and pours a *full* cup for himself, straight, no dilution. Then he adds four large pieces of sugar. Sugar comes in pieces equal to about four North American sugar cubes, so he is taking about sixteen sugar cubes in one cup. Antonia pours Sasha a cup. He adds a little water and just as much sugar as our host. Lapitsky is frowning at this procedure, watching the amount of sugar taken by Sasha very carefully. I am served next. There is almost no tea left in the pot, so Antonia adds about two thirds of a cup of water. There are only two sugar pieces left, and I take one.

"Are you not going to sit with us?" I ask Antonia and her mother.

"N-no . . ." Antonia begins.

"No, no, not necessary," Lapitsky finishes. His wife is still standing at the corner of the room holding the paintings to prevent them from falling over. Lapitsky stares at the meringues. Two are broken, they are all very stale, but this is typical of the hospitality we have been receiving in the Soviet Union. People have so little food that special occasions almost call for merely a ceremonial presentation and not an actual eating of any special delicacies that might be available. This time, however, it appears that we will be eating. Lapitsky tears the plastic that covers the two broken meringues. His movements are large and awkward, like his paintings. He gives out the two broken meringues, one each to Sasha and me. His wife is starting to say something but stops as he stares at her. Then he tears the plastic cover off the largest, most unbroken meringue and serves it to himself. He grins, and, gesturing for us to begin eating, he opens his enormous mouth and crunches down on the meringue. This is followed by a slurping from both Sasha and Lapitsky as they drink the sugary syrup that passes for tea. Antonia and her mother look on.

220

It is cool in the evening in White River. The sun goes down very late, and the mist comes up. But the pinks and purples of the sky are exciting me. We are soon going to be on a train travelling out of here. John and I make our way back to the railcar we fixed up earlier. The train is slowly starting to move. He heaves me up to the car's floor and scrambles up after me. There are voices in the gloom. "What the!" I freeze still.

"Hey, all right!" I hear a greeting. It's the two guys from Ottawa we met earlier on the highway near Wawa. And two others, older. One is Native. They are staring at us, but the others tell them to relax. "Hey, they're okay—in fact, they gave us the idea to do this."

"This is our car—we fixed it up." John is stiffly bouncing.

"So what are you gonna do about it, throw us off?" The train is picking up speed.

"How long have you been here?" I can't believe we had to be so careful, watching out for the train yard guard. These guys are practically having a party.

221

Our idea had caught on. There had been a minor revolution in the ranks of the hitchhikers, and they had followed us. "Did you talk to the old guy in the train yard?"

"Fuck, no, we just came here and piled into this car with all the hay."

One of them pulls out a harmonica and starts to play. I am cold and scared, but this moment is going to last, I tell myself. I try to enjoy the harmonica blues as the train rattles on.

Later, the two older guys are huddled in the corner with the two guys from Ottawa. They won't talk with us. One of the two we know tells us they all think maybe John and I are running from the police and they don't want us around.

"Shit." John is turning pale; he doesn't like the look on the faces of our friends.

"Why else would you suggest hopping a freight? Only guys who can't be seen on the road do that."

"Well, why did *you* want to do it?"

"Look"—the guy with the harmonica is standing up in the rocking freight car, hanging on to the slats—"everybody knows that only fucking criminals or people with something to hide do things like this. We're just following you—we're not the fucking same as you."

"I don't believe this." John is laughing. His teeth are bared, and he looks crazy.

I step in between John and the others. "Just stay the fuck on your own side of the car, then, you asshole fucking shitheads." I don't know what part of my brain is coming up with this. I sense them backing off, and I feel better now. And I was afraid of these guys?

222

When I was in Siberia I saw Lapitsky's railroad. The tracks had not lasted through even one winter and spring. They kept repairing and rebuilding and building farther across the north. But the permafrosted earth had heaved and twisted the rails. They looked like spaghetti. Lapitsky had worked on a "decorative," non-functioning railroad; it couldn't take him anywhere. For him, the railroad was a prison. It was a holocaust, so he painted the images of the Gulag camps along the railroad in Siberia and put them next to the images of the Holocaust perpetrated by the Nazis. When I walked along the Siberian tracks, I felt that curious sense of erotic exhilaration I get when I feel I am a part of something powerful and dangerous, something that is going somewhere. Maybe—when I was standing on the Gulag railroad in Siberia—maybe I was still on that train going across Canada in 1967. Maybe my feelings were just a flashback to my childhood fears and battles with life-size horrors, and did not indicate a perverse empathy with the evil of brutal dictators like Stalin. Breaking away from the mainstream ideas can lead to mental confusion; it takes time to sort things out.

223

Sometimes ideas are so extreme and so different from the mainstream that they appear to be, simply, wrong. Sometimes it's just that ideas do not find an easy nesting ground—too much change is needed for the intellectual environment to accommodate them. Lavoisier challenged the phlogiston theory and developed the oxygen theory. His new approach needed to live within an intellectual landscape that could accept a major shift in the prevailing theories of the way things work. Copernicus challenged the dominant concept of an earth-centred planetary system. He needed not corroborating evidence but rather an environment that would permit new frames of reference. Intellectual societies that will not admit new frames of reference essentially develop ideas from a teleological perspective. Their map has already been drawn.

224

But who needs Lapitsky's map of the world? His whole life has been centred on the suffering he endured in the Gulag camps. I heard once of a play that depicted severely disabled people as they really are. The playwright was asked why many of the characters were so mean and unlikeable. "What do you think happens to us when we are rejected and when people don't even want to see us? Do you think we turn out nice after that kind of life?" Lapitsky isn't nice.

Later, in 1991, he comes to Toronto to see his paintings on display. "When we picked him up at the airport, he had no suitcase, just a paper bag and he was dressed in rags, literally," the woman who acted as his host in Canada told me later. Lapitsky inundated her family and friends with requests for clothes and for presents. He never mentioned his wife and daughter. But I liked him, in a way—he was predictable, a good drinking companion. I sat up one night with him in Toronto. We ate sardines and drank whisky. He told me story after story about how he survived in the Gulag. Nothing else ever entered our conversation.

225

Scientists who guide the progress of the western civilization aren't nice either. A teleological world of ideas forces a belief in a world that justifies the images determined by those in power. The so-called pure scientific ideas are closely related to a belief in the superiority of the people themselves. The people who are seen as superior are the people who are, *at that time*, in power. During the past few centuries, it has been European scientists and philosophers who have been extolling the virtues of the Europeans. Their ideas derive from those of earlier scholars such as Aristotle, as we have seen. Of course, Aristotle himself did not see the neighbouring Europeans as superior, but rather depicted them as stupid and disorganized. He set the "Hellenic race"

above all others. It is always the same—whoever is in power places
themselves on a pinnacle. This is part of the legacy of the teleological
universe, which seeks to fulfil its self-defined image of perfection, as
Aristotle has made evident in *The Politics*:

> The nations that live in cold regions and those of Europe are full of
> spirit, but somewhat lacking in skill and intellect; for this reason,
> while remaining relatively free, they lack political cohesion and the
> ability to rule over their neighbours. On the other hand the Asiatic
> nations have in their souls both intellect and skill, but are lacking
> in spirit; so they remain enslaved and subject. The Hellenic race,
> occupying a mid-position geographically, has a measure of both,
> being both spirited and intelligent. Hence it continues to be free, to
> live under the best constitutions, and, given a *single* constitution,
> to be capable of ruling all other people.[15]

The intent is to rule over "all other people," as Aristotle states. Lapitsky survived being ruled over, only to serve the same hideous medicine
to his little family.

226

We can see the stars through the slats in the cattle car. And there is
enough moonlight to see the trees and the water and the rocks on the
shore of Lake Superior. It is damp with ground mist and it is cold; it
feels like winter. We all pile hay on top of ourselves as we travel through
the night. What if we freeze, I think. John and I hold on to each other
for body heat. The others still won't come near us; they are huddled in
their own group at the other end of the car.

Through the mist, the huge rocks out in the water loom over us,
passing us with a rush of wind. The trees by the track are hurtling
through the air just above us. But overhead the night is clear, and the
stars are holding up the sky. And the stars are holding us still and quiet
as the western half of Canada runs down the track toward us. We are

held motionless in the basket made by the stars, and the landscape flies by gently, shivering the railcar as it passes.

227

Frames of reference can be so different that they challenge the very ways we think. When I was working on an exhibition that explored the nature of prejudice, I also looked for examples of scientific logic that challenged our western way of thinking. The Canadian anthropologist John Berry told me about the Caroline Islanders in the South Pacific who travel across large expanses of open ocean using a system of navigation that employs as markers the rising and setting points of stars on the horizon. The star points are so far away that they appear to travel along with the outrigger canoes. Rather than thinking of themselves travelling with the stars, the islanders imagine that the boat and the star points are stationary and the *islands* are moving toward them.[16] In my cattle car going over the top of Lake Superior, I was sensing the stillness of the train, held by the stationary stars, watching the trees and the rocks rush by me.

228

The Caroline Island navigators use a reference island that is far to one side of the route from one island to the next. (The reference island cannot be seen, but its position is known from countless travels over known routes and a knowledge of the distances that can be travelled over a day, given certain winds.) The reference island off to their side is slowly being "pulled" under the stars. In the route depicted here, the reference island is moving from under the Great Bear rising star position until it lies under the Polaris star, then under the Great Bear setting position and on and on until it finally lies under the Vega setting position.

The stationary canoe and the moving islands can be compared to a train or car trip, where you see a distant mountain that is so far away it

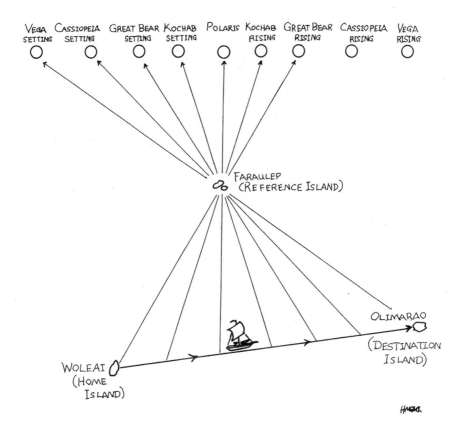

The Moving Islands of the Caroline Islanders of the South Pacific.[17]

appears to be travelling with you. You and the mountain appear to be staying still in your little personal frame of reference, while the rest of the world rushes by.

229

There is nothing wrong with the concept of keeping still while the islands come to you. It appears at first sight to be wrong, but motion is relative. As long as you and your destination island end up together, what does it matter which is moving? But it is so difficult for us to think in a new way.

When it comes to the South Sea islanders, we could argue that it is hard to think in an "old" way. Many people would consider the South Sea navigational techniques to be a part of an older primitive world; we know better now, we say—islands don't move. But all I know really is that I am resistant to alternative ways of thinking. In a different frame of reference, using a different kind of thinking, islands do move. South Sea islanders do manage to reach their destinations, or rather they manage to have their destinations reach them.

But if we look again at Kuhn's *Postscript*, we find the argument that science is progressive. Older methods of thought are too primitive to accommodate new ways of thinking. How sad. Does this means that European navigational techniques, which never had the concept of islands moving under the stars, were always more advanced? In fact, Europeans were at a loss out of sight of land until the perfection of the chronometer, in the 1700s, a device that for the first time allowed accurate measurements of longitude.[18] The South Sea islanders, on the other hand, have been travelling for long distances out of sight of land for a very, very long time.

230

The next day, we lie still under the hay for two hours. Now it is hot, but we can't show ourselves. Trainmen keep walking by. We see through the slats that we are at the end of Lake Superior, in Port Arthur. Grain elevators stand next to our train. The cars keep shunting back and forth along the tracks. We are shunted into a side rail. "What if we're stuck here? What if the car is staying here for a few days? Shouldn't we look around to see what's happening?" John is complaining.

"Shut up, we can't get caught here. What would we do?" Late in the afternoon, the car is bumped hard. Then we slowly start to move, just as a group of workers walk by. We are still under the hay. They are joined by two guys in railguard uniforms. We can see them from under the hay.

They stop next to us. "Comfortable, boys?" They laugh and walk off. As the train pulls out of Port Arthur, we all sit up and stare at one another.

"They musta known we were here all the time. Jesus, I can't move, I'm so stiff."

We are headed into another night. The stars are out again to guide the trees by us as we lie on the track. "We're going all the way to Alberta on this." The Ottawa guys are talking to us again.

"Jeez, I don't know. You're bound to get caught."

"You saw what happened there. They don't care."

"Yeah, but what about food and water?"

Earlier, the day before, we'd had a lucky break. We slowed down and stopped at a level crossing in a small town. People living by the tracks saw us and ran up, laughing.

"Water, please!" We were getting desperate. A young woman ran into her house and then chased us along the track as the train pulled out, finally handing us a plastic bottle of water and a loaf of bread. The group of people at the crossing cheered and waved and, slowly picking up speed, disappeared behind us. That wasn't likely to happen again.

"We'll get out at the next stop and stock up on supplies."

"Yeah, sure." The only long stops had been in the middle of Port Arthur train yard and someplace in the middle of nowhere the night before.

231

Ideas from older cultures can disturb scientists who believe in the building of the ultimate model of the universe. New developments are improvements, as Kuhn said, and old ideas, like moving islands, do not serve a useful purpose. Or do they?

In the exhibition about prejudice in science, one idea led to another. The image of moving islands resulted in the questioning of the pivotal concept in the history of scientific revolutions in the west. Copernicus challenged the prevalent earth-centred planetary system model. He developed the sun-centred model, and later Galileo fought for the sun-centred model. Today, we think of Galileo as a champion for the "truth." We think of the earth-centred model as being primitive and wrong. In keeping with Kuhn's *Postscript* writings, Copernicus represents the development of "better" ideas, ideas that are bringing us closer to the "correct" image of the natural world. But how rigid we have become! If islands can move while we stay still in our canoe, then surely the sun and the planets and the stars can move around us while the earth stays in one place. It is all a matter of frames of reference. At about the time of Copernicus, the Danish astronomer Tycho Brahe described a planetary system that kept all the distances and angles we associate with the planets and the sun, but centred them all on the earth. This is correct geometrically. And it works best for navigational needs and calendars. In fact, anything can be the centre of any system. If I choose to open the door to a building, I can swing the door on its hinges, or I can choose to hold the door in one place and move the building around. In the end, I can get through the doorway. Tycho Brahe's model does much the same thing. The stars and planets hang in the sky the same way, the factual observations are the same, but the way we think about it is different.

There is no "progress" to these ideas, as Kuhn and Popper and others would wish to find; there is only a "frame of reference" change. We still use an earth-centred planetary system today when necessary (for navigation and calendars, for example), and we use the sun-centred system when necessary (to produce mathematical models that further theories of gravity and thermodynamics). There has been no real revolution in science. We only talk about a revolution because it suits us to proclaim progress.

232

During the debates over moving islands and the validity of earth-centred planetary systems, many scientists working with me became upset and angry. Challenging the sun-centred Copernican system shifts the ground out from under our intellectual feet, I was told. If we accept the relativity of motion in the planetary system, then effectively we allow for universal relativity. John, an astronomer who forced me to think through these arguments a great deal during the development of the museum exhibition, was very disturbed by the relativism I was introducing into the history of science. He suggested that challenging Copernicus and Galileo could be interpreted to mean that Holocaust deniers must be allowed their say, since theirs is simply another point of view. But there is no theory behind Holocaust denial, only a wish to change history. Changing the theory within the field of facts has always been acceptable. Changing the facts to fit the theory is not acceptable.

But how, it could be asked, can I reconcile this basic tenet of scientific logic with my contention that ideas shape the reality around them? There is no conflict: realizing that the complexion, or appearance, of the facts, their relative importance to one another and their configuration within the intellectual landscape, changes with the impact of a strong theoretical thrust—this is the nature of my argument. And this is not equivalent to accepting just any point of view. For example, within an earth-centred frame of reference, the theoretical thrust lies in the concept of positioning the centre of a system around the point of view of the observer. It is not far-fetched to believe that the development of navigational systems and calendars stems from this observer centre, a perspective that is more than just an engineering viewpoint but that is, rather, a *theoretical* foundation. The idea of earth-centredness establishes itself, then, within the intellectual landscape and works with the natural world to form a viable construct. At no time, it must be noted, is there any denial of the observed facts, insofar as they can be described by using the tools of the system in question. An earth-centred perspective does not change the position or angles of the planets and the sun and the earth one to another, in other words.

Holocaust deniers, on the other hand, would assert that the murder of almost all Europe's Jews has been a fabrication (and therefore the history of the twentieth century as we know it is a sham). But this position ignores the body of observed fact, the eyewitness testimonies of the survivors, the remains of death camps, the bodies of the murdered, the physical displacement of millions of people.

Neither the proponents of the earth-centred planetary system nor the Holocaust deniers are cultural relativists, strictly speaking. Cultural relativism is the interpretation of natural or historic events from the singular and unique perspective of disparate world cultures. Unlike that of South Sea Island navigation, the two examples discussed here are both well within the western tradition. On the one hand, the sun- and earth-centred planetary models are means to understanding motion with a view to meeting different objectives. The Holocaust deniers, on the other hand, are deeply biased, willing to ignore blatant evidence that disproves their arguments.

At a still deeper level, the Holocaust deniers are perpetuating the concept of natural hierarchy. Holocaust deniers have devoted a lot of energy to preserving the hierarchial world order: at the base of their assertions is the belief in a superior race. For this reason, their position cannot be taken as simply "another point of view." It is a point of view that does not sit well within a dialectical theory that would put all perspectives at an equal level. Hierarchical ideas have as their goal the exclusion of other points of view.

In light of the foregoing argument, therefore, it does not follow that challenging the monolithic character of western scientific tradition is equivalent to accepting that any ill-founded history-distorting concept is as viable as any other; but the fact that this concern was voiced in all seriousness alerted me to the powerful passions that arguments against the mainstream scientific concepts can excite.

233

Once a new paradigm has been accepted, moving back to the old is not easy. John and I are train people now, living a new paradigm. We listen as the other four talk about their plans. They want to travel at least as far as Alberta. That's where the cattle cars are going, we think. Right now, the train is travelling through the night toward Winnipeg. "My mother has a cousin in Winnipeg," John is muttering; he wants to get off soon. The paradigm of the train hasn't taken so well with the two of us. I think it's because we are still treated with suspicion; and because we thought of the idea of hiding out in the train car, we are the revolutionaries, and they are the followers—we can change, and they can't. But mostly we just want to get off this train that is becoming a jail for us. Cattle cars took Jews to death camps. I wasn't thinking of that at the time, but there was something degrading about being carted across the country in a cattle car smelling of manure. And the odour is getting worse. We can't change cars on a moving train; one corner of ours has been designated as the toilet.

In the early morning we move slowly through the giant train yard of Winnipeg, second only in size to Chicago's. The train takes two hours to come to a stop—slowly shifting from track to track, we almost stop and then we start up, again and again. Finally we are completely stopped. John and I slide the door open for the first time in thirty-six hours. We run across the tracks, dodging slow-moving train cars and looking out for guards. But it is still partly dark. We jump over track after track after track until at last we walk out to the street.

We are greeted by a passing patrol car. "Where you coming from?" The two police officers are looking us up and down.

"Toronto."

"How'd you get here?"

"Some guy gave us a lift."

"Yeah, sure." They laugh and drive off. Later, we clean up in the washroom of a breakfast place near the train yard. My face is so black I think the mirror has clouded. And we really stink.

"Everybody seems to know exactly what we've been doing—no wonder."

234

Is reality predetermined for scientists like my astronomer friend John and people who passionately believe in the progress of science, like Thomas Kuhn? For them, does it have an end point that is obvious to all those who read the natural, and the intellectual, landscape properly? Many theoretical thinkers of the west, Hume, and Popper and Kuhn and others, and practical scientists working in many fields from astronomy to biology, believe in a sensible natural world, one that can be deciphered by humans.

The world that is predetermined is a world perceived with the map already in place. The South Sea islander map is different. There the landscape is moving and the effects of the traveller on the landscape can be thought of in a more obvious fashion. The idea of the "action" of the islands speaks to a belief in the interaction between the traveller and the landscape. The physical world is not immutable; it can actually move. But most of us living in the west see the end point, the final mapping as an unmoving constraint that shapes our journey. It becomes a kind of pretold story, a story that cannot tolerate deviation from its known course.

235

Lapitsky has a story. He elaborates on it and it grows into its self-styled final shape. His stories are like the popular images from Solzhenitsen; he talks of people gambling for food rations, crippling each other or fighting to the death for amusement. I don't know how much to believe any more. As I sit and listen, hour after hour in Leningrad, the stories become more and more extreme. Sasha sits and nods. "You know how I came to live through that horrible time?" Lapitsky is demanding my attention, but that one meringue was not enough to keep me focused. I am hungry and I want to leave now.

"No. Did you keep yourself focused by thinking of how you would eventually be painting the story of your ordeal?" I want to be helpful.

"No, no, it was a little piece of wool, that is all—a little face mask that my mother sent me, that is what kept me from death." He sits back and waits for my response. I am looking at his eyes, and they shift from my gaze. His wife and daughter nod quickly. They have heard this many times. Later, in Toronto, we want to find such a face mask, the real thing used by a prisoner in the Gulag. Somehow the story does not surprise people who know about the Gulag. These stories are very common. But are they true? Yes, true because they shape the world in which Lapitsky lives. I know I will never know the truth the way we normally think of it. It is embedded in the internal self-created world of victims like Lapitsky, a world that is defined by a very powerful map, a world predestined by the story. Does "exact truth" matter very much?

236

Being locked into our stories is like being locked into a paradigm—the normal state of affairs in science. Kuhn describes this very thoroughly in *The Structure of Scientific Revolutions*. Being wrenched out of a safe story line, away from circumstances that are understood and that guide our actions, leaving such a comfortable environment, takes a major effort or a strong external force.

Languishing on the highway south of Wawa in northern Ontario was enough to break the paradigm of hitchhiking for John and me in 1967. But leaving one paradigm can land you in another, one just as confining; we had left the train while we could still resist its attractions. However, our fellow travellers from Ottawa were not so lucky. They had been lured by John and me into the paradigm of train travel in the first place, and now they are not budging. They are trapped again, and this time we are not with them to suggest a change. They stay on the cattle car in the Winnipeg train yard while John and I leave to find his Winnipeg relatives. As we relax in town, for once well fed and rested, we imagine our friends back on the train, still heading west. Three days later, we're back on the highway, on the outskirts of Winnipeg. "Oh no!" There they are again, the two guys from Ottawa, on the highway, just down the road.

They wave at us. "Jeez, you guys were fucking right to get out of that fucking train. We were all arrested for trespassing. It was $100 fine or ten days in jail. It took our parents three days to send the money, so we just got out this morning."

A strong external force has wrenched them out of the self-delusion they were experiencing in that foul cattle car. It takes a strong force to budge someone from an established paradigm. Our friends from

Ottawa were natural followers, it seems. First they followed us to the train yards in White River to hop a freight, a radical shift in transportation style, a change they could not make on their own, and then they couldn't leave the cattle car. They would have stayed there until they reached Alberta. They had to be torn out of their comfortable berth. Paradigms are like that. They keep people ensconced. It takes a destructive force to break them down.

CHAPTER SEVEN

ESCAPE

But I reckon I got to light out for the Territory
ahead of the rest, because Aunt Sally she's going to
adopt me and sivilize me, and I can't stand it. I been
there before.

– MARK TWAIN, *Huckleberry Finn*

237

"**D**ON'T MOVE. It's better to just feel as if
you're going to move but don't actually move. Just *imagine* that the wire
will end up cutting a little line through the embryo." I'm teaching
Danielle how I insert the fine tungsten wire into the spinal cord of
the tiny chick embryo. "I tell the students to *dream* their way through
micro-surgery—it's that delicate and insignificant a movement." It is the
spring of 1979 and we are working late at night in the laboratory at the
University of Toronto. This is the only time we can work together. The
children are at home in bed, and a neighbour is babysitting for us.
Through the teaching microscope that has a double set of eyepieces, we
can work into the night. It has taken a year to develop the surgical tech-
nique. The key was the isolation of the embryos into plastic Petri dishes.

My wife is an expert at breaking the eggs open at just the right stage. It has to be exactly at stage 17, seventy-two hours old. If it's too late, the yolks break, or too early, the embryos won't continue to develop in the artificial dishes. We have enough embryos to work on tonight. We have cooled them so they won't bleed to death when we cut their spinal cords.

My experiments are designed to examine the regrowth patterns of the embryonic spinal cords over time. "This is amazing . . . It's just . . . We're so tired, and I wish we didn't have to work so late. I don't know if I can do this." She cuts through the spinal cord of the three-day-old embryo. The entire embryo is about a centimetre long, and the cut meant that she had to move her hands a distance equivalent to the width of a few hairs. The thin tungsten wire has been flattened and electrically etched so its width is so thin that it moves through the embryo like a hot knife through butter.

238

Düsseldorf is having a celebration. It is a holiday. It is 1970 in the summer, and Danielle and I have just arrived by train from Belgium. My father brought us over to London two weeks ago and told us to go to Düsseldorf in Germany. He has friends there who have promised us jobs for the summer. We're married just a few weeks now, and this is a kind of holiday for us.

Nothing is open. It is the day when Germans think about the reunification of the two Germanies. I am lugging the plastic suitcase that holds clothes for both of us. "I can't go another block." My hands are numb against the thin, hard plastic handle of the suitcase. "Let's stop and ask someone where we can find a cheap hotel." Düsseldorf is endless, with new broad streets and modern institutional buildings, but on every block there are abandoned lots that are just piles of rubble, bricks and cinder blocks and twisted metal and burnt wood, dirty and old-looking. Something has been through here—buildings are hammered flat. It is destruction masked by shiny modern buildings of glass and steel. Bank buildings and industrial headquarters are everywhere.

"Right, but who? No one is out anywhere." Danielle is not happy here. The few people we have seen haven't stopped for us, even when we shout after them. On the train as we were arriving in Germany, everything had started to feel like the 1940s of our imagination—the signs, the immigration officials, the shouted orders. Now, as we stand on a deserted street, there aren't even any restaurants in sight.

239

Twenty years after Germany, in 1990, Siberia now presents the image of an old war. I had come to the Yamal region expecting to meet only Native people. I have seen the destroyed railroad built by prisoners and the remnants of the Gulag camps. And the Yamal is melting because of the destructive natural gas drilling and the vehicles that cut through the tundra permafrost like knives through butter.

The old system is dying out. Alexander is looking for new partners. "Come to my home for a meal before you leave. We are all wanting to see you. I can tell you my plans for a tourist travel company—travel to the Yamal, eat caviar!" Alexander is the representative for the local Soviet, but he doesn't have any ideological constraints.

"I can't drink another drop of vodka, Sasha," I am muttering to him out of earshot of Alexander. "If we go for dinner, do we have to drink?" I want to get out of Siberia. I want no more of the waiting for instructions, and no more vodka drinking. It is impolite not to drink, but the bottles have tops like Coke bottles—once opened, never recapped. Sasha and I drink water glasses of the stuff at ceremonial occasions, and every meal is a ceremony. We have been "leaving" Siberia for three days now. Fiona is not expected to drink so much—it's the men who drink here. Jim doesn't drink at all and gets away with it. Later in Moscow, Jürgen will be angry at our submissiveness, the Russianness Jim and Fiona and I now wear like clothing, but the drinking and the endless days with no rest are mostly over by the time he shows up; he doesn't know that we have been brainwashed with sleep deprivation, and he doesn't know about the bottles of vodka offered to me like soft drinks. Alexander keeps pressing us to come over that night. My guts ache with the effects of too much fatty food, too little water, and no fruit or vegetables, I complain to Fiona.

"Don't argue so much—it's the custom." Fiona is looking at me darkly, so I say yes, I'll go to Alexander's. Jim is sitting in the corner, ignoring my concerns, and Tatiana is excitedly talking about her plans to take us places once we get back to Moscow. Today she is oblivious to my need for more rest. Her solicitude varies with her mood. Earlier that week, she had called a doctor in to see me because I looked pale, she said.

"Of course I'm pale. I'm not getting any rest." I sent the doctor away.

240

It is 1997, and I am leaving still another paradigm. Like all escapes, this one requires me to confront the end of an old system, the dismantling of a life that has sown the seeds of its own destruction. My daughter left Montreal a month ago, with her child. They are in Toronto with us. Now it is January and my sons are going back with me to pack up their little sister's apartment. We arrive in Montreal by train. A rental truck awaits us later in the day. "It's like goddamn Gdansk," my eldest son says. He is huddled up, his arms crossed in the black leather jacket he insists on wearing, even though it is 30 degrees below zero. The wind is blowing like solid ice off Décarie Boulevard below us. We are walking from the Métro station along an overpass. I am wearing a down-filled coat and I am freezing. To myself, I compare the walk to the one I took in Leningrad a few years ago with Sasha, the one when I lost track of my thoughts owing to the extreme cold and my hunger, but I say nothing to my sons. My younger son is looking tired and worried, and we haven't even started yet.

241

Under the microscope, the embryo is huge. Our gross hands, products of the giant world outside the microscope, have had to be trained to perform the most delicate dainty dances. And we cannot shake or hesitate even a little or the large aorta will rupture, despite the cooling of the embryo, and then the experimental exercise will be over. It takes more than an hour to complete each surgical manoeuvre, and the critical point comes only at the end of the procedure. After a typical five-to-six-hour surgical session, we are lucky to have had two successful operations.

We emerge from the sterile surgical suite bleary and shaky. "It's like another world."

"Yeah," I agree. It's one in the morning. We've been here since eight and the children will be up at six.

242

"We can get out of here by plane. Pop said he'd come and get us if we need him." I'm already reassuring Danielle that we can leave Germany anytime we need to, even though we've just arrived. My father works for the Canadian air force. He's a pilot and comes to Düsseldorf all the time. He can get us out of here. But breaking out of a place is never that easy. Right now, I can't find a public telephone, and we don't have any German coins anyway. "I'm going to ask for change for the phone, and we're going to call a few places to find a hotel room." I am standing at the door of a bar. Noisy sounds are coming from within, loud voices cheering every few seconds.

We have only been in town for an hour, and already we are feeling the oppression of the local system, the local order of life, the local paradigm. The map that guides these people is really evident today. They don't like foreigners. Their world has been ripped apart by them. "But it was so long ago." Danielle and I can't understand the scene in the bar. On a little television screen in the corner, we can see crowds of people marching in some far-off German city, flags waving. There are speeches about unity, national unity, a unity prevented by us, by foreigners. What a day to arrive.

I try my German. "I'd like change for the telephone, please."

"Get lost—we're busy." After three tries, I understand the response. We leave and continue walking. It is another hour before we find ourselves on Königstrasse. Nothing is open, but there are taxis. Cab drivers are never that unfriendly.

243

What is non-teleological thinking?

If teleological thinking presupposes that all things follow a design, or have a predetermined end point, that all things and processes have a purpose that can influence their trajectories through time, reaching back from the future, then non-teleological thinking presumes a world where things are not guided by a preordained purpose. Such a "purposeless"[1] course entails having ownership of one's own destiny, shaping it through intimate personal and local interactions with the natural and intellectual world. Non-teleological thinking leads one to a world where the maps are *not* laid out ahead of time. The maps of a non-teleological world are made through exchange between the traveller and the landscape, an event which alters both. Both the traveller and the landscape are *defined* by this mutual exchange.

This local, intimate, mutually defining act is dialectical. The landscape, or climate, against which the traveller is situated is both the negation of the person, everything that he or she is not, and the affirmation of the person. To understand this, it helps to think of something in the middle of nothingness. There is nothing for the something to be seen against, nothing to compare it with, to measure it by. The subject cannot exist without the negative backdrop of everything that it is not. The backdrop, therefore, simultaneously acts as both the negation, and, because this negation has the power to define the subject, as the affirmation of the subject. In the final analysis, the definition of a thing includes its self and its non-self. The synthesis of the self and non-self is created from local intimate interactions between the traveller and the landscape. No higher level purpose or goal need be invoked—a simple affirmation of existence is enough. No higher-level design in the universe is necessary.

244

Most of the time, we live within a teleological framework, according to a map that has purpose and an end point determined by a deity writing history from the perspective of the future, looking back in time. But sometimes we leave the framework, escape the paradigm. Those are the times when we feel the intimate nature of our mapmaking. We feel the mutual self-definition that takes place between ourselves and the landscape over which we journey. The map is made by the traveller and the place. Those are the times when we are escaping a paradigm, that we feel that the old way of life is falling apart, is being destroyed by the very act of defining itself anew. Escaping is destructive of familiar patterns. And the destruction is felt all the more keenly because we cannot, living as we are within an established paradigm, discern the eventual new growth that is ahead. When our way of life disintegrates, we see only the breakdown, the negative.

These are stories of escape. The stories take place over a period of nearly thirty years of my life. Together they have taught me most of what I know about non-teleological thinking. As the embryo grows, it destroys its former self, just as we change and mature over time, altering the old self as we go. As I left Siberia, I felt the destruction that characterizes the Siberia of today, and I was intensely aware of the upheaval that was taking place within me as I reached a new understanding about the effects of modern science and technology on the people of the world. My flight from Siberia in 1990 reminded me of the escape Danielle and I arranged from Germany twenty years before. But that escape came only after experiencing real physical hardship and disillusionment in a setting that embodied the destruction of the Second World War. And finally, the escape from Montreal in 1997 revealed for me the emotional level where we feel the departure from a paradigm the most, not as an abstract notion, or as something that only occurs when we travel to distant places, but as the dissolution of a part of one's actual everyday life.

245

"À Toronto," says the sign on the entrance to Highway 20, just under us as we walk along the overpass to my daughter's apartment. She had told us that she read the sign every time she crossed this bridge over Décarie on her way to and from the Métro station. The life with her husband had been disintegrating, leaving her feeling more and more alone in Montreal.

"Violent little excuse for a human being." My elder son is not sentimental about my son-in-law.

We are inside the apartment. It is the second floor of a house on Girouard. It stinks. The people living below smoke cigarettes constantly. I had bought potpourris and air fresheners during the weeks I had stayed here with my daughter and granddaughter the month before. Nothing worked—the smoke came up like a solid invasion.

At the doorway, I survey the apartment. "How're we going to pack up all this stuff in one day?"

246

The cab driver takes us to the cheapest hotel he knows. We have almost no money. We have to find my father's friend, the one who has the jobs for us here in Düsseldorf. "Where is the hotel?"

"It's there, down below the ground." The hotel is an old wartime bunker, a bomb shelter. We descend five storeys to the reception desk, and then more storeys to our room. Sweat is dripping from the walls, and only men are down here with us, singing old war songs. We sit in bed in our little room and wait for the morning. We cannot turn off the light, because without the light it is darker than anything I have ever experienced.

247

Sasha is pouring us another drink. There is a tumbler for both of us, filled with vodka. He is topping mine up for the tenth time, it seems. "We have a time here, we relax." He thinks we should wait a little longer before leaving for the airport. Alexander is laughing.

"Play us a song, Alexander," says Jim, who is filming everything. Later in Toronto, we will review the film. Jim had even recorded the table covered in dishes. Alexander and his family must have spent a month's salary on the meal. We eat caviar, sturgeon, Russian delicacies—pastries filled with savoury meat, and fruit and vegetables that have to be specially flown up to this Arctic Circle city. And we have vodka, a commodity in very short supply in 1990. Each large glass must be drunk in one go. Sasha is the champion. I have been mercifully spared these acts of bravado. I have attempted to nurse the same glass for an hour now, although it is topped up frequently by Sasha and Alexander. Alexander's wife and daughter are smiling a lot at Jim, the only man who isn't completely incapacitated. Tatiana is rolling after so much eating and drinking.

"Who is going to drive us to the airport?" I'm becoming alarmed, because no one is currently capable of doing so. Jim and Fiona and I can't drive here, and the plane was due to take off from the airport an hour ago. Our escape is being heralded by a complete breakdown of everyone involved, it seems.

"I phoned the airport." Alexander is laughing and clutching his sides; Sasha is holding on to Alexander with one hand and his next full glass of vodka with the other. He is laughing too. "They'll hold the plane for you or there'll be trouble. I called Viktor." Alexander thinks this is so funny. Viktor is the local chief of transport, the one who spent the afternoon the day before giving us gift after gift.

"Oh, Jesus Christ." I can only guess at the power of this local politician and his friends. We are holding up the airport schedule because of a drunken party.

248

The escape from a paradigm that contains a body of work, scientific, historical, literary, or personal, involves the consideration of everything the paradigm is not, that is to say, of *any* other approach or system. The rest of the dynamic interrelated universe, in fact, is a necessary element in the history of that paradigm. In other words, paradigms break apart, or cease to be the sole source of influence as maps or filters, because they must self-define through interaction with systems that they cannot encompass. All orders of things eventually break down, *not* because they are deposed by the society's acceptance of new and better ways of doing things, as Thomas Kuhn proposed in his *Postscript* to *The Structure of Scientific Revolutions*, but because they contain the seeds of their own destruction. The destruction of the old order results in a new synthesis. The positive and negative interact, come together. These paradigm shifts are a constant feature of our lives, new orders growing from the destruction of the old, and the destruction is inevitable because everything is always juxtaposed against its backdrop, namely everything that it is not. The essential difference between this perspective, the dialectical model I am proposing, and the hypothesis model of modern science is that there is no progress toward a better system inherent in the former.

The escape from an older paradigm, with its familiar, seemingly positive aspects, into a new order, the new synthesis produced through dialectical exchange, often entails calamity and upheaval. It is a hard journey, for two reasons. First, there is no preconceived map—the map is made as the journey progresses, and this can be arduous. And second, before a new order can be established, many things will die or change utterly.

249

In 1979, I am well into my Ph.D. work in the field of developmental biology, specializing in the study of regeneration. "It's really a medieval study, not modern in any way." Rick Elinson is a professor down the hall in our zoology department; he disparages the work done in regeneration. "You cut animals up and wait to see what happens." Not really, we say at the time. We're trying to develop hypotheses that can be measured. We cut limbs from newts and spinal cords in chick embryos, but we do it under various conditions. The limbs are examined for results, with and without the presence of nerves, and with and without various hormones. The limbs grow back well in adult newts when the nerves and hormone-producing organs are intact, but not well at all when they are removed. Chick embryo spinal cords restore their contiguity and eventual function when they are cut at early embryo stages and not when they are cut at older stages. Experiments are far more detailed and subtle than this, but in general that is the lay of the land. This is not medieval but very modern. We suggest that experiments can change one small aspect of a system, and we can then test the importance of that aspect to the whole system. This is following in the line of Karl Popper and others who designated the hypothesis that can be falsified as being at the heart of all good science. And falsification must take place in an experimental mode, by isolating measurable pieces of the world. In the case of the newt limb regeneration, for example, when we remove the nerves, we are doing so under a general hypothesis—namely that nerves are necessary for regeneration. The hypothetical question, Are nerves necessary for regeneration, is valid under Karl Popper's suggested rules because it can be falsified. If we remove the nerves and find that the limbs can still regenerate, the hypothesis has been proven false. Hence, since the hypothesis has the *potential* to be proven false, it is considered by modern scientists to be a good hypothesis. However, at a much deeper level, we are changing the newt limbs profoundly by removing the peripheral nerves that activate them and give them the sense of touch. Because I could sense the profound changes that followed any surgical procedure on an animal even as I worked on the hypotheses that guided our work in the developmental biology labs, doubts were beginning to form in my mind as to the validity of such a strict, Popper-style approach to scientific investigations.

But meanwhile, I accepted the rules of the regime. Nerves and regrowing limbs are measurable. For years I worked with the developmental biologist Richard Liversage, along with other colleagues, including my wife, cutting the nerves from newts and measuring the levels of various biochemical components, eventually comparing them with newts that had been allowed to keep their nerve axons uncut and intact in their limbs. We had changed one aspect of the world, we had taken out the nerves of the newt limb, and we controlled the rest of the parameters so that we could measure the effect of this one little change, or so we thought.

We hypothesized that levels of cyclic nucleotides, key chemical components of the biochemistry of all animals, would change significantly in the nerveless limbs. Our belief was that nerves controlled cyclic nucleotide levels and that this was one of the main reasons that nerves were so important in regenerating limbs. If we were to find that levels of cyclic nucleotides *were* changed due to the removal of nerves, we would be able to accept our hypothesis as being valid, and we would then make a further test to bring us closer to a more complete understanding of the process of regeneration. If we were to find that taking out the nerves had *no* effect on the levels of cyclic nucleotides, we would have proven our hypothesis wrong. Having a hypothesis that could be falsified made us good scientists.

250

There are no jobs for us in Düsseldorf. My father's friend never heard we were coming. And other possibilities are not proving very fruitful. We have been here almost two weeks. Now we have to get back to Canada. We have to escape. Each day is endless and lonely. And we have no money for food. We sit in the grassy parks and eat sausages. We try to make what little food we have last as long as possible. The *Vollkornbrot*, the dense, chewy black bread we keep to make sandwiches, sits in the corner of our hotel room and grows fly maggots because it is kept so long.

One of the people we meet is friendly; he tells us about the bombed-out sites we see on every street. Twenty-five years after the war, they are still rebuilding. He was born during the war, and his father named him Falke, after the falcon that symbolized the Third Reich, but he has since changed it to Reiner. He is ashamed to be German. A friend of his, Ilse, an older woman, keeps muttering to herself. Reiner tells us Ilse cannot forget escaping the city of Essen after the Allied bombing attack. A young woman then, she crawled for three days over dead bodies. We listen to Reiner, but his story is not our story. He doesn't find sympathy in us. We think more about finding food to eat—we are beginning to starve. One day we come to Reiner's apartment. His wife tries to stop me as I walk in, smiling a greeting at Reiner, who, I suddenly realize, is attempting to hide in the far room, holding a plate of food. Not welcome, we leave.

No one in Canada answers our telegram, sent from a post office. "Please send money or come to get us. We are desperate." No answer. We hear nothing for over two weeks.

Twenty years later in Siberia, the night before Alexander's party, I ask about telephoning my home in Canada. There are virtually no connections, and it isn't worth the effort to try. Later that week, after returning to Moscow, I sit for two hours listening to the telephone ring in my ear, waiting for the overseas operator to come on the line. She never did. Foreign hotels with outside phone lines are the only way to escape the country for a few expensive minutes. And foreign hotels were remote from us—we always stayed in Russian hotels and Party residences.

251

"We're taking apart a home." The inanimate objects in my daughter's apartment in Montreal are like living things to my younger son. He can't stand the process of dismantling the old life, the one that is already fading for us all.

"Get over it. He was a joyless bastard." By citing the negative image of the hated husband, my other son keeps us going in what is at some level a cruel act of destruction.

I am reminded of dreams, or nightmares, I had on nights following my vivisection of living animals back in my days in the regeneration laboratory. The animals pulsed with blood; there is nothing quite like the feeling of living flesh warm under your fingers being cut by your scalpel. And discovery lay ahead of each cut. But I had to steel myself more and more over the years. I couldn't bring myself to cut on the days after I had the dreams, the dreams in which people I knew would take the place of the animals of my experiments.

252

We found that the levels of cyclic nucleotides were significantly affected by taking out the nerves from the newt limbs. As corroborating evidence, we also found, in animals that had a complete set of intact nerves, that cyclic nucleotides are present in higher levels in the regrowing tips of regenerating limbs at certain key stages of regrowth, compared with ordinary intact limbs that were not cut in any way. In other words, cyclic nucleotides were starting to become a focus of attention for us because, using the established scientific method, our hypothesis had not been falsified by our experiments. Because we found that cyclic nucleotides were associated with the regenerating limbs of newts, and were strongly implicated in the regeneration-stimulating activity of the limb's nerves, our hypothesis had so far held up to scrutiny.[2]

But there are alternative conclusions for any hypothesis. Perturbation experiments will allow a scientist to test a hypothesis only within a limited framework of ideas. The larger issues are never discussed under these conditions. The hypothesis we were working under did not take sufficient notice of the fact that the internal environment, the landscape of the limb, is utterly changed by the act of cutting it open, or the act of taking out its nerves. We did note that a simple sham operation, in which the limb is cut open but the nerve axons are left untouched, also resulted in changes in the cyclic nucleotide levels, but even this evidence for a profound shift in the tissue environment resulting from injury alone was attributed to possible effects on the nerves due to their exposure to new biochemical and ionic conditions; in other words, the possibility that the entire system undergoes significant global change even with a mere surgical opening of the skin, and that therefore no real determinations can be made as to the effects of the perturbation experiment, was never seriously entertained.

The new system of cut limb or nerveless limb is completely different from the old order—the intact, untouched limb. It is not possible to believe that only one parameter is being changed in such perturbation experiments. Yet this is the situation I found myself in. Those of us working on these experiments had come from an old tradition, passed down from the days of pure classical scientific experimentation, a tradition that accepted only empirically based scientific methods. This meant putting in something new, taking something out, or replacing something with something else—add, subtract, or replace. The belief was that only one parameter was being changed at a time. Liversage's teachers had been Elmer G. Butler of Princeton and Oscar Schotté of Amherst, who had both studied in Germany with the German embryologist Hans Spemann (1869–1941), who won the Nobel Prize in Physiology and Medicine in 1935.[3] Who was I to argue the philosophy of science in this rarefied atmosphere of pure experimental research?

253

The escape from an old order, the escape from a paradigm, requires destruction. The old order comes up against *what it is not,* and a new synthesis occurs. That is the heart of a non-teleological mapping. The intimate juxtaposition of the thing and its opposite—its landscape, its non-being—is what creates the map. Self-generated, a result of the exchange between the negative and the positive, it is not laid out beforehand; the map is not waiting for all things to adapt within it.

254

Hegel writes about the principle of the self-generation of new paradigms, and of their inevitable birth through self-destruction.

> The life of a people ripens a certain fruit; its activity aims at the complete manifestation of the principle which it embodies. But this fruit does not fall back into the bosom of the people that produced and matured it; on the contrary, it becomes a poison-draught to it. That poison-draught it cannot let alone, for it has an insatiable thirst for it: the taste of the draught is its annihilation, though at the same time the rise of a new principle.[4]

255

There *cannot* be only one minor change to a system in our perturbation experiments. Any experimental change, any addition, subtraction, or replacement of an element, however apparently insignificant, utterly shifts the system into a new state. It is a new system, one resulting from internal upheaval. Under the concept of dialectical interchange, we can imagine all components within a newly developing system interacting, forming confrontational zones that eventually shake down to a new synthesis. The cutting of living tissue forces this shakedown, because it imposes new conditions for the existent material of the living thing. The living tissue is constantly forming a relationship with the rest of the world. This is most obvious at the boundary of the living animal and its environment. When we cut into the embryo, a new relationship is suddenly formed with the outside, and this is what forces a new set of exchanges between the living animal and the rest of the world.

Under more natural conditions, the upheavals of newly forming systems also occur, but usually at a slower rate. The developmental stages of animals reveal these system changes, but the creatures involved do not easily yield information to scientists who practice perturbation, hypothesis-filled experimentation. My work on the chick embryos was a result of my need to find a better route to understanding nature. While I worked on the newts and the classic hypotheses by day, at night I was watching as the embryos developed from one stage to the next, observing the natural development of successive new microscopic paradigms unveiling themselves before my eyes.[5] These new social orders under my microscope, the size of the tip of my finger, were teaching me something new.

After years of observing the chick embryos, I realized that cutting into the spinal cords was an act that creates a new juxtaposition of opposites—the exposed interior of the embryo itself abruptly put up against its surrounding landscape or environment. That forced juxtaposition creates a new "social" order at the microscopic level of the living tissue. A new map is created at the intimate level of tissue/environment interchange. The new order comes from the destruction of the old, but it is created artificially, by the surgical cut. My investigations led me to the written works and forgotten speculations of scientists whose ideas had been ignored for years because they did not fit the major developmental biology paradigm. In 1947, Johannes Holtfreter, a distinguished student of Hans Spemann's,[6] had speculated that in normally developing embryos there is a stage at which the presumptive spinal cord and brain cells undergo self-generated injury, and that this destruction leads to the development of the central nervous system tissue. Later, others would speculate that common salts, naturally occurring in the embryonic tissue, are pumped into the tiny space between the incipient prespinal cord[7] and the underlying tissue. The salts are thought to result in a self-injury, an embryonic breaking apart of the intercellular bonds in the prespinal cord tissue. The reaction to the injury is a rounding of the flat prespinal cord into a long tube that serves as the basis for the rest of the central nervous system development.[8]

This self-injury paradigm does not sit easily with those who would concentrate on special factors, and lately special genes, for every aspect of a living being. For most scientists working in this area, the metamorphosis of the prespinal cord into the mature spinal cord comes about

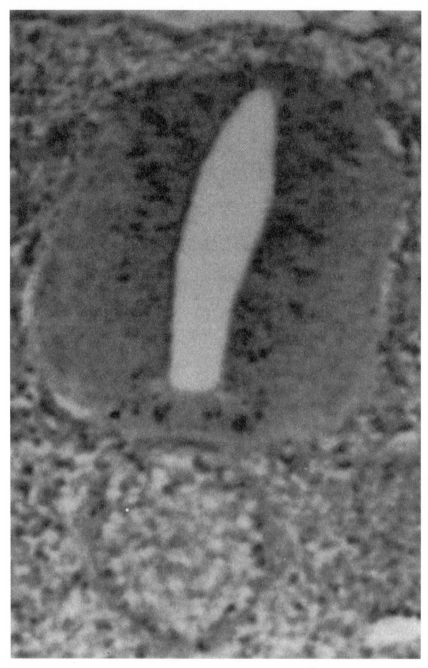

Photomicrograph of the cross-section of the normal spinal cord of a chick embryo at about four and a half days of development—diameter magnified 400 times.[9]

through signals sent from cell to cell, signals made up of specialized molecules that are cued by the genes, which are, in turn, thought to be following a program. The destruction theory, although distantly connected to genes and their products, is much more dialectical; the embryonic tissues react with each other at a very intimate and local level—there is no set program. In fact, the developmental trajectory, the journey down the embryo's map, can be *altered* by changing the physical conditions of the tissues, and anything that can be changed through a mere shift in gross anatomical juxtapositions is obviously not following a prescribed, genetically controlled course of development—some, at least, of the developmental outcome must be due to the statistically likely proximity of certain tissues at the early stages of life.

In my experiments, I cut through the tissue of embryos that had already formed the spinal cord tube; but this advanced stage of spinal cord development regressed after being cut—I saw the tissue return to that earlier stage, before the tube formation, a stage characterized by the ability to form entire new spinal cord tubes; I witnessed the development of whorls and subsidiary tubes that mimicked the original tube "formation through self-destruction." Interestingly, the chick embryos with the new unusual whorled spinal cords were eventually hatched and displayed normal behaviour, even though they hid inside themselves the architecture of a new-order spinal cord shape, created through the act of a knife imitating nature, a new order that was built on the same biological principles of destruction as can be found in the original naturally forming nervous system organ.

256

A cut can be made across the body of a preserved embryo to reveal the cross-section of the tube that makes up the early spinal cord. The early spinal cord tube will be the avenue down which the nerves will grow, nerves that, in turn, are responsible for feeling and movement in the body of the hatched chick. Our own human development is very similar.

In the centre of the cross-section photograph, there is a long oblong white space. This is the hollow centre of the spinal cord tube. Surrounding the tube are the cells of the spinal cord's inner epithelium, or "skin." The black blotches are the dividing cells in the growing spinal cord tissue. The embryo has been injected with radioactive thymidine that ends up as a part of the newly forming DNA of the dividing cells. DNA is found in every developing cell of all animals and plants and is the storehouse for our genetic information.

The spinal cord tube of a normal embryo is the result of the natural interaction between the embryo's tissues and the inner environment of the embryo. It is a dialectical mapping that has resulted in the characteristic tube shape. In an earlier stage of the embryo, the tube was not yet formed. The incipient spinal cord tissue underwent a form of internal disaggregation, or self-injury, and the result was a rounding-up of the original long "plate" into the "tube" shape. In the natural course of development, the embryo produced high levels of salts; the consumption of these products at the cellular level led to the embryo's own eventual local tissue breakdown. The loss of structural order, in the original "plate" of incipient spinal cord cells, resulted in what I term *an injury response*, and the "tube" was born. This is not unlike Hegel's discussion of a new order coming out of the self-destruction of the old order.

257

The growth patterns of the normal spinal cord tissue are similar to what happens when the spinal cord is cut with a scalpel and starts to *regrow*. In the experiments described here, however, injury was not inflicted with a scalpel, but rather by slow infusion, directly into the spinal cord tissue, of the chemical compound 0.02 per cent ethylene-diamine-tetra-acetic acid disodium salt (EDTA). EDTA has the effect of scooping up all available calcium in the spinal cord's inner tissue environment. In an earlier stage of the embryo than the one we see here, there is a natural disaggregation of the incipient spinal cord tissue, a kind of self-injury. This normal stage of development leads to an

Photomicrograph of the cross-section of the spinal cord of a chick embryo at about four and a half days of development, after being artificially infused with a disrupting chemical compound—diameter magnified 400 times.[10]

injury response; the incipient spinal cord, starting off as a long, flat "plate" of tissue, rounds into a "tube." EDTA mimics the action of the natural self-injury that originally formed the tube of the spinal cord. The EDTA, by scooping up the calcium, causes the cells to disassociate from one another, a kind of wide-spread injury.

Instead of the smooth tube with one inner lumen, as we see in photomicrographs of normal spinal cords, EDTA injury creates a conflagration of many symmetrical tubes—the newly ordered spinal cord of the embryo. Black blotches indicate the actively dividing cells of the spinal cord epithelium, an indication of rapid injury response and of tissue that is healthy, although injured.

This new system has grown from the injury that was caused by poisoning the spinal cord tissue with EDTA. In this case, the injury has been inflicted artificially, but it is a direct parallel to the normal actions of the embryo as it naturally grows from one stage to the next. This experiment provides a glimpse into the possible general mechanisms of embryo growth.

So rather than the shape of the embryo being held in the genes,[11] like a map of destiny waiting to be fulfilled, we have here an example of the map of development unfolding as an interaction of the tissue with its own inner landscape. This is not a classic perturbation experiment, one that relies on the changing of only one parameter to measure its contribution to the whole system. Rather, this is an experiment that acknowledges that any change leads to an entirely new system, one that has been changed profoundly from the old and is now guided by new tissue/landscape juxtapositions. In developing the experiments that have led to these new embryonic microscopic systems, I have made a parallel to Hegel's concept of a society ripening a fruit that acts as a poison to itself. The embryo, during its natural development, ripens tissue products that act as a poison to its original cellular integrity. Self-injury results in the formation of a new shape. My experiments are an artificial re-enactment of the original natural injury events. By injuring the embryo anew, if the plan goes according to Hegel, I should also see a re-enactment of the original tube formation of the spinal cord. And I do. There are now several tubes all reacting to the injury in a fashion reminiscent of the original, natural spinal cord formation. I put this down to a normal dialectical tissue/inner-landscape interaction, a non-teleological mapmaking.

258

For Hegel, the new principle that grows out of the old, destroyed system is the result of the coming into being of a new synthesis from the juxtaposition of opposites, the most essential opposites being "Being" and "Nothing," coming together as "Becoming." Discussing the dialectical nature of Hegel and his understanding of the scientific process, the twentieth-century German philosopher Hans-Georg Gadamer writes:

> The actual beginning of . . . [Hegel's *Science of*] *Logic* consists of only a few lines, which, nevertheless, pose the essential problems of Hegel's logic: the beginning with the idea of Being, the identity of it with Nothing, and the synthesis of the two opposed ideas of Being and Nothing, called Becoming. According to Hegel, that constitutes the content of that with which science must begin.[12]

259

Unlike the chick embryo experiments, my cyclic nucleotide measurements in newt limbs without nerves were teleological. To understand this, we have to imagine being inside the newt limb. As a scientist working in the laboratory, I always did just this. I pictured the landscape, the structure, the biochemical soup, and all the components that make up living tissue. I imagined it to be a place that could potentially be described, given enough experiments. Then I imagined what it would be like without nerves. The removal of nerves would lead to there being no special molecular factors being released from the nerve endings, no electrical impulses to the muscles and no exchanges of salts over the nerve cell membranes. But I saw everything else remaining pretty much as it was before the nerves were removed. The difference was that those things that happen only in the presence of living nerves were not happening. There is a further implication—if I could replace the nerves with some additive, I would observe a fully functioning limb, not discernible from the real thing. This image of events is teleological precisely because the end result can be imagined; it is imagined to be only a slight variation on the old system, with one element, like a puzzle piece, removed. The map of the internal landscape of the living newt limb tissue, the animal's inner landscape, is thought to "anticipate" the nerveless state and to act as a template to mould it into a predictable shape. To think otherwise is to preclude our ability to form hypotheses. But of course to think this way is to postulate a grand design, to think teleologically.

In my case, in my classical newt limb experiments, I imagined that the cyclic nucleotides would change if the nerves were removed from the limb. This was a fairly safe bet, in retrospect. Actually, I had imagined that the nerveless limbs would have "lowered" levels of cyclic nucleotides, thus pointing to the "stimulating" effects of nerves on this important factor in the biochemical mix. For years people had been looking for the "factor" that could explain the importance of nerves. But I found that the levels fluctuated wildly up and down after the removal of nerves, or, for that matter, even after cutting open the tissue without injuring the nerves themselves. So I then postulated that the products of the cut nerves were flooding the limb tissue after the injury, or that the general injury of the tissue had some indeterminate, but temporary, effects. I was attempting to salvage the hypothesis, as scientists often do. Looking back, I believe that I ignored the major effects of an injury on the "system" of the limb. Why? Perhaps because a non-teleological approach, in stepping out of the classical scientific system of hypothesis testing, would not yield results that would satisfy my colleagues. A non-teleological approach would not have produced any hypothesis worth measuring—using such a mental construct one would imagine the inner landscape of the newt's limb tissue and would see that once the nerves had been removed, or after the tissue had been exposed to the external environment owing to cutting, the entire system is changed. There can be no prediction as to the results. Any number of things could happen because the elements have to shake down to a new order. The new order of tissue interactions may have a typical shape that we can discern after several episodes of the same scenario, but the pathway to get there will not be easy to describe, because the system is entirely changed every time it is injured in any way.

260

Opposites are the very foundation of the non-teleological map, because opposites form the definition of the coming together of the object and its landscape—its background, everything that it is not.

It is 1968. My future wife and I are studying Chinese philosophy with Leonard Priestley, our professor of philosophy at the University of Toronto. "There won't be a final exam because I can't think of a suitable question," he'd told us. We are studying Chuang-tzu, a philosopher who wrote in China sometime between the years 551 and 233 B.C.E., a time known as the period of the hundred philosophers. We have taken the entire fall term to discuss the implications of only four pages of a translation of Chuang-tzu's work. We have nothing concrete to show for the effort, and there will be no exam.

Chuang-tzu exemplifies for me the essence of opposites in his description of a horse, which is both the horse and its opposite, the non-horse: "To use a horse to show that a horse is not a horse is not as good as using a non-horse to show that a horse is not a horse, Heaven and earth are one attribute; the ten thousand things are one horse."[13] Chuang-tzu means to say that the "ten thousand things," that is, all things in the universe, are ultimately one unity. A horse is its opposite as well as itself, or it ceases to be at all, at a deeper level.[14]

261

Two years after the dialectical lessons of Chuang-tzu, in 1970, Danielle and I are witnessing the destruction that Germany brought about for

itself, the poisons that built up inside, the poisons that eventually destroyed it. Reiner is part of a group that meets with Israelis to try to
repay Jews for the Holocaust. He doesn't want to talk about it. Instead,
we walk past ruins on the streets; they look like self-inflicted wounds.
He is proud of the damage that befell Germany during the war. "It
was so long ago," we keep saying, "so why is there so much rubble?
Couldn't somebody at least take it away?" Reiner just looks at us. I
think he would not be happy to see the piles of rubble go.

When I am in Leningrad, the winter after visiting Siberia in 1990,
the Jewish painter Lapitsky will draw for me the parallels between the
Gulag camps of Stalin's northern railroad and the concentration
camps of the Holocaust perpetrated by the Nazis. Meanwhile, waiting
for Alexander's drunken party to finish, I have had enough of these
stories. Sasha takes me aside. "We are speaking of important stories
when we fly back together tonight, but not now. Later, remind me and I
will tell you about the history of the Gulag." I can't imagine that he will
be awake. He can barely look me straight in the eye, and his head keeps
nodding. I am overtired and really sick of the Gulag stories. I hope he
falls asleep.

Finally, Yuri is called, a friend of Alexander's, to drive us to the airport. It is now almost two hours past the plane's takeoff time. Yuri lives
in the next apartment block and arrives in only a few minutes. His little
car is packed with all of us—me and Fiona and Jim and Sasha. Tatiana
will come in Alexander's car with the luggage. I don't even ask if
Alexander is going to attempt to drive.

262

In the shakedown toward a new system after a major disruption of the
old system, all elements self-define anew through interactions with
each other and with the entire landscape of the "whole." This is a dialectical response. This shakedown results in the system going through
a confrontation with its negation, this new "other" that has developed
within it. The result is an entirely new system.

In the embryonic spinal cord injury experiments, I imagined that the injury led to a complete shakedown of the embryo's nervous system. The dialectical approach encouraged me to suppose that all the elements—cells, tissue—confronted the new landscape, the exposed landscape of the injured system. The only thing I had to go on for anything close to a hypothesis able to predict the embryo's response to injury was the original, natural spinal cord tube formation in an earlier stage of the embryo. A natural self-injury stage resulted in the original formation of a tube. Therefore, I imagined that a new, artificially produced injury, at a slightly later stage in the embryo's development, would also result in a classic injury response—tube formation. The fact that new tubes did indeed form does not explain the details of the processes that went on. I imagine that the system breakdown was profound. The new stable post-injury system has shapes reminiscent of the old system, but we cannot easily explain the process. Classical science, by changing one parameter at a time, attempts to pin down the active parts of a system, but I have argued that this very method is suspect; the classical tools, the perturbation experiments that attempt to isolate one factor from the rest of the system, are themselves responsible for initiating profound change. Studying systems is not easy because there are no interventions that do not profoundly change everything. The new and the old systems of embryonic tissue, the post-injury and the pre-injury systems, are utterly different from each other. There is no convenient map laid out to show how they might relate.

Experimental scientists believe that we can slowly put together the pieces of these puzzles, that although the systems are different they are enough alike that we can ascribe roles to the many elements within a system. Taking out an element like nerves leads to changes that can be tracked adequately well, it is believed. I argue that the hypotheses are always set within a known mapping that we have decided *a priori* fits the reality of the system we are attempting to describe. Believing that we are describing a rather static reality as the basis for hypothesis setting, we will always come up with the same result—when we remove an element from a system, we will identify a change and ascribe the change to the removal of the element; when we add an element to a system, we will identify a change and attribute the change to the addition; when we exchange one element for another we will assume the changes result from the exchange. In all cases, we focus on the elements under scrutiny and do not think of the inevitable profound changes to the system as a whole and the dialectical interchanges that will have to shake down the system until it settles into a new stable whole. With the focus never on the whole system, we will always be looking for ways to justify the scientific results in terms of our original hypothesizing. In the case of our measurements of the cyclic nucleotides, we observed extreme fluctuations, both positive and negative in direction, following the removal of the limb nerves. This should have alerted us to the possibility of general system changes, and it should have led us away from postulating a major role for nerves *per se* in the regenerative process. As I said earlier, this wasn't our first response; we tried to defend the original hypothesis by imagining nerve products pouring out of the cut nerve cells into the limb tissue.

The concept of systems changing was getting through to me at some other level, though, and this new approach led to my conclusions for the chick embryo work. A few years after concluding the cyclic nucleotide experiments, I spoke at a conference where I postulated that the massive search in regeneration labs around the world for factors coming from nerves was misguided and that we should instead look for general changes to the surrounding milieu. This was bringing back an older idea, one that had, in fact, despite the tradition of experimental science he personified for me, long been a favourite of Liversage's.[15]

263

As I write this, I am aware of the parallels between my experiments in the laboratory and the stories about my life's experiences. The escapes from Germany, from Siberia and from Montreal are all non-teleological. They are all dialectical shakedowns that follow from an injury to an established system. If I look at the purely personal aspects of the experiences, I am aware that classic perturbation experiments were being performed, with me or members of my family and my friends serving as the variable agents in the experiment. The escape from Montreal, the removal of my son-in-law from my daughter's immediate life, which was a result of a poisoning from within, was an extirpation experiment: the seed yielded a fruit that poisoned the system and led to its inevitable breakdown, only to result in a new principle, one for which my sons and I were agents. In a classic laboratory setting, a scientist would watch for the system to react to a simple removal of one element. Everything else would be expected to remain more or less stable. This is the classical teleological approach. What's the big deal, we say. Removing one person from the scene simply means we adjust the circumstances slightly, but the rules of the system do not change, the order is intact. Wrong. The non-teleological approach tells us that we know nothing about the map once an element has been taken from the system. The entire system must adjust to a new order. The story of the escape from Montreal tells this kind of story.

In Germany, Danielle and I were put into a foreign system and told that all our experiences up to that point would allow us to manage perfectly well. We were additives to an experimental system. The outcome should have been predictable. But the system, our internal systems and the system into which we were landed, all changed on our arrival, although our personal lives were perhaps the ones that registered this development most obviously.

The trip to Siberia changed my perspective on many things. This too was a profound change, not the one I had glibly predicted before we left Canada. And our presence in Siberia obviously affected the people we met there. The farewell party at Alexander's was an act of self-destruction. We were all becoming drunk, in one way or another, hiding from the fact that we had to tear apart this new relationship, one so quickly but profoundly formed. We had to leave one another and we were acting out like children.

264

It is the escape from Montreal that fits the model of necessary destruction most of all. In Siberia and Germany, we underwent personal hardship, but there we were also witnessing the aftermath of real societal destruction. Montreal is very personal. And it is the personal that holds the key to understanding non-teleological maps, the intimate exchange between the individual and the landscape that produces the local, personal mappings. The maps we draw from these adventures will be filled with the perspective of the moment, with the dailyness of routine. These maps are like those of the reindeer herders who travel through the tundra, unaware of the cataclysm that is melting the Yamal terrain but committed to the creation of the map every single day. This is very real.

The living room is filled with boxes and plastic garbage bags containing my daughter's belongings. We have been packing for hours. My sons and I are exhausted, our muscles ache, and there is no food we feel like eating. We decide to take the Métro to find somewhere to eat. Mostly we can't stand the sight of the apartment any more—we are taking apart a home, as my youngest son said earlier in the day. Outside, it is minus 45 with the wind chill. It is frightening, it is so cold. "Shit, I hate this place." Nothing is open anyway, it seems, and we walk too far looking for a restaurant. Montreal is dying. This night it seems to me that a poison is creeping into her tissue and inflicting injury after injury. This is necessary for new growth, but can we, who are simply travelling through, withstand the process of Montreal's self-destruction? Later, we will feel better after the huge Italian meal, the conversation with the murderous maître d' who suits our mood very well, but now we walk through the Gdansk of Montreal, longing to escape.

265

Plato (ca. 428 to 348 B.C.E.) worked as a philosopher in Greece about the same time as Chuang-tzu in China. Hegel found justification for his concept of a new synthesis coming out of the juxtaposition of opposites in the writings of Plato. Gadamer writes about this unusual philosophical marriage

> confirmed in the *Sophist*, where the exposition of the dialectic of the species remains itself basically "dialectical." Once the dialectical correlation of "difference" itself with "sameness" itself, of not-being with being, has been asserted, there can be no simple characterization of the respect in which something is different. A philosophical statement, which in division of the ideas undertakes to determine the nature of things, specifically presupposes the speculative relationship of unity in what is opposite. To this extent Hegel is not completely unjustified in seeking support for his views in Plato.[16]

In Plato's *Sophist* dialogue we do find the roots of the discussion and arguments that develop when one considers systems in which opposites become the one unity of all things.

> STRANGER: . . . Imagine them here before us, and let us put this question, "You who say that hot and cold or some such pair *really are* all things, what exactly does this expression convey that you apply to both when you say that both are 'real' or each of them is 'real'? How are we to understand this 'reality' you speak of? . . . For surely you do not give the name 'reality' to one of the two and then say that both alike are real, for then there will be only one thing, whichever of the two it may be, and not two."
>
> THEAETETUS: True.
>
> STRANGER: "Well then, do you intend to give the name 'reality' to the pair of them?"
>
> THEAETETUS: Perhaps.
>
> STRANGER: "But that again," we shall object, "will clearly be speaking of your two things as one."
>
> THEAETETUS: You are quite right.[17]

To me, it does not seem like such a stretch. Hegel found dialectical underpinnings in the great philosophers of old. He was seeking the mechanisms that would help us understand the workings of existence, and he believed that his formulation, since he regarded it as true, would be found in the works of the classic philosophers.

This desire for philosophical foundations speaks to a more essential aspect of Hegel, however. Although I find in the dialectics of Hegel the philosophical guideposts for my deliberations on non-teleological mappings, I also sense in his work his need for the hierarchy of western civilization. His harking back to the classical philosophers is a symptom of this need. All through the scientific age of Europe, an era in which we still reside, justification has been sought in the classics. It is as if this points us in the right direction, bringing us closer and closer to an ideal. The civilization as a whole is seen, especially by proponents of the western scientific method, as climbing a ladder toward a more and more perfect world. This is the classical ideal that can be traced back to the Greek philosophers.

Despite the dialectical proposals of Hegel, an approach that teaches me to travel on intellectual avenues that take me away from the hierarchical models of modern science, I find an extreme posture of superiority in his work. It cannot go unnoticed because it also teaches me something. For one thing, the belief in the supremacy of Europeans, and of Germans in particular, as expressed by Hegel, leads me to an understanding of the trip Danielle and I took to Düsseldorf in 1970. The nationalist fervour and the self-aggrandisement associated with that passion are obviously far stronger in people than the belief in an intimately developed personal map, made through the dialectical interchange with one's local landscape. Even the intellectuals who objectify our collective points of view are not immune to these passions for power.

Then why should I be surprised by the immorality that guides those who perpetrate Gulag camps and Holocausts? Prejudice, born of a belief in the hierarchy, is obviously more deeply seated than the will to understand.

266

Hegel writes of the German people as the culmination of intellectual and spiritual history. *Despite* his principles of dialectical development and of free will, which seemingly would yield relative truths, Hegel speaks of the attainment of absolutes.

> The German Spirit is the Spirit of the new World. Its aim is the realization of absolute Truth as the unlimited self-determination of Freedom—*that* Freedom which has its own absolute form itself as its purport. The destiny of the German peoples is to be the bearers of the Christian principle.[18]

Even though this "absolute Truth" takes the form of a formula invoking free action, I doubt that purely relative standards are the point to Hegel. He still alludes to the hierarchy of the west, essentially the Great Chain of Being of the scientists and philosophers since the Middle Ages of Europe. This is made more clear by the comparisons he makes between Germans or Europeans and the apparently more inferior Asians or Native Americans or Africans, for example.

> And as the germ bears in itself the whole nature of the tree, and the taste and form of its fruits, so do the first traces of Spirit virtually contain the whole of that History. The Orientals have not attained the knowledge that Spirit—Man *as such*—is free; and because they do not know this, they are not free. . . . The consciousness of Freedom first arose among the Greeks, and therefore they were free; but they, and the Romans likewise, knew only that *some* are free—not man as such. Even Plato and Aristotle did not know this. The Greeks, therefore, had slaves; and their whole life and maintenance of their splendid liberty, was implicated with the institution of slavery: a fact moreover, which made that liberty on the one hand only an accidental, transient and limited growth; on the other hand, constituted it as a rigorous thraldom of our common nature—of the

Human. The German nations, under the influence of Christianity, were the first to attain the consciousness, that man, as man, is free: that it is the *freedom* of Spirit which constitutes its essence. . . .[19]

A mild and passionless disposition, want of spirit, and a crouching submissiveness towards a Creole, and still more towards a European, are the chief characteristics of the native Americans; and it will be long before the Europeans succeed in producing any independence of feeling in them. The inferiority of these individuals in all respects, even in regard to size, is very manifest; only the quite southern races in Patagonia are more vigorous natures, but still abiding in their natural condition of rudeness and barbarism. . . .[20]

The Negro, as already observed, exhibits the natural man in his completely wild and untamed state. We must lay aside all thought of reverence and morality—all that we call feeling—if we would rightly comprehend him; there is nothing harmonious with humanity to be found in this type of character. . . .[21]

At this point, we leave Africa, not to mention it again. For it is no historical part of the World; it has no movement or development to exhibit. Historical movements in it—that is in its northern part—belong to the Asiatic or European World. . . . Egypt will be considered in reference to the passage of the human mind from its Eastern to its Western phase, but it does not belong to the African Spirit. What we properly understand by Africa, is the Unhistorical, Undeveloped Spirit, still involved in the conditions of mere nature, and which had to be presented here only as on the threshold of the World's History.[22]

And with regard to the slavery that does not hinder the German people, as indicated in the quotation referring to the "Oriental" peoples and the slavery at the time of the Greeks, it appears that, for Hegel, it may be the natural lot of Africans, since their position on the hierarchical ladder is apparently much below that of the Europeans.

From these various traits it is manifest that want of self-control distinguishes the character of the Negroes. This condition is capable
of no development or culture, and as we see them at this day, such
have they always been. The only essential connection that has existed and continued between the Negroes and the Europeans is
that of slavery. In this the Negroes see nothing unbecoming them,
and the English who have done most for abolishing the slave-trade
and slavery, are treated by the Negroes themselves as enemies. For
it is a point of first importance with the Kings to sell their captured
enemies, or even their own subjects; and viewed in the light of such
facts, we may conclude *slavery* to have been the occasion of the in-
crease of human feeling among the Negroes. . . . Slavery is in and
for itself *injustice*, for the essence of humanity is *Freedom*; but for
this man must be matured. The gradual abolition of slavery is
therefore wiser and more equitable than its sudden removal.[23]

267

The hierarchy is sought by even those who detail the dialectical mapmaking skills. And this belief in ever-improving civilizations is passed
into the realm of the study of the natural world. If for Hegel, who
believed in the ultimate freedom of the Spirit of humankind and who
postulated that this freedom would allow for the natural development
of laws, for example, an attribute that I interpret as meaning that
the map is not predetermined for him and therefore is not teleological
in nature, if for this Hegel there is still a natural hierarchy, a ladder
of achievement of civilizations and of ideas, then it is not surprising
to me that scientists easily believe in the hierarchy of all living things
as well. The embryonic spinal cord development that I see as the result
of local tissue/environment interactions, the result of self-injury leading to the inevitable emergence of a new shape, or new order, this
same development could be construed by the classical scientist, I
suppose, as having followed a preordained destiny of sorts through
this arcane mechanism. So is all development, are all maps, ultimately

teleological, after all? I choose to think not. Even the minor experiments I performed on the chick embryo point in a different direction. Changes to the embryo/landscape interaction—even though they are rare in the development of an organism that is swathed in the maternal juices containing the most conservative of environments—lead to different outcomes. Radical changes, such as scalpel cuts, show this. This proves to some degree that the hierarchy is not inevitably there, not absolute. This also warns me to be sceptical of human absolutes.

268

At the Salekhard airport, people have been waiting for us for more than two hours. Sasha tries to talk to one of the officials, but he is ignored. Tatiana asks one of the airport officials to talk with her privately. "She is KGB, KGB. We will be okay." Sasha is not smiling when he says this. The plane is waiting on the corrugated metal runway. It is a large Antonov cargo plane. "No, no, we go in the back, not the door." Sasha, weaving as he walks, guides us to the rear of the plane, where there is a mesh net on the gangplank to help us walk up into it. Inside, we are greeted by hostile stares from the other passengers. There are about thirty of them, their luggage taking up the space in the middle of the plane's main compartment. We all have to sit on two rows of wooden benches, one on each side of the plane. There are no seat belts that fit, only long loose pieces of canvas webbing that can have no practical use, and there is nothing to tie down the luggage that consists mostly of large sacks of what looks like food, and boxes of heavy equipment. The passengers are men, except for Tatiana and Fiona. Fiona sits down at the end of a bench. Most of the places are occupied by the men who want a place to lie down later. The trip will take us ten hours overnight to Izhevsk, south of here in the Urals, and then to Moscow.

"Move down, move down." Tatiana is now in charge. Sasha cannot even stand; the alcohol has finally taken hold. Room is made for us all, farther up. Then our luggage comes in.

Alexander is here. "Greetings, and goodbye," he says, bowing. Sasha wakes up with a grin on his face, and more vodka appears. Alexander and Jim hurl our bags onto the already substantial pile in the middle of the plane.

"Let's drink outside." Sasha crawls down the mesh gangplank with Alexander and I am now a little concerned. Maybe he will be left behind, and then what?

269

Escape from Germany—the concept has clouded my thinking process. We are standing on the edge of the airport tarmac in Düsseldorf. My father has come to get us, but it won't be easy for a while yet. Crew members of military planes are not checked by German border officials. We are dressed like crew in their civilian clothes, neat and conservative; in case we are questioned, we can say it was all a misunderstanding. We are waiting for the signal to walk quietly and calmly over the tarmac with the regular crew. "They won't ask anything, they won't even be looking, but act as if you've just heard a good joke and we're all getting ready to move out as usual." My father's co-pilot and crew are happy enough with the arrangements. I am terrified, but Danielle is too tired to care. We walk.

At the plane, I wonder whether I look casual enough. "Will they come in here to check us? Are we safe in here?"

"Just let them try." My father is too preoccupied checking the instruments on the Yukon turboprop to pay much attention, but his expression is not entirely reassuring. I am shaken up by the German experience. Hunger was a part of it, but the shiny impersonal bank buildings amid the ruined bombsites were more upsetting, and the swearing and obscene gestures by passersby on the street in the poor neighbourhood near the railway station where we had lived for three weeks the worst memory.

"Telephone call for you," the concierge had said the week before.

"What?" We had taken to sleeping most of the day by then. I stumbled downstairs to the one phone in the lobby. A friend of my father's was on the line, saying my father would be coming on Tuesday to pick us up. I went back upstairs. "He's coming Tuesday—that's in two days. Hurray!" But that hadn't been the message. My father's friend spoke in English and I was now thinking half the time in German, so I had mixed up my mental translations, confusing *Dienstag*, Tuesday, with *Donnerstag*, Thursday, but I didn't know that until later. Meanwhile, we got ready to go in two days, using up all our money to buy food. When Tuesday came and no one showed up, I began to have doubts about what I had heard. We waited two more excruciatingly long days with virtually nothing to eat.

Sitting in the cargo plane in Siberia twenty years later, I feel the fear I had in Germany. Really breaking away from a place, from a system of rules, from a paradigm, requires extreme actions. Cargo planes seem to fill the bill.

270

The truck in Montreal is a cargo plane. It is big. My sons and I work all morning Sunday loading it up. The washing machine is the worst. "Don't move, or my fingers'll be crushed. Move it to the left a little, the left!" The stairs are dented as we ease the monster down. Outside, the greasy downstairs neighbour is trying to get his car started.

"Hey, give us a push down the street. I've gotta get this thing moving." He is standing on the street with another anglophone, a relative or a friend of his. I don't think his French neighbours talk to him. I think maybe a little help in his direction will yield some reciprocal help for us. My sons and I shove his car around the street for a while, with no luck, and no help is offered to us in return.

"What a fucking place." We are resigned to finish the moving job alone.

271

It is embarrassing. We have far too much baggage in the cargo plane. Sasha has made the whole trip up to now using an overnight bag, but I have two large suitcases and Jim has a giant duffel bag filled with food in case he doesn't want to eat the food we are served. And then there are the gifts. We have carvings and artifacts, preserved and mounted fish, and a huge stuffed reindeer head with antlers. The antlers are sticking into one of the men sitting near us on the bench. He heaves it away from his section of the cargo hold, shouting "Put it down there!" He isn't gentle with it. We have to adjust the luggage and the antlers without any help. But most of the passengers are quiet, huddled up, looking at us from their corners.

272

For Hegel, the coming together of opposites, of Being and Nothing, leads to a Becoming, a constant renewal, an ever-present reality. For me, this is the key to a non-teleological map, an ever-present reality that is not predestined by a map lying in wait for our adaptation. The *flow* of events is the unravelling of a life lived in a place, of the life in Montreal. This is a becoming, even for my sons and me, mere agents in this unravelling. We are closing the truck's compartment, cleaning the apartment, the floors, the bathroom, the kitchen, sweeping the stairs, locking the door, riding in the cab, turning onto Highway 20, leaving the province of Quebec, driving down the road, moving away from Montreal. Road passing under our feet, Quebec cars passing under our gaze, slippery ice passing under our tires. Feeling only the passage into a new present. Relaxing for the first time in two days, for a few hours, not talking much.

273

At the time of the breakdown, the destruction of an old order, are we keenly aware that the future cannot be predicted or understood? We can only experience things in the present. Plato suggests that perhaps in an existence beyond human experience, there is only a present tense.

> [H]e [the creator] resolved to have a moving image of eternity. . . . For there were no days and nights and months and years before the heaven was created, but when the heaven was created he created them also. They are all parts of time, and the past and future are created species of time, which we unconsciously but wrongly transfer to the eternal being, for we say that it "was," or "is," or "will be," but the truth is that "is" alone is properly attributed to it, and that "was" and "will be" are only to be spoken of becoming in time, for they are motions, but that which is immovably the same forever cannot become older or younger by time, nor can it be said that it came into being in the past, or has come into being now, or will come into being in the future.[24]

During all the escapes of my life, I was keenly aware that there was no apparent future ahead. Every moment of the present stayed with me, like an immovable thing.

274

The escapes from binding paradigms, the escape from Germany in 1970, the escape from Siberia in 1990, and the escape from Montreal in 1997, are all in the present tense for me as they are happening. The torment of the immovable present is like an unending sojourn in hell. Nothing seems to happen. We are doomed to repeat the same actions over and over again.

"Everybody out." My heart stops for a second. Why are we getting out of the cargo plane? We haven't even started the trip, we are still sitting in the Salekhard airport, and now why do we have to disembark? The Russians along the benches just move out as ordered.

"Is something wrong?" Everything is possible in this regime. We can be arrested. We shouldn't even be on this plane—we know that. Who ever heard of foreigners travelling through the Soviet Union on top of piles of junk? We stand on the metal mesh that acts as a tarmac, looking down, trying to avoid eye contact with the uniformed airport guards, but nothing happens. One hundred-pound bag of potatoes is dragged out. Shouts of anger quiet my heartbeats because they are directed at someone else. The guilty individual just gets back into the plane and sits on a stack of other bags of potatoes. It's routine to smuggle food away from Siberia, the same food that was delivered from the south only the day before.

We are left alone. Slightly distracted from what is obviously a business transaction, bribery I guess, uniformed guards just look at us briefly as we get back into the plane's cargo compartment. Tatiana has taken care of any details concerning us. She has our passports; she is smiling to herself.

275

"Checking what?" My father doesn't want any more interference. He has just been told that the airport officials need more information, but let's get this airplane out of Germany, okay?

"Will we have to get out?" I can't take much more tension. I couldn't last another day here—I've really lost perspective on this place.

"No, no, just stay in the back, on the packing cases for now. You can both sit up in the galley during takeoff, but stay out of sight for a while."

276

The weather is very bad. As the night wears on, the truck is ploughing through thick snow and ice that strafes the windshield. Other cars on the road are sliding as we pass, heavily laden and deliberate. "I can't get over the dismal feeling of that city." I want to express my anger and relief at leaving Montreal. "Uptight place. How about that little jerk downstairs?" The smell of the downstairs neighbour's smoking alone, even during the short two-day period we had spent packing up the apartment, was enough to leave a literal bad taste in our mouths. "Everybody smokes in Montreal—it's in the air everywhere."

In Moscow, I had noticed a constant smell. On the streets, it was the exhaust from ancient automobiles and trucks. The air was almost visible at times. Inside, cigarette smoke was a thing you inserted into your nose; it fitted right into the back of your throat like an elaborate gagging device. In the cargo plane on the way back, the men all light up cigarettes. My eyes are watering. I breathe shallowly to try to reduce the impact of the cigarettes.

277

Tatiana is trying to give pieces of a chocolate bar to the other passengers, but they are refusing. "Sasha said something." Jim worrying about Tatiana. "Something about the KGB, he says she's KGB, and now they won't even take her chocolate."

"So what?" I reply. "Maybe she is KGB. She got us out of Salekhard pretty easily. What did she say to the guards anyway?" Tatiana sits in a corner and looks down, refusing to talk to us; Sasha is grinning in a kind of evil way.

"We have time for talking now." He starts his story. Fiona sits up to listen, but the curve of the plane doesn't allow her to sit straight. She is groggy from sleeping uncomfortably on a very smelly bag filled with the skin of a reindeer, one of our many gifts. We can barely hear Sasha because the engines are too loud. I have never been next to such a loud noise in my life—it's like standing inside a jet engine. Sasha yells into our ears. As he talks, listening is harder and harder. I realize that the plane isn't pressurized, and as we climb to a higher altitude, our ears begin to plug up.

278

We are finally off. Danielle and I leave the seats and clamber all over the plane. We can see Germany under us as we climb into the sky. We can move around all over the plane because we are the only passengers. I lean back over a soft bag of something in the main storage area. "Ah, this is the life, eh?"

"When we get back to Canada, it should be fine," my father reassures us. "You don't have to worry about not leaving Germany through the regular channels—no one will know. We do this all the time with family and friends." Good, good, just get us out of here.

279

Tatiana is staring out of the little window of the plane; she is crying.

"It is nothing—KGB. She must think not to telephone the KGB when we arrive to Izhevsk." Sasha is saying times have changed—KGB was then and now we have this project. "She must think about the project." Maybe it would be better for her to leave the project and leave us all alone, he says. We have been seen in Salekhard photographing evidence of the Gulag, so Tatiana is worried, Sasha says, and we don't have visas for our destination. All our visas, for every destination in the Soviet Union, had to be approved before the whole trip was started. Even though the last-minute trip up the Ob River the week before had been to a very remote region, we had been obliged to obtain special permission from the local KGB office in Salekhard. Izhevsk is a big place, and the guards at the airport will be even more concerned than isolated Soviet officials in a little village on the Ob. Visas? Suddenly, the escape vehicle, our cargo plane, doesn't feel so safe any more.

280

"Jesus!" The highway is blurry ahead, and ice coats the windshield. It feels as if we are driving on grease. But the truck is so heavy it just keeps moving on. "Let's stop for a while and see if this lets up a bit." We don't want to stop, but weather conditions are getting worse and worse. The journey out, the escape, is not all clear sailing, wasn't just the final locking of my daughter's apartment door. I ease the truck into the inner lane as we approach a service centre. Tailgating cars to the right of me bunch up behind as I change lanes. Everyone is driving slowly but too close together.

281

Fiona is now convinced that Tatiana is a member of the KGB. "She just pushed her way into the cabin and tried to give chocolate to the crew." Fiona had been up there too, trying to stretch her legs and her back. "They refused to take any. Sasha says it's because they want her to know they know who she is."

Sasha starts to tell us his stories again. "We published article in newspaper in 1986, a bad time for Gulag stories. There was woman I know. She had diaries of her father." Sasha has a lot of women friends; we keep meeting them on this trip. This story is horrendous. The diaries related that Stalin put the woman's mother in prison and had her sexually tortured, and her father could do nothing, even though he was a high-level minister in Stalin's government. He knew his life depended on not saying anything. Stalin was a psychopath. Sasha wrote a newspaper story based on the diary and published it. He and the editor of the newspaper stayed up all night waiting to be arrested. There is a really tangible sense of danger in the cargo plane as Sasha tells the story.

We are living in a time that has not changed; in 1986 Sasha feared arrest, and today in the cargo plane he fears arrest. We have not escaped. Real escape from an old order is a long process, painful and destructive.

282

Today, as I write this, I read in my diary, the one I wrote in during the flight out of Siberia, "Strange vibrations seem to come from this area of the world. I can't describe it exactly, but you can almost sense the danger. I don't know how long the flight is. I have had some time to contemplate my own situation in life, but to be honest, I have seen the results of so much hardship here that I can't stand to think about sadness any longer. I keep looking for rays of hope. Is there one in my own life? I don't know exactly." I find the phrases to be curiously disjointed, revealing the suffering I felt at the time.

The process of destruction is almost inevitably associated with its opposite, the constructive desire for the positive. On the flight out of Siberia, I looked for a ray of hope. On the flight out of Germany, a place that only hours before had been oppressive, I lay back on the packing cases, relieved. A feeling came to me from the vibrations of the plane: my father was flying this plane, and I could almost feel his hands holding me up, cradling me, as we started over the Atlantic toward home.

283

Sasha is telling me and Fiona about Stalin, about how he treated his own son. Jim is busy playing match tricks with the guys in the back of the plane. The arrangement of the matches proves certain mathematical rules, I think. Jim is testing the men. They've all been away from their families for four months working on the oil- and gas-drilling stations. They like to play games like this. Jim doesn't have to listen to Sasha. He is the designer on the project; he isn't concerned with every story we hear.

Stalin's first son was arrested by German troops in 1941. Hitler proposed a swap for a German general who had been captured by the Soviets. "Stalin says, 'Not allowed to be capture by Germany army,' so his son is killed, killed in concentration camp in 1944." Sasha is holding his head. I know his own little son sits with him in their tiny Moscow apartment while Sasha writes his books about Arctic exploration. "Stalin's camps much harder than Germany camps." Sasha is more sober now, and his stories keep coming at us over the night flight into the Urals. According to Sasha, Stalin had every member of any village captured by the Germans sent to the Gulag camps. Being captured was a crime. Once people were captured, there was never any escape. This is the nature of a paradigm—the rulers cannot brook any escapes, not even if the escape amounts to being captured by the enemy. "In 1946, after concentration camps, soldiers of Soviet Union taken from the Germany concentration camps and all sent to Gulag." Sasha is looking at my eyes for confirmation of the horror he is telling us.

284

"Three! That's three cars upside down in the ditch! Can you believe this?" We are on the highway again, and the ice is worse, blowing in off Lake Ontario near Brockville. In the course of the past ten minutes, we have counted three cars in the ditch. Other cars have pulled off the road, surrounding the upturned vehicles. The last one we saw had people crawling out of windows. There are no ambulances yet. The road is sheer ice. We do not stop. All around us, the physical world is reflecting the destruction we have been wreaking on the old regime of Montreal. It is a literal reflection of the moral chaos of our own lives.

285

Stalin's daughter was married in 1942 to a Jewish man. They were married for about three years; Sasha knows the man well. "When she is sixteen; she is having affair with thirty-five-years-old man. Now he is great cinema producer." Sasha's stories are fascinating but entirely disjointed. The main message is the inhumanity of Stalin. Stalin hated Jews, especially because of his daughter's marriage. Stalin's daughter's thirty-five-year-old lover is sent to the Gulag camps. She was followed around by the NKVD; she could not walk freely in Moscow. Stalin's second son was a general at the end of the Second World War, a "very bad man. He drank too much and was self-loving," Sasha tells us. He was like Stalin. All the brothers and sisters of Stalin's second wife were sent to die in the camps before the Second World War. Stalin frequently killed off people he knew; even close associates who fell slightly out of favour were sent to the Gulag camps. It was said that simply being taller than Stalin was considered a crime. "Stalin was only 165 centimetres tall." Sasha is shaking his head, shaking with the recalling of the stories.

286

We count eleven cars that have gone off the road in a ten-mile stretch, seven of them upside down. "Shit! Look out!" A few minutes before, a black car had come swerving past us, screeching tires and disappearing around a curve. That was number eleven. We saw it as we lumbered around the curve ourselves a moment afterwards; it was accompanied by two other ditched vehicles. People ran over to help, so we kept on going. But we are barely moving. Everyone suddenly has slowed down to a crawl, and we're boxed into a convoy of frightened motorists. The scene around us is like a movie, my sons and I realize, a drama for us to watch. We cannot participate. It is the last attempt of the old regime, the dying embers of the old paradigm, to draw us back in. Flashing lights are set up around the last overturned car by the police that have now swarmed onto the highway. The journey has taken on a new bizarre form. We are travellers on a sheet of treacherous ice; destruction lies ahead if we make one false move.

287

Destruction leading to the emergence of a new principle, one that is inherent in the old order, does not conform to the map hoped for by those who believe in a destiny that is designed. Destruction is a consequence of leaving the established way of doing things, but does it lead to a new resurgence of life? Wasn't destruction of the order of things linked with the tearing of the very fabric of the earth in Ulysses' speech in *Troilus and Cressida*?

> The heavens themselves, the planets, and this centre,
> Observe degree, priority, and place . . .
>   but, when the planets,
> In evil mixture, to disorder wander,
> What plagues and what portents! What mutiny!
> What raging of the sea! Shaking of earth!
> Commotion in the winds! . . . what discord follows![25]

I see the cars in the ditch, wheels spinning in the air, as we travel on the 401 highway from Montreal to Toronto, and I see the natural world reflecting the destruction of our connections to Montreal, the emergence of a new order of life accompanied by the death of the old. Nature falls apart when the order is challenged.

But another more optimistic philosophy is available to us, as we have seen in the writings of Chuang-tzu and Hegel, and even in some of Plato's works, and in images like Indra's fishing net that Wignarajah reminded me of when I was investigating the Hindu calendar—a juxtaposition of opposites that reflect each other in themselves, a juxtaposition that, in turn, leads to the concept of *birth* from death, of creation of a new principle from the ashes of the old. Writing during the century following Shakespeare, John Milton talks about the development of a new principle from the ashes of the old. This is an escape from a paradigm, an escape filled with the inevitable destruction, and as he states, the new principle rises like a phoenix from a holocaust.

But he, though blind of sight,
Despised, and thought extinguished quite,
With inward eyes illuminated,
His fiery virtue roused
From under ashes into sudden flame,
And as the evening dragon came,
Assailant on the perched roosts
And nests in order ranged
Of tame villatic fowl; but as an eagle
His cloudless thunder bolted on their heads.
So virtue, given for lost,
Depressed, and overthrown, as seemed,
Like that self-begotten bird
In the Arabian woods embost,
That no second knows nor third,
And lay erewhile a holocaust,
From out her ashy womb now teemed,
Revives, reflourishes, then vigorous most
When most unactive deemed,
And though her body die, her fame survives,
A secular bird, ages of lives.[26]

288

I am lifted up by the escape from Germany. It is the new hope springing out of the old despair. Danielle takes it a step further. She is really in control now. My father turns the controls of this huge aircraft over to her as we fly over the icy whiteness of Greenland. "We have to turn left about here. Just ease the steering mechanism like this." Moving the airplane controls, she leans into the left and we all feel the slight swell of the turn.

"Now this makes the trip worthwhile, doesn't it?"

289

Sasha is telling us more. After the revolution, Lenin said the old regime had to be destroyed to make way for the new. "Lenin says it is necessary to kill all intellectuals. Stalin was not clever man and he knew it. He acted on Lenin's ideas."

"Do you think that communism is responsible for the deaths in the camps? Is this the reason why so many intellectuals and others had to die?" I am searching for Sasha's beliefs.

"Yes, I am thinking communism and fascism are the same. Communism is the same word as killing!" Sasha is pursing his lips and looking over at Tatiana.

290

Is Sasha right about communism being synonymous with killing? Why do leaders of Communist movements, or left-wing revolutionary governments, kill off intellectuals? If I look back to Hegel's definition of change in a society, I see the seed bearing a poisonous fruit, one that leads to the demise of the society and the development of a new system. In the artificially injured embryonic tissue of my experiments, I sought to shake up the system to create a new system. I imagine revolutionary leaders are practising a harsh form of surgery on their subjects, cutting open the tissue of a society to stimulate the shakedown that will yield new growth. The power elite of the old system includes the intellectuals of the institutions, and that group is responsible for entrenching old values maybe more than any other. We can see that in the persistence of the prejudiced views that are detailed in the writings of the philosophers that define the culture of the west. So maybe what Sasha hated so much is a likely aspect of any revolutionary movement. Frantz Fanon, writing about Algerian, and more generally African, decolonization movements in the 1960s, found himself advocating violence if necessary, in order for the oppressed to relieve themselves of the bond they had with their oppressors. He thought violence inevitable. "National liberation, national renaissance, the restoration of nationhood to the people, commonwealth: whatever may be the headings used or the new formulas introduced, decolonization is always a violent phenomenon."[27] He considered intellectuals in a burgeoning new system to be holding the people back, keeping the values of the former oppressors alive.

> But it so happens sometimes that decolonization occurs in areas which have not been sufficiently shaken by the struggle for libera-tion, and there may be found those same know-all, smart, wily intellectuals. We find intact in them the manners and forms of thought picked up during their association with the colonialist bourgeoisie. Spoilt children of yesterday's colonialism and of today's national government's, they organize the loot of whatever national resources exist. . . . [T]he success of their depredations is swift to call forth the violence and anger of the people. For this same people, poverty-stricken yet independent, comes very quickly to possess a social conscience in the African and interna-tional context of today; and this the petty individualists will quickly learn.[28]

But where, we might ask, is the moral foundation in this argument? If breaking paradigms is destructive, and if it can be translated into vio-lence in our societies, and by some into "necessary" violence, where are our traditional human values? Is there an argument for swift surgery when something is diseased? Each situation is different, but does this mean that sometimes pain is necessary? Looking back, I am sure I would not describe the horrors I saw evidence of in Siberia as either quick or necessary. In any case, Fanon's prescription has been equated with medical treatment by some. In an article comparing the violent solutions of Fanon to the not-so-violent approaches of Nelson Mandela and the distinctly non-violent ones of Gandhi, Gail Presbey, a political theorist and Africa specialist, quotes Fanon's description of the colonizers of Algeria as "a gangrene germ": "The independence of Algeria is not only the end of colonialism, but the disappearance,

in this part of the world, of a gangrene germ and the source of an epi-
demic."[29] She concludes that one cannot decide absolutely which
method is best; it depends on the individual cultural situation:

> Just which of these approaches is the most humanistic: the quick
> and total violence described by Fanon, which claims to be human-
> istic because it quickly creates the social climate in which health
> can be gained; the limited violence directed toward material re-
> sources advocated by Mandela, which hopes to force the enemy to
> give in while preserving as much as possible the future hope of
> healing the community; or the nonviolent challenge advocated by
> Gandhi, which preserves the lives of the opponent in hopes of win-
> ning them to the right cause, but requires more patience and self-
> control than the other methods? All three put limits on violence
> and injustice that are often ignored in both the daily workings of an
> oppressive system and the specific acts of violence used to enforce
> the system. Any of the three, when compared to the unhindered
> continuance of domination, emerge as humanistic. Which of the
> three strategies is best may have to be left up to the concrete cir-
> cumstances of each situation, where history and culture play a role
> in shaping the consciousness of the people.[30]

I would add that this is effectively a realization that the situation, even
that of a human society, defines itself. In situations of extreme societal
change, there is no map by which people can guide themselves. Any action in such a situation depends entirely on the intimate interrelationship between the people involved and their newly evolving landscape,
a landscape of physical reality and intellectual ideas. Unfortunately, the
immorality of killing in these situations is weighed against the immorality of keeping the oppressed under the control of a repressive regime.
There is no easy solution.

I could not argue this with Sasha. I could not argue that his equating
Marx's or even Lenin's ideals with Stalin's regime of butchery was his
personal view and not necessarily mine. He expected instant respect
for his opinions when he painted mental pictures of violence for us. But

it is not always so simple. In my whole time in the Soviet Union, I met few people, intellectual or otherwise, who could see the development of the non-teleological process of dialectical thought as a move away from a belief in a design, a move away from a belief in the Great Chain of Being of the European Middle Ages. They had equated Communist theory with the brutality of the political leaders who camouflaged themselves with dialectical colours; they had associated dialectical ideology with the immediate source of their pain.

291

Izhevsk. It is two in the morning. No visas means trouble, but Tatiana is subdued. We keep quiet and walk into the airport from the tarmac. The guards are confused. Sasha tells them a story and they laugh. They advise us to stay in the airport. There will be no trouble.

292

Back home, we see the Trenton military base outside the windows of the plane. My father is coaching us. "Now, each of you take a bottle; we're only allowed one each, so you two will make up the difference." Military crew have to enter through customs too, it seems, and my father and the co-pilot want to bring in a couple of extra bottles of booze. The other crew members, the navigator and the cabin crew and the radio operator, all have their quota, so now Danielle and I will each take one.

"Ah Jeez, Ted, you know they aren't old enough." The customs officer is an old friend, but we are underage, or at least he thinks so. Danielle is under the drinking age and I am just legal, but I look really young. My father shrugs. They all laugh and we get through. Back at my parents' home, I see a couple of bottles of rye whisky we've had in the house for a while. They are all distilled in Canada and they all have imported duty-free stickers on them. I'd never noticed them before this trip. My father has been flying overseas since I was five.

293

Fiona and Jim and I are aware that our trip to Siberia has been a descent into a dark place. The trip has done something to us. Now we have to pick up the pieces and start again, like little children, in a way. We have lost our sense of privacy and our sense of personal free will. The regime that captured so many prisoners to build the Gulag railroad has had an effect on us after only a short time.

Back on the plane, our last leg of the journey to Moscow, Fiona has to use the toilet. "It's just a hole in the floor," she is telling me when she returns. "A hole in the floor of the plane—can you believe it?" Of course I can believe it. Most of the toilets since we left Moscow have lacked seats, and squatting is necessary. Fiona has travelled to many countries where conditions have been worse, but this is a moving airplane and somehow we have never imagined aircraft to be this primitive. And we feel more vulnerable in this vibrating machine; if the toilet is primitive, how likely is it that the machinery that is holding us up in the sky is reliable? "But the worst thing was," she continues, "there's no door—just a curtain and it sways back and forth, back and forth." She is imitating the swaying motion, laughing at the memory. "And this soldier guy up there was sitting across from me the whole time, just staring, each time the curtain swayed back and forth, back and forth." She is really laughing now, swinging her arms and then pointing at the guy in shabby military gear. I look up at the soldier who is still sitting across from the one-hole toilet, glaring at us. He knows what she is laughing at, knows he has paid dearly for that sleazy voyeur's moment. "And all the time he doesn't even look at my face, he just stares at—" She stops herself.

Before we left for Siberia, while we were still in Moscow, Jim and Fiona and I were on our own, taking the Metro into town one night. "Fuck!"

Jim turned to her. "Fiona! I don't believe I heard that! You never swear."

"Yes I do, when I'm really pissed off. I just don't like certain words and . . . I don't swear much."

"What words?"

"Well, the C word, for instance."

"The what?" Jim pries for this intimate information.

"The C word."

But I hadn't been listening. "You mean 'cunt'?" Jim started swatting me over the head with his hat and yelling my name in a loud voice. The people around us turned with narrowed eyes. Pronouncing my name, with its rude Russian meaning, inside a Moscow subway car got us a lot more attention than the English word *cunt*. But we didn't understand their reaction at the time, and we were embarrassed by their stares.

Now, when we are flying from Siberia, all Fiona's defences are down. "I don't care any more. If the jerk wants to watch, let him. God, it's amazing how much I don't care any more on this trip. What's happening to us?"

CHAPTER EIGHT

ARABIA

Enoch . . . pointing to a typewritten card at the man's foot, "it says he was once as tall as you or me. Some A-rabs did it to him in six months."

– FLANNERY O'CONNOR, *Wise Blood*

294

T HE WOMAN is walking with her family, and there are three other women, and a group of children. The boys are wearing khaki pants and long-sleeved shirts and they are running up ahead to the security station in the airport's main departure area. Five little girls, dressed in loose clothing, in subdued colours, are walking quietly, corralled by a couple of the slower-moving women. Three men are ahead of the group; two are young with small beards and one older with a heavier grey beard. They are ignoring the boys—at least eight of them, ranging in age from five to eleven—who are swarming around them. The men have head coverings that distinguish them as the very religious Muslims, the Matowa. They wear only the cloth scarf, without the heavy cloth ring, the circlet, that many men, less orthodox, use on top of their heads to hold the scarves in place. Their long white robes come to their feet. The woman who first caught my eye is walking with her head down. She is dressed like the other adult women in her group and like the many Saudi women I have seen during our stay in Riyadh. She is completely covered in black, loose robes falling to her feet. Not even her hands show outside the clothing. And her face is veiled, even her eyes. There is nothing to suggest what she looks like or how old she is. The oldest man is making arrangements with the security people. The woman is now the centre of the family's attention. She kneels and hugs each one of the children, her veil never exposing her face, her small white hands emerging to stroke the faces of the children. The older women hold her head against theirs in prolonged embraces. There is much talking and crying. The men move even farther from the group and look on quietly.

295

When we live inside a paradigm, the facts are laid out for us as truth. We cannot imagine that we have set up for ourselves a world in our image. Our actions are consistent with results we have seen time and time again when we do not depart from the rules that have laid down the original map. This is a form of slavery. We are enslaved by this destiny that dictates the trajectory of our lives. And we in turn enslave others. Their enslavement to our pursuits, and their literal enslavement to the service of our material needs, is an inevitable part of the hierarchy that we see as natural.

296

Jürgen and I have been in Saudi Arabia for about a week. Now we wait in the Riyadh airport to fly home. I will be going via Paris and Jürgen is going through Munich. He has people he wants to see there. It is early in March 1992. A week ago, I had hurriedly set up the trip. First, I went to Ottawa to obtain visa stamps in our passports. Stepping into the

Saudi embassy offices in Ottawa, I was already leaving the European world view behind. Two other Canadians sat waiting in the little office. They gave the impression that the wait had been days long. A clerk finally came to the tiny window with the sliding-glass front. He took the documents I had prepared and Jürgen's and my passports and left. I sat there for another hour. The other couple said nothing to me during the entire hour of waiting. It was eleven-thirty in the morning, and my flight to New York for the connecting flight to Riyadh would depart from Toronto at six-thirty. The final leg of my journey would be a thirteen-hour flight that left New York at almost midnight. It could not be missed—there would be an important meeting of scholars the morning after I was due to arrive in Riyadh. We would discuss the nature of the future science museum being built under the auspices of Prince Sultan ibn Salman ibn 'Abd al-'Aziz.[1] That was the main purpose of my trip. But all this had been arranged only in the past two days, and the visas were necessary in spite of the invitation from a prince and the urgency of my attendance at the meeting. Jürgen would be joining me for the business negotiations the following day.

297

The belief in truth rests on the foundation of a belief in facts. The facts that make up our world are not reducible to simple objects—facts involve *relationships* between objects; objects, or things, alone are not facts. Ludwig Wittgenstein, in his *Tractatus Logico-Philosophicus*, begins by stating that "the world is the totality of facts, not of things,"[2] and a little later that "the world divides into facts." The point, for those who seek to understand the scientific logic of the natural world, is that a catalogue of "things" is immediately recognized as incomplete. A thing is an object, like a stone or a pencil. A fact is a relationship, like "the stone is next to the pencil."

If we take the world as reality, then reality does "divide into facts." However, the disposition of these facts depends on where you are coming from. Wittgenstein covers this by accepting that there are an unlimited number of combinations possible.[3] So we can imagine that although we may only see the world from our individual perspective, there are, existing in the continuum of all reality, all possible combinations of relationships of things. A more problematic issue is the nature of a thing, an object. For Wittgenstein, there has to be some immutable foundation, and that lies with his notion of the *simple* object. Objects can be complex, consisting of many parts—for example, pencils and stones are complex, and human beings are certainly complex—but after dividing complex objects into their parts, there are, finally, simple objects.[4] For the philosophy of science in the west, objects and their interrelationships form reality, at some irreducible level—an "atomic" level, as described by the philosopher Bertrand Russell in his introduction to Wittgenstein's *Tractatus*. At this point in our scientific history, we are searching to discover what we consider to be the fundamental atomic level—quarks, subatomic particles that, through their relationships, create the building blocks of our reality. By beginning at the lowest atomic level with an understanding of these quarks, their properties and their potential interrelationships, western scientists hope to understand the many higher levels of complexity.

298

I'll be late for my flight, I'm thinking to myself. These people don't care—I'm not important to them. I imagine that the Saudi reality considers levels of complexity that fit into a hierarchy that is different from mine. Even if we were to agree that the object of our social reality, the individual human being, is consistent between cultures, I suspect that the importance I ascribe to myself in my society does not translate easily to theirs.

In the waiting room of the Saudi embassy in Ottawa, I am finally required to come up to the little window again. I am becoming alarmed about the time I have left to make it to the Ottawa airport. We were told that getting a visa was a formality, since the prince was inviting us. "Please complete the form—it is incomplete."

"What? What do you mean incomplete? Didn't they tell you that I am in a hurry, that I came to Ottawa myself for the visas because this is a last-minute emergency?"

"All parts of the form must be completed in full." The man is not looking at me; he is reluctant to point out the nature of the problem on the form.

"Okay, okay, I'm sorry. Look, can you tell me what is not complete exactly?" He points at the section on religion. "It is complete," I respond quickly. "I put *none*—that is my answer to the question."

At this point, the couple who have been waiting with me in this tiny room start to shift in their chairs. "Just put down *Christian* and shut up before it's too late, for Christ's sake. These guys don't understand your answer, but you better hope they don't start to." The man is looking worried. "Look, it's none of my business, but just don't get upset about it. Put down Christian and they won't start thinking you're Jewish or something." While this conversation is going on, the man behind the window is looking more and more impatient; he is slowly pulling my papers away from my grasp, and the passports are nowhere in sight. I feel really nervous; my fellow Canadians are acting as if we aren't in Ottawa at all.

"All right, I'll complete the forms." I grab the papers back from the man behind the window. After he disappears from sight, I ask my new-found advisors, "What if I'm Jewish—then what do I put down?"

"Don't be foolish, they only let Muslims and Christians in.[5] Don't think you can go there and act the way you do in Canada. They're all real bastards over there." I fill the forms out, putting in Christian for myself and Jürgen.

"Do you go over there often?" I ask the question more as a way to say thank-you for the advice than for the information.

"We go over as little as possible." The man looks over at his companion, who is snickering to herself.

"If we didn't have to ever see the place again it would be too soon." She has a really nasty look to her mouth, as if she just tasted something that's gone bad.

I pound on the window for a response. If this process takes much longer, I'll miss my flight. "Here, I've completed the forms. How long will it take? I have a plane to catch in two hours."

"It takes a minimum of two hours, assuming we can do it at all today." My arguing is not working. My new friends are rolling their eyes resignedly; I give up. Out in the hallway, I telephone Toronto to complain to the people in my office. By some miracle, they connect to the prince's assistant in Riyadh, and I have the visas within the hour. The rest of my stay in Ottawa consists of tearing across town in a taxi to the airport.

299

Wittgenstein defines the process of model-building in the western scientific imagination: "We picture facts to ourselves."[6] And then he proceeds to connect the picture we have in our minds to the reality of the world. Throughout his *Tractatus*, and certainly displayed in the following section, his "reality" is not questioned; I find the assumption that there is an unassailable concrete world of objects to be the most problematic aspect of scientific philosophy in the west.

2.12   A picture is a model of reality. . . .

2.161   There must be something identical in a picture and what it
        depicts, to enable the one to be a picture of the other at all.

2.17   What a picture must have in common with reality, in order
        to be able to depict it—correctly or incorrectly—in the way
        it does, is its pictorial form.

2.171   A picture can depict any reality whose form it has. . . .

2.19   Logical pictures can depict the world.[7]

Scientists make models of reality—pictures. Nevertheless, despite the fact that they are mere models, it is expected that these *pictures* can be tested against the backdrop of the "real" reality to ascertain their truth. In the 1922 edition of the *Tractatus*, Bertrand Russell's introduction speaks of Wittgenstein's approach to the verification of the "truth" embodied by models of reality: "A picture, he [Wittgenstein] says, is a model of reality, and to the objects in the reality correspond the elements of the picture."[8] But a reality that is immutable, and that can be used for the testing of the validity of a model, remains unquestioned—in other words, "reality" is assumed to just *be*. This acceptance of a fixed reality allows for the illusion of a progression toward the final design, of progress in western science. Thus, the *model*, or picture in the mind of a scientist, often becomes reality itself.

Headed into Saudi Arabia, I was entering a place where the *pictures*—the images that assailed my eyes—did not match my reality. In contrast to the ideology that would accept an external world that is the "ideal" and immutable—that underlies our experiences—my philosophy creates *pictures* that are useful only for an instant—they change with each new interaction. In my view, facts can be the *product* of models or intellectual approaches—the models form reality rather than the other way around. How can I explain my dialectical model to western scientists who believe the reality of irreducible objects such as quarks and other subatomic particles? My answer to an immutable reality might be as follows: if intellectual models can form environmental niches for themselves, why not simple objects also? The reality we see, therefore, may be a result of objects creating an existence for themselves through interactions with other objects around them.[9] In Saudi Arabia, I am seeing evidence of the creation of reality at a social level; for me, this is indicative of changes that may be as deeply set as *physical* reality—even at the so-called irreducible atomic level. In other words, if I see evidence for the "survival" of an abhorrent concept in a society, such as the subjugation of women, a way of thinking that should not compete well unless it has had a role in ensconcing *itself* in that society—unless it has been instrumental in changing the intellectual and physical environment until it has made itself a comfortable nest— then why can't I imagine this dialectical interchange reaching down into the atomic level? After all, I witness a physical reality in Saudi Arabia so different that the interchange between the objects of the world may be playing out a very different dialectic from that which I see in my own world.

My experiences in Saudi Arabia and later in South Africa would expose me to practices that could only exist if an idea had *created* a place for itself. Apartheid in South Africa and the subjugation of women in Saudi Arabia were ideas that had created niches for themselves, altering the landscape both intellectually and physically. Have the societies in Saudi Arabia and South Africa transformed their world at *all* levels, from the societal to the atomic? Is social behaviour manifested in the fabric of the clothing, and even in the chemical nature of the people? I sense that it may indeed be so. Ideas can generate changes in our reality so profound that the world becomes an entirely different place. The questions we ask, and even the physical reality we picture to ourselves, may not match the experiences of someone from another culture. Therefore, if I assume that the physical reality I can perceive with my senses is always related in some fashion to the irreducible atomic level, I would postulate that our physical reality can be changed even down to the atomic level. To think otherwise is to assume that cultural differences are merely a veneer, and that universals can be found that rise above these differences. But, if the "idea" comes first, and can generate a niche for itself, transforming all that is around it while it is being changed within a particular natural landscape in return—if such a dialectical exchange takes place—then cultural perspectives are not a veneer. They are intrinsically part of the reality-generating idea itself.

Such ideas, ones that attempt to question our sense of what is real, appear bizarre when first encountered. However, is it so incredible to imagine that the interaction of objects in the universe can have profound effects? Science is not so omniscient as to preclude such possibilities. And in any case, I am offering these thoughts as a route into questioning the tacit assumption that we have it all tied up, that we are on the brink of solving the mysteries of the universe, that we will soon know "the mind of God." It is that level of arrogance that these arguments seek to undermine with doubts about the perceived tangibility of the physical fabric of reality we think we feel and see around us. Furthermore, it is interesting to note that it is western science that allows for the most extreme interventions into nature—we change the physical reality around us constantly, by delving into the earth, by shifting the balance of the ecosystem, by genetically engineering the biosphere. Everything we touch is changed at a profound level. And finally, any of us who have travelled have had the sense, at times, that the nature of human communication has taken on new, unintelligible dimensions, the fabric and tissue of the concrete things around us have relationships to one another that are following new and uncertain rules—essentially, that nothing is what it was meant to be, that the very ground has shifted beneath our feet. My travels to Saudi Arabia and South Africa had this quality on more than one occasion, and those experiences cause me to doubt that I know very much at all about the ways of the universe.

300

My stay in Saudi Arabia has been like a passage into bondage. The idea of the world that formed this place is not anything like what we know in the west. As I watch the woman at the airport, I am overwhelmed by this sense of bondage—this slavery. The prince has sent his men to take care of our security clearance out of the country. They move like white birds, gracefully flowing robes drifting from one airport official to another, taking Jürgen and me along with their breeze, bags and crumpled suits in tow. Our passage out of the bondage that defines Saudi Arabia for me is a movement back to the familiar, where the activities of my daily life are clearly defined, where business deals are not shrouded in the etiquette of an indecipherable culture. The woman stays in my field of vision. She is leaving the country on her own, which is very unusual, as women do not travel without male relatives as companions in Saudi Arabia. Then I realize that once through the security gates, she is free.

She is free to redefine the objects in her world, herself included. Her family watches from above, behind the railing that separates Saudi Arabia from the rest of the world. We have taken the escalator down, past the security gates, where no one who is not travelling is allowed, but the Saudi family can still see the woman and yell farewells.

The prince's men pass in and out of the Kingdom of Saudi Arabia, completing the task of our departure; they come to us in the outer world and hand us our passports. "Give the prince our best." Jürgen is matter-of-fact.

301

In the west, we think we have the elements of reality in our "picture" of the world. Essentially, we are locked into a belief in a real world external to our inner selves, one that is not produced by our subjective interpretation; the real world is one that we approximate with our "pictures," but, we say, it exists nevertheless.

Wittgenstein says in his introduction to the *Tractatus* that he is indifferent whether his ideas have been anticipated by others. He further states that the concepts he has related in the work constitute the "final solution of the problems." Wittgenstein is posing as the philosophical naïf here, assuming that his concepts are basic enough not to be challenged. This is the same position as that of empirical scientists, who also fail to question the fundamental premises that underlie their philosophical approach to the empirical study of the natural world. The logic goes thus: the more simple the concepts, and the more simple the language used to describe it, the closer the model must be to reality. Simplicity, sometimes called elegance, is taken as proof of the basic premises. Unfortunately for western scientists, simplicity also indicates that little explanation is necessary to explain terminology and basic assumptions are left unquestioned; this attribute suggests that scientists are often *too* familiar with the basic tenets of a given paradigm and therefore tend to be indifferent to the constraints this can put on their imagination. Thus, a reference to the simplicity of an argument can serve to reinforce the status quo. Radical departures from an established intellectual model, on the other hand, can require a considerable degree of explanation, especially if the goal is to lure followers from the mainstream. New concepts, therefore, often do not present themselves in a simple form.

The idea of an objective "external" reality was anticipated by western philosophers before Wittgenstein. The concept of a "real" reality, ideal and unsullied by the prejudices of the observer, is basic to western philosophy. It is from this philosophical principle that we postulate the final design of the universe, an ideal that I maintain is responsible for the hierarchy, for the teleological world. It is also final design that guides the evolution of ideas in the minds of our philosophers. Yet the western concept of a final design is a very *human-shaped* one that cannot but be questioned when we consider that it also creates the idea of superior and inferior human beings—a convenience for the developers of this scientific logic, and one that has to have clouded their vision.

302

The woman is changing. First, she lifts her veil. She looks up to the railing above us and smiles at the women who were sending her off a few minutes before. The children are yelling her name and laughing and singing. The women wave their arms and wipe unseen tears from inside their veils. She is sitting near me, and I can see that her eyes have exquisite markings—mauve eyeshadow and kohl outlining their edges. Red lipstick and deep-coloured blush set off her dark eyebrows. She is about thirty years old; I didn't know that before she took off her veil.

She sheds her outer robe. She is swathed in layers that wrap around. Removing these garments is an elaborate process, and I'm amazed that she is doing this in full view of everyone, including her family. They all continue to wave. She is wearing a black Chanel-style dress, short above her knees, with no sleeves at all. Her breasts are outlined by the silk that drapes her lightly, sharp pointed nipples indicating the most delicate of camisoles, the lace showing at the neckline of the dress. I can't help staring—her transformation to an object of western desire is dramatic. Even the men up above are waving now; this is a jewel they are proud to display, as long as it is outside their controlled world of Muslim facts. She stands to smooth her skirt and steps from the tangled drapery at her feet. For a brief moment, her pubic mound is gently shaped against the thin fabric, her thighs parting a little as she lifts her arm to wave back and call to the women and the children and the men in the lobby above. No one else is looking. The final transformation—she takes off the head covering to reveal gold-and-diamond earrings and rich red-black hair flowing down her bare neck. All the garments are bundled into a small travel bag. She is on my plane, going to Paris.

303

Plato painted the image of an ideal reality existing beyond the grasp of humans. It is not considered to be the result of interaction between the observer and the observed. It is idealized outside the experience of those living in the landscape, whether the landscape of the physical world or the intellectual world of ideas doesn't matter. Plato describes the true reality (his "fifth entity") as something derived from the concepts of the naming, the describing, the imaging or picturing, and the formulation of the knowledge of object. Effectively, he accepts the same preconditions as Wittgenstein—an external reality—and ends with the concept of the perfect reality. Wittgenstein, and his legion of scientific followers of the twentieth century, start with the concept of the relationship of objects, consider the language used to name, describe, and picture such relationships and end with an approach to the truth of our knowledge about these relationships. Empiricists today do not question but rather *assume* the existence of atomistic facts and objects within the reality alluded to by Plato in the passage below. The reality of today's scientist comes close to the Platonic ideals of classical philosophy. In the case described here by Plato, the reality of the "circle" acts as an example of the idealized world.

For everything that exists there are three classes of objects [1. name, 2. description, 3. image] through which knowledge about it must come; the knowledge itself is a fourth, and we must put as a fifth entity the actual object of knowledge which is the true reality. We have then, first, a name, second, a description, third, an image, and fourth, a knowledge of the object. Take a particular case if you want to understand the meaning of what I have just said; then apply the theory to every object in the same way. There is something for instance called a circle, the name of which is the very word I just now uttered. In the second place there is a description of it which is composed of nouns and verbal expressions. For example the description of that which is named round and circumference and circle would run as follows: the thing which is everywhere equal distances between its extremities and its centre. In the third place there is the class of object which is drawn and erased and turned on the lathe and destroyed—processes which do not affect the *real circle* to which these other circles are all related, because it is different to them. In the fourth place there are knowledge and understanding and correct opinion concerning them, all of which we must set down as one thing more that is found not in sounds nor in shapes of bodies, but in minds, whereby it evidently differs in its nature from the real circle and from the aforementioned three. Of all these four [entities, classes of object], understanding approaches nearest in affinity and likeness to the fifth entity [*true reality*], while the others are more remote from it.[10]

The blurry picture we think we have of the "real" reality is described graphically in Plato's *Republic*, where he depicts prisoners who live in a cave, separated from the real world, seeing only shadows of reality. These prisoners are like all of us, according to Plato. The essential point here is the belief in a reality that is ideal and separate from our experience, which is the foundation of our empirical science of the west. This is the assumption that Wittgenstein and others do not notice they are making. Empirical scientists believe we are living in this cave and that we are attempting to improve the indistinct picture of shadows on the wall so that it better matches the "real" reality.[11]

304

On the flight to Riyadh in February 1992, I sit next to a military man from the States. He is sleeping, but I can't. "Why can't we fly business class?" Jürgen complained to me in Toronto the day before my flight, before we had the arrangements made. "The government regulations are ridiculous. How can we manage to work under these conditions?" My flight follows immediately after my trip to Ottawa for the visas, so I will have travelled for over twenty-four hours once I arrive. I will weather an eight-hour jet lag and then face the day-long meeting with the scholars and scientists and engineers from across Saudi Arabia. I agree with Jürgen. Now I am wedged between the military man and a woman who is slowly covering herself more and more as the trip progresses.

"I work with strategic stuff," the man had said before falling asleep. "I can't tell you anything." I didn't know what to say next. "Back in the States, my family and I go on these outings, right? These vacations for military families, where we re-enact the battles from the Civil War. The kids love it—we all play our traditional parts, right?"

"What do the women do then? They don't get to shoot the guns and see the action of the old battlefields? They just stay behind and cook?"

"Yeah, right, well, it's supposed to be authentic. My son and I really get close during those weekends. It's all subsidized for us too."

My bladder is tight, it's so full, but the toilets are clogged at my end of the aircraft. The plane is filled with children in diapers, and the smell from the nearby washrooms is nauseating. Even on the wet floors, men and women kneel to pray. In Riyadh, prayer takes place five times a day. The Matowa, the religious police, stream through the streets in Land Rovers and Jeeps equipped with loudspeakers, calling people to prayer in commanding voices. On the plane there is no agreement on the time, so prayer is constant. There is no agreement on direction, so they pray facing all sides of the plane and then argue about it. Their individual realities are not matching well. Some of the men are becoming frantic. I fall fitfully asleep. I have no choice but to lean against the unconscious military man. He squeals and shakes as I snuggle into his shoulder, but he doesn't wake up. This doesn't work—every time he shakes I spring up, looking around. I am exhausted but unable to rest.

305

"Yes, oh yes, this is luxury." Five and a half years later, it's 1997, and Jim and I are on a flight to Johannesburg. The airplane is luxurious. It is South African Airlines, not Air Saudia, and not a cargo plane out of Siberia. There is room for my hand luggage in a compartment next to my arm. Jim and I are on the top deck of this huge plane, which isn't even full. We will be travelling for fourteen hours on the longest flight in the repertoire of the world's commercial airlines.

Halfway through the flight, Jim and the rest of the passengers are asleep. The blinds are drawn; we don't know that it is blazingly sunny outside the plane. The stewardess asks me if I would like to spend some time in the cockpit with the crew. "Sit right down here, then. Make yourself at home." The co-pilot looks at me with bleary eyes. "Where did you say you'd be working in Joh'burg—downtown? You've missed me there—why would you be doing that? Whites don't go there now."

"The blacks are not to be trusted," the pilot tells me. He is an older man, close to retirement. He lives in Pretoria, and he hasn't been to Johannesburg in years. "They'll kill you soon as ask your permission." I ask for more details, and they come at me—car hijackings at gunpoint, killings for the change in your pocket, and home invasions—raping the women and killing the men. The pilot is warming to the subject. "They need one kind of law, the kind that works. They don't need any of this reconciliation, the blacks don't—they aren't educated."

"They know nothing and they don't want to know," the co-pilot goes on, as he plays with the instruments.

"Where are we?" I want to know when we are going to cross the equator—it will be my first time.

"Here, look at this map. Well, it's not a very good map for showing you where we really are—it doesn't look like anything you could call the real thing." He displays a map that indicates a faint outline of the lower portion of the edge of the east coast of Africa. But it is distorted— it has a series of lines that give bearings and that allow for the trajectory of a flight to be more or less a straight line. "It doesn't really show you Africa at all." He breaks off to radio to a remote station in Cameroon. "She isn't answering." He is yawning.

"Must be break time, feeding the goats." The pilot smirks. "See what I mean—it's the same all over Africa."

The co-pilot tries again to make radio contact. "What we'll do, see, is obtain a bearing, then correct the instruments and then we can tell you when we're crossing the equator. Should be in the next half hour or so."

306

Gerard Mercator first made his famous map projection in 1569. Today, it is the most commonly used map of the world. This format was intended to assist navigators travelling long distances by sea. Mercator maps are often used by navigators of any means of long-distance transportation, including aircraft.[12] We have become used to the Mercator map, even though it means that in our vision of the world map the continents do not closely resemble their actual shapes.

The distortions in the size of northern and southern land masses occur as a result of flattening the map to produce a grid with 90-degree angles of longitude and latitude from top to bottom. The grid is further distorted by the stretching of the longitude lines as the map progresses to the North and South Poles. As we come closer to the poles, the continental shapes are stretched and widened. Greenland, for example, is seen to be about the same size as South America, whereas it is only one-eighth in size in actuality. The "reality" of the map appears to be compromised. But from another point of view, there is another reality, one more important to the navigator.

Before Mercator, world maps were based on the "plane-chart," a spread-out globe using a grid that maintained a constant ratio between

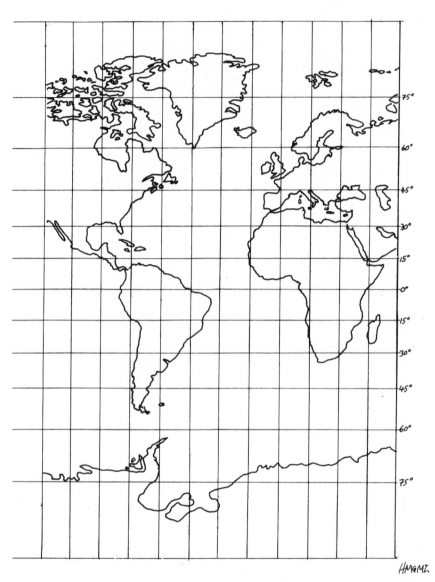

HMGMZ

Map of North and South America, Europe, Africa, Greenland, and Antarctica, using
a Mercator Projection. This projection allows navigators to maintain a straight-line
course, but it distorts the continental shapes near the poles.

latitude and longitude. The continental shapes approaching the poles
became spread out horizontally, since, on a flat sheet of paper, the longitudinal lines were not narrowed near the top and the bottom as they

are on a globe. However, the latitudinal lines were kept equidistant from each other, 45 degrees north being the same distance on the map from 60 degrees north, as 60 is from 75, and so forth. The accuracy of the latitudinal lines maintained a closer degree of verisimilitude between the flat map and the sphere, especially in the limited region of the Mediterranean, but these maps were not helpful to navigators travelling long distances to the north and south over vast oceans. The problem was that the ratio between the length of the latitude lines of a section compared with the length of a longitude line became distorted closer to the poles. Mercator solved the problem by allowing the longitudinal lines of a section of the map's grid to lengthen (the distance between 60 degrees north and 75 degrees north is greater than the distance between 45 and 60 degrees, for example) in proportion to the artificial widening of the latitudinal lines in each grid section, thus maintaining the actual ratio of latitude to longitude over the whole flat representation of the world map. This meant that the course of an ocean-going vessel, travelling over the Atlantic between Africa and North America for example, could be plotted as a *straight* line—a rhumb line, a line of constant compass bearing. By maintaining straight lines of navigation, the "reality" of the *navigator* is more closely approximated by the Mercator map than it is by maps that do not distort the most northerly and southerly portions of the world map. Thus, we can question the degree to which reality can ever be equally represented or understood when comparing contexts that have varying needs and perspectives—the map of our "reality" varies, depending on what we are doing with it.

307

The world of the non-European is seen as lacking the external reality that results in logical maps of the world, and logical science. The historian Edward Said implicates western civilization in this negative view of the near "Orient," the Arab world: "On the one hand there are Westerners, and on the other there are Arab-Orientals; the former are (in no particular order) rational, peaceful, liberal, logical, capable of holding real values, without natural suspicion; the latter are none of these things."[13] Said backs this analysis of western scholarly prejudice using quotations from academic and political commentators who have described the Arab world over the past century. For Said, Henry Kissinger sums up the view of the west with respect to Arab science:

> [H]e [Kissinger] speaks consciously as an authoritative voice for the major Western power [the United States], whose recent history and present reality have placed it before a world that does not easily accept its power and dominance. Kissinger feels that the United States can deal less problematically with the industrial, developed West than it can with the developing world. . . . [H]e divides [the world] . . . into two halves, the developed and the developing countries. The first half, which is the West, "is deeply committed to the notion that the real world is external to the observer, that knowledge consists of recording and classifying data—the more accurately the better." Kissinger's proof for this is the Newtonian revolution, which has not taken place in the developing world: "Cultures which escaped the early impact of Newtonian thinking have retained the essentially pre-Newtonian view that the real world is almost completely *internal* to the observer." Consequently, he adds, "empirical reality has a much different significance for many of the new countries than for the West because in a certain sense they never went through the process of discovering it. . . ." [T]he point [Kissinger] makes is sufficiently unarguable to require no special validation. We had our Newtonian revolution; they didn't.[14]

The implication is that there is a hierarchy of ideas, and that an understanding that the real world is external to the observer is a mark of the superiority of a civilization. But how is this reality defined? Is it not from the point of view of the observer, who must use it to some end? For the pure Platonic observer, the western empirical scientist, it is imagined that there is a perfect "circle" somewhere in the zone of reality. But for the navigator sailing across the ocean, the picture of reality must be distorted from the true circle to create a map with constant straight lines, or we will not reach our destination. I would question the degree to which we really subcribe to an external reality that can be described and held to be true by everyone, given that the definition of this reality must develop from the use we make of it; the navigator's reality is different from that of the mapmaker interested in mathematically accurate shapes for continents, for example.

308

My bags are opened, every pocket unzipped. My toothpaste is squeezed. My business papers are laid out in a mess on the table. I am searched for pictures of my western reality. The Arab world I find on landing in Riyadh has a great interest in these "pictures of our reality." The mysterious internal reality that Kissinger and others ascribe to the Arab mind has no connection with the airport security guards. Later in the week, I am in a convenience store with Lawrence, an American who runs the small prototype of a science museum they have in Riyadh. His home is in Oklahoma, but he lives here most of the year. I am pulling at his arm. "Why are all these photos blacked out?"

"It is a sacrilege to depict the human face." This is the image of the reality that these people do indeed understand. Every human face in every edition of every foreign magazine and newspaper is obliterated with marking pen. I feel chilled. There are no faces. Every advertisement in the windows of modern shops has blank faces, no features. Mannequins have smooth heads, with no eyes, no mouths. After three days, I see no women, only black-draped shapes. A glimpse of a female face in a newspaper will give me an erection—I am sure of that. The guards at the airport are looking for pornography, women's faces. There are none. They are not expecting to find drugs, only pictures of my reality.

The Saudis have not eliminated pornography—at least not in the minds of visitors from the decadent west, like me. They have brought it to new levels. Even after a week I become sensitive to the most subtle indication of female qualities. I secretly seek out the curves under the drapery.

309

Edward Said does not analyze the scientific approach to reality taken by the Arab scholar, the "Oriental": "I have no interest in, much less capacity for, showing what the true Orient and Islam really are."[15] He is interested in the image the west has of the orient—in particular, of the Arab world. He argues that western scholars have treated the world of the near east as an exotic mystery, and that they have invented it, describing it as having illogical concepts, devoid of scientific understanding and modern progress. But despite his accurate description of the bias held by the west, and even though he does not outline "what the true Orient" is, Said implies that the Arabia where I am headed in 1992 has been maligned *even though it too can boast an understanding of the empirical reality we all know will gain us control over the natural world.* Henry Kissinger's description of the west's greater devotion to a reality external to the observer may well be accurate, but we do not have to assume that this is a badge of progress, and therefore attempt to defend the "Orient" as having made the same leap to modernity. Said seems to be making this tacit assumption, that modernity is certainly to be found in the philosophy of the middle-eastern mind, and that of course it must take the shape of the western reality. In other words, even those who would defend non-western cultures from being maligned also assume that the Platonic version of an external reality is the only progressive model for a scientist to hold.

What is modern about our picture of a reality that is external to the observer? It is an old idea, after all, one rooted in our belief in the superiority of the European human, near the top of the arbitrarily real Great Chain of Being, the model that has been developing for centuries. In Riyadh airport, this external reality is manifested as an infection from the west; pictures of reality have a real, unavoidable influence. The world of Arabia does understand this external immovable reality, then, but it is seen as an invasion. It cannot cope with the invasion; the pictures are hunted down and exterminated.

But even though the external reality of the west is recognized, is the world of Arabia a reality that is "internal to the observer"? And does this mean that reality is formed as an interchange between the traveller and the landscape? Is this a dialectical world I am entering? My western mind, my scientific training is strained here; my empirical reality finds no foothold. In Riyadh airport, at the end of our stay, my eyes rest on the recently unveiled woman's nipples and the brief shape of her pubic mound against the fabric of her dress—that is my reality. This is what the naked truth really is, the empirical reality that I use to objectify my world. Is this culture of Arabia trying to tell me something about the meaning of bondage? Women completely draped in black, a reality hidden from our eyes, is really "interior." The covering preserves the privacy of human sexual urges, I am told; women are not in bondage here. Yet my eyes rest on nipples and curves, holding the woman objectified in the empirical bondage of the west. It is all bondage.

310

The reality of the west, a reality external to the observer that owes nothing to its interaction with that observer, is the reality that must be invoked when I watch the television in my hotel room in Johannesburg in November 1997. Winnie Madikizela-Mandela, the president's former wife, is on trial at the Truth and Reconciliation Commission, an extra-judicial body presided over by Archbishop Desmond Tutu.[16] There is a truth that is sought, and the implication is that it is the "real" reality, one that does not depend on the point of view of the observer, or the perpetrator.

The establishment of a "commission" for truth says enough. Chairman Tutu and the leadership of the country believe in the reality they are uncovering. Winnie doesn't; she is an observer with a different point of view:

[W]hen you see the TRC [Truth and Reconciliation Commission], when you see Desmond Tutu hugging Pik Botha when he walks into the TRC and actually applauds and thanks the perpetrators of the worst brutality and atrocities any country has ever known.

When you see them smiling and you see a Winnie Mandela walking into the TRC . . . "Oh! she is connected to eight murders, Oh! in fact she is going to be questioned about 18 violations. . . ."

I was not even given the courtesy of a phone call to ask me if I would be prepared to answer any questions the TRC might have had. The idea was not to establish any truth because there is no truth to be established there in all those lies that are told there.[17]

"I think she could have done it. It's in her nature—a proud woman, is it?" My friend Hemant, an official in the education ministry of Mandela's government, is leaning back in a chair in his living room. "I brought her food when she was in prison all those years ago. She wanted some kind of special granola that only came from the United States. I said, 'My God, what do you think we're running here—a five-star hotel? This is a prisoners' relief organization.' She always liked luxury, she was haughty, she could take the law into her own hands if she thought she was right." But there are so many opinions. Every day of the Truth Commission hearings, women from Soweto come to protest her treatment. "So what if Stompie [Seipei][18] was killed? So what if he was so young? It was a war then. Winnie should be treated like a hero, not a criminal."

The truth is relative. You can see that in the differing opinions about what is happening in the Truth Commission hearings. So where is this desire for the "absolute truth" coming from? And why does making a public confession wipe out a crime in this country? I think it is imported along with the belief in the European hierarchy. Absolute reality must exist out there somewhere, and when we uncover it the universe gains a new luminance, a sanctity that wipes out wrong. But a relative truth, I seem to be hearing in South Africa, cannot lead to a purification. No, we need absolutes, I am hearing here.

311

The problem lies in the belief in ultimate knowledge, a belief imported from the west. The great divider that apparently separates modern scientific civilizations from primitive pre-scientific societies is a belief in that external reality, the ideal circle of Plato, the reality that the scientific positivists following Wittgenstein picture to themselves. This is a conviction that has characterized western science since the Renaissance, the time when the very order of the universe was changed with new scientific theories and the sun was put at the centre by Copernicus: "[W]e have acknowledged, at the very heart of the Copernican undertaking, the conviction that man can know the world order in its reality and totality. The Copernican revolution is based on the idea of an alliance between God and man, an idea characteristic of the Neoplatonism of the Renaissance."[19] But it is a fictitious reality, one that invents itself and then proceeds to maintain its existence by feeding on itself.

The Relativity of Positive Science

What positive science knows is . . . not the immediate truth, but something that is an object for its investigation by virtue of being presupposed. Not only does its analysis proceed from a predetermined content, but its knowing is itself predetermined in that it takes for granted its own relationship to its object.

Consequently, positive science can only result in knowledge that is relative both with regard to its form and content. What its cognition addresses is not true reality. . . . [A]ll debate in the positive sciences . . . rests on nothing more than common assumptions that can just as easily be superseded by the adoption of a different set of terms establishing a new paradigm of science. . . . [T]here is nothing problematic in the knowing of positive science so long as its relative status is acknowledged.[20]

In South Africa, five years after my journey to Saudi Arabia, I am learning about bondage again. I see that apartheid has the power to self-define and to invent its own environment. Like all ideas, it is forming in relationship to its intellectual environment, its landscape. It is so strong that it has its own Truth Commission that will entrench its particular truth and its justifications, leading to amnesty and purification for all those who speak of the "reality" that occurred during its reign. Maybe Winnie Madikizela-Mandela is right. I wonder why Pik Botha, the former president of the ideology of apartheid, is likely to be embraced by Archbishop Tutu if he testifies before the Truth Commission?

It is so easy for me, as a western scientist, to expect that the Truth Commission can unveil the reality of the apartheid period, the true facts. But they are being related by the perpetrators, or by the victims whose reality was also defined by the powerful idea that was and is apartheid; the facts revealed at the hearings are re-establishing the hierarchy of apartheid. This is even more apparent when we consider that the commission is granting amnesty to those who bring the abhorrent methods of that racist era to the public; amnesty is, after all, a reward of sorts.

There are alternatives to staying within the paradigm of a racist ideology. "I am an Africanist," Professor Tshimpaka Yanga tells me. He is not happy with my repeated appeals for a discussion of racism in South Africa. We are in his office in the University of Witwatersrand. "I am interested in the civilization of Africa," he says. "I have no time for the discussion of discrimination and race. It is a discussion for those who choose to accept the control of colonialists." Reject the argument against racism completely? I am dumbfounded, but in his narrowed view there is a new sense of what it takes to reject a paradigm. Apartheid is a bondage system that exists both in and out of power, and Yanga knows this. It is 1997, and I still haven't learned anything. I come now with my badge of anti-racism and I am still rejected. But they are not working for us, for me, as Jean-Paul Sartre said in his preface to Frantz Fanon's *Wretched of the Earth*. Those who are fighting colonialism in Africa are not trying to speak to me; they couldn't care less:

> Europeans, you must open this book and enter into it. After a few steps in the darkness you will see strangers gathered around a fire: . . . They will see you, perhaps, but they will go on talking among themselves, without even lowering their voices. This indifference strikes home.[21]

312

Why is the empirical reality of the west the root of bondage?

The "pictures" of our reality, our models for the natural world that we use in our empirical, our experimental science, illustrate an ideal reality, the Platonic perfection that lies beyond our murky cave. The sheer belief in such an ideal, as a fixed reality, one that lies outside the observer, becomes the τέλος, the end point, our ultimate goal. We aspire to it. The image of an end point becomes the purpose that reaches back from the future to act as a template for all activity and models of the world. This is the basis for the image of a ladder of achievement. Such a ladder has an intrinsic image of one thing being superior to the next, and thus subservience is born of this idea. Bondage is a natural child of such a teleological model of the world. The west has been enamoured of the climb to perfection for centuries. This model has led to all the colonial conquests, and we have exported our image of bondage into every land we touch.

313

The sun is blazing overhead. White robes move silently across the immaculate stone walkway, their course unhurried. There are other images of superiority, and they are all not strictly European.

Khallid, the young man designated as our personal guide and helper while we are in Riyadh, is walking with me in the compound that is the territory of foreign visitors and high-level Saudis, a subdivision of embassies and offices for senior bureaucrats and royalty. We are surrounded by security, immune to the life of the city around. Our palace has nineteen rooms. Only a few are filled. The rocks in the gardens and the stone pathways are swept daily by Philippine servants. The palace is for foreigners; it sits in the centre of the compound. And our palace has many meeting rooms—the night before, I was waved through the gates when they saw my white face, sub-machine guns lifted away only then. "What is happening here?" Our driver, Muham-mad, smiling, tells me.

"You ask Muhammad, who knows—he keeps his ears open. I will tell you." We're left with the impression that there's a plan to assassi-nate a political leader in another country. His smile widened as we drove into the palace grounds, while white-robed men moved past us to the main meeting hall. I know I will see into that hall later from the windows that line the corridor outside my bedroom, but something this sensitive is going on so close to me?

"You're kidding. Why do they let us in, then, if it's so important?"

"They don't care about what you think. You are a foreigner." Muhammad asks us if he will be needed later.

"Yes, we'll go out for dinner. Can you take us somewhere authentic?"

But Jürgen and Joe, a museum colleague who has joined us from California, are tired of authentic. "Let's just rest for a while."

"Yeah, okay." I was nervous and would have preferred to leave immediately. A few minutes later, I did look into the meeting of would-be assassins from the corridor outside my room. Several of the men glanced up and gestured in my direction. I went into my room and hoped for no repercussions. And today I am walking with Khallid. "Why are all the cleaning staff Filipinos? Why is every nation segre-gated into specific jobs here?"

"Yes?" Khallid is not helpful. He does nothing I can detect is work, and he guides us from one aborted meeting to another.

The hierarchy here is not one I am accustomed to. Europeans and North Americans are used for their scientific skill. Canadians are usually wanted for telecommunications work. Jürgen and I are unusual; we are here for museum work. We are treated with great solicitude, almost like pet animals. Khallid takes us to his home one night. He and his young wife have white fluffy kittens. "Look, she is so soft, yes?" His wife stays in the narrow kitchen of their apartment. She brings us fruit drinks and leaves the room immediately. I never see her face. Now walking in the compound, we come to an old man. Khallid and the man stop, almost touching bellies, wrapped in their flowing white robes.

"Khallid, you are growing fat." The old man is poking Khallid in the belly.

"Yes?" Khallid introduces me to his friend. His name ends with al-Sidari. Walking on, a few minutes later, I ask Khallid if I had heard right. The man has traced his family name back to the favourite wife of 'Abd al-'Aziz, the founding monarch of modern-day Saudi Arabia. "Yes, he is the king's uncle." Now I understand that Khallid has no work to do because he is part of the upper echelon of this hierarchy.

Not all hierarchies match. But if they don't, how can only one be approaching the ultimate true reality? Is it possible that hierarchies could be turned upside down? For example, could the lower elements in a ladder of achievement become the highest levels of success in Saudi Arabia?

314

The scholarship of the Islamic mapmakers of the twelfth century reflected the long history of academic work in the Islamic world. For centuries, Muslims had been connected to sources of knowledge, translating classical Greek texts and gaining knowledge from trade routes into the far east and Africa. Their maps covered the same territory as the medieval Christian Mappae Mundi, such as the Hereford Mappa Mundi, but there were no monsters or other elaborations drawn onto the Islamic maps—they were far more exacting and scientifically accurate.

The important point here is that the map derives from a different set of hierarchical premises. Al-Idrisi was an Islamic scholar who worked in North Africa and Southern Europe. The centre of his world was certainly the Islamic world that covered the Mediterranean and near eastern regions. If we assume that up and down in a map is arbitrary, we can then see that a mapmaker might make the centre of his world the "top" of a map. Today, we have become so used to Europe lying at the top of a map of the world that we think of North as a convention born of necessity rather than politics. In al-Idrisi's map, Africa and the near

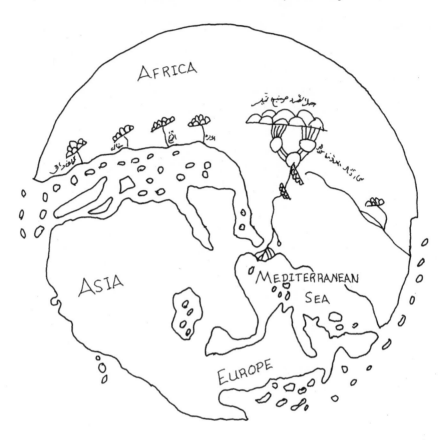

Author's version of the map of the world drawn by the twelfth-century Islamic map-maker, al-Idrisi.[22] This is a map that reveals a different frame of reference from that of the European—Africa is at the top and Europe is at the bottom. This map is a recreation of the 1456 reproduction of original. At the top, slightly to the right, its name written in Arabic, is the source of the Nile, the Mountains of the Moon. At the lower right is Europe, just under the Mediterranean. The body of water that cuts the left-hand side of the land masses in two separates Africa (to the top) from Asia (below). (Africa spreads out across the whole top of the map. This was the shape given to that continent following the information first put together by Ptolemy in his map from the year 150. Islamic scholars had knowledge of Ptolemy's work for centuries before it became available to Europeans.)

The al-Idrisi map becomes clearer to us if it is turned upside down to approximate our modern north-south projections.

east are on top, and Europe is on the bottom. This orientation is significant, I believe, with regard to the hierarchy that guided Islamic scholars. The Islamic world was the top of their world and all other
regions were there to be conquered.

When I walked with Khallid in Riyadh, I was seen as a foreign servant, and the Saudis saw themselves as the superior beings. For them,
the map can be drawn with the Islamic world on top. Al-Idrisi's map
would still hold.

315

Yanga is shifting uneasily in his chair. The door opens, admitting his
colleague from next door who has just arrived. "I invited Dr. Nyesi to
join us." Fine, I think, anything to break the ice, but Dr. Nyesi, a lin-
guistics professor at the University of Witwatersrand, says nothing,
and looks placidly happy at my sweating forehead. He says nothing
during the entire hour I am there interviewing Professor Yanga. My
friend Monty sits quietly beside me during most of the interview; I
know that he senses the tension I am feeling.

When I was in Khallid's company in Saudi Arabia, I found in him
an accomplice who was adept as I was at accepting hierarchies, whatever their form. But with Professor Yanga, I am introduced to another
perspective entirely. He is breaking down the paradigm of hierarchy
that I understand. The superiority of Africans with respect to the rest
of the world might be implied by his dismissive haughtiness, but it is
not an issue. He will talk with me about Africa, but on the whole I sense
that he considers my opinions irrelevant. "What do you know of
African philosophy, in any case?" He is brooding.

Aware of my unease, Monty replies, "Yes, well, our project, the new
science museum, would include discussions with people such as yourself, to guide the process." But who would be the audience, and how
can we begin to think that Africans would care to converse with Europeans? I am trying to communicate, but what is the point—I will get
nowhere here.

But I persevere: "I can imagine that you need a place where issues can be discussed with members of the public, a meeting place for scholars and ordinary people, all African, to discuss the emerging new synthesis that is Africa. We know it takes resources, money, and ideas to bring about such a place," I say to Yanga. Yes, but why me? Why should a white man of European descent be the one to bring this about? Is my logic just another form of the west's seduction? Am I luring in the prospective victim, trying subtly to make him subservient to my way of seeing things?

In Toronto, long before the South Africa trip, I had heard this before. "Let us do it ourselves. You and your institution have no credibility. You are not black. You cannot exhibit the issue of slavery and black suffering in your museum." But for years, meeting after meeting, I convinced them our exhibition work linking racism and science was valid. Recently, though, my confidence began to unravel. Just after I announced that I was going to South Africa, my colleague Emma wouldn't speak to me for the entire week before I left.

"Three white guys are going where? To talk about science museums in the centre of Johannesburg? And why can't I go? At least I'm the right colour. They won't even look at you. They'll talk about you behind your back—you're not the goods. You think you created this work all by yourself, a white guy? You know, the more I talk about this, the madder I'm getting. You are all without integrity. This place is making me ill. Let me out of here." Now I'm arguing with Yanga and I wish Emma had come with us.

After an hour of sparring, he concludes with "Yes, well, let's please keep in touch, shall we? I am sure your enterprise will be most rewarding." Yanga is being sincere. I have won him over. It's more than I thought possible. But in the parking lot with Monty afterwards, I'm disturbed.

"You know, Monty, we can't deliver what Yanga wants. We would have to have a board of directors that didn't care what kind of science and technology was on display. Yanga's Africanist themes are not accepted by the mainstream of western scientists. I can't see your major South African corporations being so lenient in their educational donations.

And if we follow Yanga's logic, we could be creating a museum that consciously excludes the topic of racism. Can we live with that? And how many blacks are such pure Africanists that they can choose to forget the history of apartheid?"

Monty is smiling. "When you've been around here long enough, you'll see that we're ready to open the door to almost any discussion. Yanga isn't typical, he's from the Congo. His experience is much different. The South African black, or white for that matter, is not going to forget apartheid—it's part of us." But Monty's reasoned words are not comforting. I am afraid that I am negotiating in bad faith. I liked Yanga's initial idea that all discussions of apartheid are suspect, his subtle suggestion that the Truth Commission is a part of the white supremacist's plot to keep the idea of apartheid alive. My soft words that won Yanga over were my attempt to get close to the discussion around the fire that Sartre talked about in his preface to Fanon's book, the circle of thinkers who would reforge Africa. But was I undermining Yanga's ideals just by being there, and just by being white?

Monty's car is stifling. He hasn't fixed the window, so it is firmly closed. "Monty, can we at least open the roof hatch? I'm dying in here." No Africans, white or black, feel the heat like me—they like hot stuffy cars.

316

What can I learn by being subservient in the society of white-robed Arabs? If the hierarchy is upside down, and the "Orientals" are on top, can I feel what it's like to be lower down on the ladder? Not easily. I am treated with such care, like one of Khallid's fluffy white kittens. I fear no beatings; I'm just put in my place. "Please, it is necessary for us to pray now. You will wait in the adjoining room." We are not a part of ebb and flow of life here; we are put places.

Our calendars do not matter. "We have to stay an extra day or two? The prince needs to see us, but he is busy. I don't believe this. What kind of a place is this?" Jürgen is pacing outside the office of Khallid's older brother Zahir. The calendar by which the world does business does not matter here. Later that night I am wakened by sounds from the mosque I can see from my window calling people to prayer; but it is in the middle of the night, and the announcements go on all night. In the morning, the French-style café where we eat breakfast is closed, the local store is closed, and there is no food anywhere. Ramadan, the month of fasting during daylight hours, has started a day earlier than expected. Sky watchers in the desert announced the night before that they had (unexpectedly) seen the crescent moon, and the calendar, without regard for the rest of the world, was changed in Saudi Arabia. Zahir is apologetic but unmoving. Now we will stay even longer. The prince can only see us after dark, if he is available. Joe is going anyway, he announces, but his ticket back to San Francisco is no longer valid. All routes out depend on the needs of our hosts, our superiors. We stay in the palace and wait.

317

Frantz Fanon warned of the African intellectuals who would fall prey to the seduction of the west, intellectuals who would accept the trappings and the spoils of the European colonialists. They are the ones who seek to prosper in any new situation, to act the part of the revolutionary but to be deprived of nothing, not even the praise of western institutions. Fanon claims that the people rise up quickly against this new-styled oppressor, and violence ensues.

It is difficult to assess the actions of an intellectual, a person who lives in the world of ideas, so how can the average uneducated person rise up against them? When the uprising is a part of an organized political movement, things are different. As Sasha told me in the cargo plane coming back from Siberia, Stalin sent the intellectuals to Siberia. Stalin accepted the challenge of the effete intellectual and meted out violence. The effect was not always death and oblivion, however. In Leningrad, when we first visited there in the summer of 1990, we met with the director of the Arctic and Antarctic Institute, Rudolph Itz. He had been studying northern Siberian peoples for decades. He had a huge face that blended into his neck and body. A deep gravelly voice spoke to us in English. "Every anthropologist who is my age today in Soviet Union studied at our 'northern university.'" He chuckled to himself. "We have nothing to do there, you see. We study what we find. I am ten years in Gulag camp. I study people of north."

"You mean," I asked with care—it was after my cargo flight conversation about communism with Sasha, and he was in the room with us— "you mean that the Gulag experience was good for you? You learned something because of it?"

"It was best thing for me. I am too comfortable sitting on ass in Moscow before I go to Gulag." He laughed so hard he choked up phlegm. I looked over at Sasha. He was laughing. We all laughed.

In South Africa, I don't know which intellectuals Fanon would sanction. All the black professors at the universities are comfortable, They are not being re-educated in the countryside, not leaving their western accreditation behind. Business cards read "B.A. Oxford," or "Ph.D. (California)," and prize posts in the University of Witwatersrand, formerly held by white professors, are now filled by black academics. The hierarchy is still well in place, despite some theoretical forays by scholars like Yanga.

318

Zahir is explaining, "Women are separate but equal in our society." His office building is all men, and there is an adjacent one staffed by women, he tells us.

"But women can't even drive in your country." I am bored, so I am willing to risk insulting our keepers here. Jürgen and Joe and I are waiting in Zahir's office for a message from the prince.

"Women have different roles. They are protected from men, and men's lustful actions. Driving exposes them to danger. Anyway, let's talk of lunch, shall we? I know a good place, Lebanese." Lebanese food is the best authentic middle eastern food we can get here, apparently. The night before, our driver, Muhammad, had offered to take us to a

Yemeni place where he and his friends eat. But he stinks—he never changes his clothes, and we can't breathe in the car.

"I'm not going anywhere this guy thinks is okay." Joe is worried about his health. He works out all the time; his body fat is so low that you can count his muscle fibres, and greasy Yemeni food is out.

On the way to lunch with Zahir, we walk through a soukh, a marketplace; this one sells only computer software. Foreign women cover their hair, but we can see their faces; there are a few of them shopping here. A Saudi woman is crouched on the ground, covered completely in black. Her head lifts up to us as we pass—her hands, still in her robes, are reaching out to us. I know she is begging for money. Zahir rushes past, Khallid, Jürgen, Joe, and me behind. As the others go ahead, I stop to give her money. A little hand comes out to grab the bill and disappears again. I look around for problems. "You can get yourself in trouble with the religious police for having anything to do with a woman here. She will probably be beaten for hanging around in the soukh begging," Lawrence tells me the next day. "I would be a little cautious about such things in the future." Lawrence is afraid of the prince's men, stiff around them. He is older by twenty years, but he obeys his superiors. "They haven't hired us; they've bought us." But he is not a fearful man. He is a herpetologist, who picks up snakes with his bare hands. One night we go to his house for dinner. He has two "baby" sand vipers as pets. I think of Khallid's kittens.

"Deadly poisonous snakes aren't very cuddly, are they?"

"Well, actually, they like to snuggle up around warm things. That's why I put these lamps in their bowls. Last night one of them got loose. I couldn't find it till this morning. They're just as likely to curl up with you when you sleep. Sure, they like to get close." Jürgen is squirming. The next day we go out with Lawrence to the ruined old city, Dir 'iyya, in the centre of modern Riyadh. "The place is infested with snakes, cobras, and even the burrowing asp. I think that might have been what killed Cleopatra."

"But Khallid says there aren't any snakes in Riyadh."

"Khallid doesn't know anything—typical Saudi, no education, too much lazing around in cafés. The average Saudi doesn't know anything about the fauna and flora of his country." We have just spent hours crawling over rocks and ducking into tunnels.

"Well, surely we won't see any snakes in March?"

"Oh yeah, it was a year ago almost to the day when someone was killed by an asp, right around here. They have fangs that can move completely independently. They're little snakes, only about six inches long or so. There's no antidote for the poison, but mostly they hide when they hear you coming."

"What? Where?" Jürgen moves up behind us, baby-stepping between our feet as Lawrence and I walk. Lawrence goes on about other nasty things we probably should have been warned about before we crawled around these rocks. Scorpions and solfugids, a cross between a scorpion and a spider is the way he put it—not venomous but very aggressive. They run out and tear chunks out of unwary passersby.

"You get to be a bit of a fatalist here. If it's your time—well, then. Anyway, I've seen so many snakes it doesn't bother me any more." Lawrence is oblivious to Jürgen's mounting panic. I am happy to be distracted. Poisonous snakes, and even scorpions, are more inviting than human servitude.

319

The chicken is slathered in piri piri sauce, dripping and wet, oily and reddish, little hot peppers smothering the skin. Makgoba sinks the long dark fingers of his right hand into the oozing chicken meat, while his left hand holds the flesh in place. Dripping, it comes to his mouth and he leans forward to suck his fingers. His chin is greased when he emerges; his tongue licks the remaining oil from his chin. He tears more white flesh open, scooping the thick sauce with his fingertips. The sauce gushes over the exposed breast meat as he pries it open with two hands. I am glad Jim and Jürgen are not here. They are in Pretoria for the day. Their questions would have spoiled this moment of pure lustful pleasure. Monty and I look on. I am not eating the fish I have ordered. We have given up talking for now. No answers are coming to our questions.

320

Zahir is primly wiping his mouth; we have eaten a sumptuous lunch, in a beautiful room—white tablecloths, sunlight coming in from immaculate windows. "It's debatable whether laws produce good behaviour, but what can we do? That is our way."

"Have you heard about the laws they have in Singapore? Gum chewing is outlawed. What next?" Joe and Jürgen and I are laughing.

Zahir smiles. "Yes, but have you ever been there, I mean recently? You cannot walk down the street without sticking to the sidewalk. There should be laws there. The people are not able to control themselves."

321

It is a Tuesday in November 1997. Our lunch with William Makgoba, who is a professor of molecular immunology at Witwatersrand University, and a leading intellectual in South Africa, was hurriedly set. "We're lucky he'll see us." Monty is squeezing the BMW through the partially opened gates of the university. "Hello. Listen here, you always let me through to the inner section. We have an important appointment. Yes, thank you." We continue, not stopping for protests from the guards at the gate. "This may prove to be a vital meeting. Makgoba is very important." We hope that we can get critical interest in our museum project. We'll be featuring issues on race discrimination and we need black support. We park and run into the doorway of a nondescript-looking building. "I've been here once, I think," Monty tells me. "I just can't remember." The medical research laboratories are in several connected buildings. "It's here—over this little bridge." And we're at Makgoba's door, a little office filled with journals and papers.

Makgoba's handshake is languid; no pressure greets mine. His eyes wander to Monty. "Yes?"

Makgoba has a degree from Oxford but has been under attack from colleagues regarding the validity of his credentials. He has responded by charging that the university is filled with racist academics who haven't learned anything from the fall of apartheid. His fight is well known to everyone. The Friday before our meeting, he wrote a newspaper article challenging white academics to come forward to confess their conspiracy during apartheid to the Truth and Reconciliation Commission.

> The Committee of University Principals, the Committee of Technikon Principals and several leading universities in our country should prepare their submissions to the TRC. This sector owes the nation full disclosure of how its shortsighted activities and curriculum contributed directly or indirectly to gross human rights violations against the oppressed. . . . Many talented and gifted members of the oppressed suffered, were denied opportunities and could not develop their full potential as a result of this discriminatory curriculum. Our academics and intellectuals provided the theoretical basis and support for discrimination and apartheid.[23]

He sums up what I have been learning in my visits to South Africa, Saudi Arabia, and Siberia. He sums up what I believe has happened during the history of western science: our European society has supported and attempted to justify prejudice and discrimination.

Yes, he endorses our museum project. "It is interesting. Where did you say you were from?" But he isn't surprised by our lack of black support. "Don't think that a black businessman is going to be interested. What makes you think that they want anything different from the whites? They want to be rich."

"What about your call to bring the academics up before the Truth Commission?" I am trying to change the subject. His allusions to my naïveté are embarrassing me. But Makgoba is eating again, his hands dipping into the soft oily chicken like a lover's. He needs more water, so he signals the black waiter. Our glasses are filled from the jug at the side table. "No, no, I had Perrier, not this stuff." He continues to eat. I repeat my question.

322

Makgoba fought for his western credentials. The ladder of success is important to him. The European Great Chain of Being is a part of his life. And he wants to use the Truth and Reconciliation Commission to humble his oppressors. But I see the commission as an extension of the old apartheid rule. Condemning the actions of the oppressors, and allowing them to describe their actions as a requirement for amnesty, gives the atrocities new life. It reminds me of a murderer or rapist, facing inevitable conviction for heinous crimes, deciding to undergo an ordeal on the witness stand. Such a person delights in hearing it all again, in exposing his lustful cruelty to the victims and their families. "But we are looking for peace, we are forgiving the past once we understand it, we are looking for remorse" go the heavy arguments from my white friends in South Africa.

And the Truth and Reconciliation Commission goes on and on with graphic descriptions of beatings, torture, and murder.

Yanga dismisses my conversation on anti-racist science exhibits for the public. Makgoba uses for his own needs the ever-present colonial system of the South African government and condemns us all with his indifference.

Fanon said of the African intellectuals who keep the trappings and the power of the European colonialists alive: "Spoilt children of yesterday's colonialism and of today's national government's, they organize the loot of whatever national resources exist. . . . [T]he success of their depredations is swift to call forth the violence and anger of the people."[24] I am unable to judge. Who are the "spoilt children of yesterday's colonialism"? All I know is that I am not a participant in the discussion.

323

"Splat!"

"Yes, yes, that's all that's to be done with them." Giggling, the chief steward is agreeing with the pilot.

"Just line them up against a wall, and splat." The pilot on the South African Airways 747 is explaining to me his view of the problem in South Africa. "All this talk of forgiveness and living together in harmony is just not realistic. The blacks want everything and they have nothing to give in exchange. Crime is the problem and there's only one way to deal with that."

"Look here—" The co-pilot is indicating the instruments we have been watching for the past half hour. The numbers are approaching zero. "We're crossing the equator. Welcome to the Southern Hemisphere!"

A week later, I am in a rich suburb of Johannesburg. I've been here an hour talking with Brian, the head of a local design firm, about his life in this country. Jürgen and Jim have just arrived. "Whoa, look here, a gun? Or, what is this?" Jürgen is reaching for the black plastic Glock lying on Brian's desk. I am too wrapped up in my thoughts until almost too late.

"Hey, don't touch that! It's a loaded pistol and there's a bullet ready in the chamber!"

"You're kidding." Jürgen is still about to pick it up.

"No, I'm not kidding." I am rattled. Jürgen doesn't get it. I have to sound almost angry to stop him.

"Well, what kind of a thing is that to do then, leaving a loaded gun around?" Glowering, he turns to sit down and we wait for Brian to return.

"Just ask him yourself. I don't know what exactly he needs it for."

Before Jürgen and Jim arrived, Brian had asked me if I carry a gun. "No? Look here," and he pulled the Glock out from his waistband at the small of his back. He cocked the gun, putting a bullet into the chamber, readied it for firing, and handed it to me.

"You just loaded this?"

"Of course."

"Do you use it?"

"I used it last week to scare off hijackers on the highway, at night it gives off a really beautiful blue flame." He shows me the kind of bullets he uses in the gun—they are 39 calibre, hollow-tipped. The Glock feels great. I pick it up and aim at the wall surrounding his garden.

324

"Tonight we go out to a café. You'll like it, I think." Khallid is guiding us into a dark alley; palm trees are silhouettes against the blue sky. We look into a collection of tents. Men in white robes are lying on their sides, leaning against cushions, some sucking on hookahs, some eating ordered-in pizza, small male servants clustering around them like wives. The ruling class is what I seem to have been trained into during my life in a western country, so I find I am inevitably liking the café already. At the door a little man greets us. His movements are like those of someone performing a magic trick. "You want coffee?" Khallid tells us we will be served here at the door while they prepare a tent for us. The little man is smiling at me. In his left hand he holds a coffee pot, his right hand gestures openly toward me, and a small cup appears from his sleeve. He looks me in the eye as he pours amber coffee. I accept the cup and then he presses sweet dates into the palm of my right hand. Jürgen is laughing at my stupefied expression.

"But I really like this," I protest.

We sit back into our cushions. We are watching forbidden Israeli television stations picked up by satellite. "But that place is illegal," the prince will smile and scold us gently two days later. Hookahs are brought out for us to smoke, and sweet fruit and juices to drink. The servants wait for our call at the edges of our view.

"This really is the life, isn't it?"

325

The café in Riyadh was a picture of the fruits of heaven that await us, the perfect reality that is the end point of our existence. We aspire to it, and because we picture its ideal reality, we see our lives as a climb toward this perfection. And this creates in us the image of inferior and superior beings. But we can't condemn this belief system as utterly inappropriate; it is pleasurable—the amber coffee and the dates were warm and sweet and, as I rested against the cushions in our tent, I felt wanted and important.

I think back to Sasha's conversation in the cargo plane coming back from Siberia—no pleasure there—when his condemnation of communism left me with so many questions. Is destruction necessary to end a regime, to rid society of the control of a dominant group? More important, must the breakdown of a hierarchical society lead to a purging of its leaders, of its intellectuals? After all, how can we be asked to give up such power voluntarily, we who enjoy such pleasure, lying on our cushions and dreaming of heaven?

326

Brian's country house is on his private game farm. Everything is white marble. The sun is so bright against the floors and walls on the upper deck that I cannot see. I crash into the perfectly clean glass sliding doors on my way back from getting another beer. "Yeow!"

Jürgen and Jim are lounging back enjoying the sun. "Hey haven't you had enough to drink, walking into walls?"

"Jeez," I'm laughing, "I'm blind—everything is so damn white here." We're feeling good today. Brian invited us to his farm last week when we visited him in his office.

"Let's go and try the gun, shall we?" Brian is up on his feet, bouncing a little. We step off the patio. The house is ringed with brush and termite mounds. "We'd find cobras in any of those termite nests. Just knock them over and they'd come out. I saw a really big one last month." Brian wants to turn the whole farm into a natural habitat, and snakes are no problem. "Just be careful walking through the brush—you really should have high boots on. See that zebra running there—he's limping. I think a snake bit him a while back. Here, let's try the gun out. Want to shoot first?"

The struggle to be European in the wide world of discovered lands is not so easy. I feel the power of the gun in my hands, liking the western hardness of it, the simple politics of it, the politics I heard in the cockpit of the 747 as I crossed into the Southern Hemisphere on my way to

South Africa. How can I reconcile this with my desire to expose the misguided belief we have in the superiority of one group over another? It is not so difficult to understand, given the setting. As guests on Brian's private game farm, Jürgen and Jim and I were treated like special people. Brian and his companion, Ingrid, had prepared the lunch, and they had waited on us at the table like servants—and this despite the fact that Brian made more money a year than all of us combined, and despite the fact that Ingrid could not use one of her hands very well because of a spider bite she had received in their bedroom the night before. Makgoba had ignored my questions and had made me wait. Watching him eat his chicken, I felt like a voyeur. Sartre said it is not for me that the Africans are speaking, but at Brian's game farm, it *is* for me that Africa is speaking, even if it is a white Africa.

Twice I knock the little plastic film canister off the old metal frame. "There's no hole in it, so you didn't really hit it. You must have hit the frame it's sitting on." Jim is examining my latest efforts.

"It's only two inches high; what did you expect? Anyway, it fell, so I came close." I can't understand Jim's fussiness. "Here, you try it." I hand him the gun. Jim looks professional holding the Glock. He's had military experience, but he hits nothing—the canister doesn't budge. I try again, moving constantly, swinging my arm toward the target like a dancer.

"No, no we're too far away, let's try it at hijacker distance." Brian stops me, and now he's pacing out the proper distance, walking toward us from the target.

"Hijacker distance?" Am I hearing this right?

"Yeah, there's a proper distance before you should start shooting, or you'll never hit anything. You wait until the hijackers are within range. It takes guts." Brian counts out fifteen large paces as he walks toward us from the target area. Jim doesn't like the sound of this. He tries again and hits nothing again. He looks grim.

I swing the gun up, once more in my dance. The film canister is not really holding my attention—I am entranced by the feeling of holding the gun. I imagine I am shooting at assailants. I feel light and relaxed. The shots rocket through my skull, the sound is so loud. Three explosions, and the canister flies off the frame. Hijacker distance—I plug it dead-on. Jim brings it back from the target. The hollow-tipped bullet has ripped the top of the tiny film canister wide open. "I have to tell you. I really don't like this kind of thing," Jim mutters to me, as he hands me the canister.

327

I am confused. What am I finding here? On the one hand, I see the need to destroy the paradigm of superiority. On the other, I enjoy the power I wield and I fear changes in the hierarchy of our society, because any change could mean violence. Am I arguing that all points of view should be re-examined, be given their due, because I could propose that all are relative and therefore equally valid, depending on their context? I enjoy shooting the pistol at Brian's farm, I recognize my enjoyment when I am cared for by loving servants in Saudi Arabia, and I recognize my discomfort when ignored by Makgoba. Could I end up justifying the apartheid regime if I continue in this way? I think back to John's caution when we argued about the relativity of the planetary models. He claimed that if I choose to make all knowledge relative, dependent on the local conditions and the relationship of the thinker to the intellectual landscape, then all moral judgments are also necessarily relative. John had argued that such a moral danger lay waiting hidden in my contention that earth-centred models satisfy our observations just as well as sun-centred planetary models. He felt that such a relativist attitude could allow for the acceptance of the arguments of people such as Holocaust deniers. I had argued back that although scientific models of reality are just ways in which we configure our observations and that no "picture" of reality could be seen as absolute truth, the Holocaust deniers are not simply positing an alternative point of view. Rather, they are choosing to deny physical observations and thereby creating false models.

But there is more to it than that. Extreme positions such as those taken by Holocaust deniers aside, historically apartheid and the Holocaust were seen by some as being valid points of view. Scientific observations made by their champions fitted their picture of the world. It would be difficult to contest the validity of apartheid by arguing with the pilots I met in the cockpit of the 747 jet that blacks are equal to whites; all their experience and their observation of the world tell them otherwise. It does not help to say that they are seeing the world through biased eyes; we all are, and we all think we are seeing reality. We all think our particular picture of the world is reality.

Escaping from a paradigm means there will be destruction, a breaking-down of the old and a birth of the new. Why break it down if it seems to fit the picture we think of as being reality? Why break it down if we will have to endure destruction and even violence? Is that is what keeps us back—enjoyment of the spoils of domination on the one hand and fear of violence on the other? Partly, but also the conviction that we are right, that our picture of the world is closing in on the absolute truth. Yet even Ludwig Wittgenstein, who codified the scientific pursuit in terms of "pictures" that are "models of reality" tells us, at the end of his *Tractatus*, that all our philosophical progress is mere posturing:

> 6.54 My propositions serve as elucidations in the following way: anyone who understands me eventually recognizes them as nonsensical, when he has used them—as steps—to climb up beyond them. (He must, so to speak, throw away the ladder after he has climbed up it.) He must transcend these propositions, and then he will see the world aright.[25]

328

I came to the view that models in science are relative from a detailed examination of the point of view of the observer. Points of view can change the way we see the universe around us. I define reality as the configuration of "things" in our universe, their *relationships* to one another, but I see this reality as depending on the point of view of the observer. Ultimately, our reality is the discernment of things themselves, what we choose to see as important and worth breaking out of the continuum of our universe. If I look at Africa from the point of view of a white man from Canada, my view will differ from Makgoba's, even though we are observing the same phenomena.

It is important to understand that the interactive, dialectical relationship that I can have with the natural world around me is a distinct philosophical point of view. It differs from the hierarchical concepts that dictate the need for an end point that acts as a guiding map or template calling us from the future to conform to a prefigured destiny. A paradigm shift out of the hierarchical model requires our accepting that the *interactivity* with our environment will ultimately form our life's trajectory.

A rejection of the hierarchical model does not lead to an acceptance of all possible configurations of things in the universe, however. I do not have to accept the arguments of the architects of the Holocaust or of apartheid.

It is not as easy to postulate the validity of relative moral values as it is to claim equal efficacy for contrasting models of motion for the planets. The reason that moral perspectives are not as "relative" as the laws of physics or biology can be derived from an understanding of the power of the notion of absolute truth—namely, a paradigm that is based on this concept has a *configuration*, or shape, that is much different from a philosophical approach that rejects it. In a truly dialectical model of reality, as an example of an approach that counters the basic tenets of the most common western hierarchical models of reality, in this alternative observer/observed interactive model, one where the observer is an actor forming a relationship with the landscape, there can be no truth. And, although at first glance this seems to indicate that therefore any model can be tolerated, there is at least one model that cannot exist in such a system. With no absolute truth, there is no teleological drive, there is no ultimate perfect picture of a reality that lies external to the observer, there is nothing that acts as the goal toward which all things strive, through life, through evolution, through time. Therefore, *there is no Great Chain of Being, and there is no ladder of success*. And therefore, there is no concept of superiority that can hold in a purely dialectical interactive system.[26]

The Holocaust and apartheid were built on the concept of a natural hierarchy, a human reflection of the superiority and inferiority perceived by many of us to be natural and correct. In a dialectical system, such concepts of superiority and inferiority are inadmissible because they do not fit the paradigm. The personal forging of one's own world through interaction with the local landscape does not lead to the acceptance of global models of hierarchies with the absolute perfect reality lying at the end point. Therefore, there can be no acceptance of the Holocaust or apartheid as just another "point of view." Such systems are intrinsically hierarchical, based on a belief in the ultimate "perfect reality." And this perfect reality has a way of being defined by the dominant society, the Nazis in Germany, the Nationalist Government in South Africa, the European colonialists over the past five hundred years.

329

But back to Sasha's condemnation of communism—in a dialectical revolution, must we purge the intellectuals? Makgoba called for the academics to be investigated by the Truth and Reconciliation Commission, a kind of purging. But he seems to fit Fanon's definition of a spoiled, indulged intellectual dependent on the former colonialists. In a radically altered South Africa, would he himself have to answer for his collusion with the enemy? Or is his passive-aggressive style an acceptable method of guerrilla warfare? Intellectuals form the basis for our education, and they articulate our philosophical justification of dominance, just as Makgoba said in his newspaper article. They are in many ways the most powerful people in any society, so to make a societal change must they be changed, through re-education, like Rudolph Itz and his colleagues who were sent to Siberia, or through the violence of the followers of Fanon?

The intellectual foundation of our society is so firmly based on a belief in an external reality that there is an almost inevitable acceptance of its corollary, the end point, the τέλος. What good would it do to rid society of its intellectuals? The intellectual landscape is too rich and too established to notice any temporary loss. It permeates our society. As Makgoba said, why do I think that black businessmen would want to help fight racism? They are too busy pursuing their end point—wealth—just another way to climb the ladder. The teleological philosophical view of the universe is everywhere.

Some even say that morality, this arbiter of conduct, is in our genes. The American sociobiologist E. O. Wilson calls for an examination of the morality that is coded into us through evolution. The physical basis for behaviour and spiritual integrity is seen as a scientific puzzle, one that will yield to the investigator who sees reality as an absolute, something that can be figured out:

> Which world view prevails, religious transcendentalism or scientific empiricism, will make a great difference in the way humanity claims the future. . . . Ethics and religion are still too complex for present-day science to explain in depth. They are, however, far more a product of autonomous evolution than has hitherto been conceded by most theologians. . . . Science, for its part, will test relentlessly every assumption about the human condition and in time uncover the bedrock of moral and religious sentiments.[27]

The deeper danger lies not in a belief in genetic codes for behaviour, but rather in the belief in the external reality that captures all things under its wings, the living and the non-living, the animals and plants, the human race, but also the rocks, the gases of the sun and the distant galaxies. All living things, even their moral judgment, are seen by the science of the west to be reducible to basic elements that follow the laws of the universe. Again, in Wilson's words:

> The central theme of the enlightenment, enhanced across three centuries by the natural sciences, is that all phenomena tangible to the human mind can be rationally explained by cause and effect. Thus humanity can—all on its own—know; and by knowing, understand; and by understanding, choose wisely. The idea is amplified

by . . . the conviction that all tangible phenomena share a common material base and are reducible to the general laws of nature.[28]

The behaviour, and therefore the morality, of the human is seen as a reflection, as a part, of the hierarchical nature of the universe as a whole—all complex things owe their nature to the "lower" atomic levels of existence, and ultimately reflect the general laws of the simplest irreducible things. So we often hear it said that we cannot change the nature of people. It is intrinsic in us to want to outshine each other, to compete, to spontaneously generate the concept of superiority and inferiority. Therefore, why fight it, and why destroy the fabric of a culture, and why have a revolution at all?

330

There are better reasons for not killing off intellectuals. It is an absurd concept. To kill off a portion of the society is to express a belief in the genetic, inevitable nature of the morality of a human being. And yet, an understanding of morality as a fixed biological component of an individual is precisely what reductionist scientists are expounding. Morality is seen as an inherited trait. But *correlation* of biological traits to groups within the human population does not add up to cause and effect. One could go to South Africa and line up everyone who is hijacking cars in Johannesburg. Chances are we would see mainly black faces. We would then decide that the genetic or biological traits that we could perhaps find in common with many of the criminals were markers for all their behaviour. We could claim the correlation was an indication of their criminal lineage, that of course their genetic background was a causal effect. But there is nothing to support this. In another situation, in another world, there would be black owners of cars complaining about white criminals, and they could examine the genetic traits and hope to find some correlation to a criminal genetic inheritance. The same thing applies to intellectuals. To kill them off implies that the leaders of a regime believe that intellectuals are genetically programmed to be intellectuals with a certain kind of morality built in, a perverted morality that is characterized by a natural tendency to justify the oppression of the uneducated. So killing off the intellectuals reflects the same perverted morality; it is cut from the same cloth. I would postulate that it is wrong, therefore. After all, intellectuals have had advantages in life, and their view of the world can be attributed as much to those favoured circumstances as to any intellect they are gifted with genetically.

Sasha had a right to be afraid of a regime that targets individuals for what they are, for what they cannot change in themselves, their genetically unique selves. At its heart, such a political system is espousing the western motif, the belief in the natural ladder of success, the Great Chain of Being. The system he labelled as communism was not the dialectical approach outlined by Hegel, nor was it akin to the philosophical approach I am suggesting can act as a counterpart to the western hierarchy. Hegel talked of a society reaching a natural point where its fruit poisons its members and a new order is born from the destruction. Such a poetic description has inspired those who would apply his theories, but they have often done so with an eye to the ladder of success, not with a view to eliminating the concept of superiority and inferiority, not with a view to individual destinies carried out by each person paddling a metaphorical canoe up a river, forming the landscape and being formed by it. Political applications of Hegel's dialectical theory remind me of my surgical interventions in chick embryos. Cutting the tissue forces an injury reaction. We hope the surgery mimics the *natural* action of the evolution of societies through self-destruction. We hope to see a new stable order as a result of the intervention. But more often than not, the political surgeons hope for the tables to be turned and for the establishment of a new elite, a new superior class, that includes themselves.

The old paradigm re-establishes itself again and again. A new would-be superior group is always waiting in the wings to replace the one on its way out. A symptom of this self-fulfilling philosophical mechanism is our unmoving belief in a perfectly formed reality that is completely beyond the control of the observer. That external absolute truth is best seen in our science. It is western science's need to achieve a complete understanding of the natural world that is the indicator, the litmus paper, for the subtly disguised Great Chain of Being, the paradigm that has the ultimate end point, the τέλος, waiting for us to complete the divine design. When the scientists, the thinkers in a society, talk of reaching a complete understanding, that is when I am afraid. So, I think Sasha was fearing the wrong thing—to blame communism was not relevant. To blame the teleological drive for perfection, the belief in absolutes, the belief in the heritability of irreducible and unchangeable human morality and intellectual abilities, the belief in a perfect reality and the belief in our ability to picture it—that would be closer to the real issue.

331

If Sasha had said to me that he distrusted the political regime in his country simply because it was a regime, a group of powerful people who held on to their elite positions, who kept everyone in a state of subservience, then I would not question his hatred.

The interactive dialectic, the making of our own maps, requires that we act with humility. We are not going to accomplish the task of uncovering the secrets of the universe. These "secrets" belong to each of us as an individual human, and they cannot ever be universal in a society; they require an intimate knowledge that occurs at every step we take. Every action of any creature in the natural world results in changes to both the creature and its landscape, its environment. The slow additive effect of creature-to-landscape interaction will result in occasional breakdowns of the status quo in a society, as predicted by Hegel, but this is hard to artificially recreate. Dramatic surgical operations such as the execution of a class of people, the exile of political opponents, will create a change. That much is true. Physical systems that undergo the removal of a part of the whole, or the addition of a new element, will be changed irrevocably, to become entirely new systems operating under new conditions. There can be no comparison of a new system with the old. But the changes that ensue following such an intervention are not predictable. The surgeons cannot guarantee any particular outcome because there is no way of knowing the nature of the new system until the parts, the constituents of the system, have settled down into a new stable relationship with one another.

332

At last we can see the prince. It has been days of waiting, and the final notice comes with no warning. We arrive in an entourage of cars. The prince's men are at the gates of his palatial home, waving us through, but the guard in the little gatehouse carries an automatic weapon levelled at the driver as we stop for identification. There is shouting, and the men inside the compound argue that we are not to be detained. We drive into the courtyard. "Quickly, quickly"—Zahir is rushing us out of the car—"he will not want to be kept waiting." It is an honour for us to be received, we have been told. I sense a change in the demeanour of our hosts. We have been elevated to a new level, we are special tonight, we are allowed to speak to the prince.

Jürgen and Joe and I enter a large living room and sit on comfortable chairs looking at each other. Lawrence, the herpetologist, arrives just after us. He is favoured tonight as well. Khallid is not with us—too low in rank, I suspect. Zahir is looking like an appointment secretary. He is flustered. "The prince is coming. Please stand to greet him." I expect a very sober austere man. I find myself consciously putting my left hand behind my back, not wanting to risk any offence.[29]

The prince rushes in. He is exuberant and very relaxed. "Ah, my Lawrence." He grins at us, making an obvious joke about Lawrences and Arabia. He holds Lawrence by the shoulders and embraces him. Then he rushes to me. My right hand is outstretched, and he grabs my entire arm with *both* of his hands, right and left! I am dumbfounded that he is so at ease. Our conversation is so easy too—everything can be discussed. He is not held by the restrictions of his culture, as far as I can see.

Zahir says nothing. The conversation is all centred on us.

333

In South Africa, we are waited on by Brian and Ingrid on their private game farm. They are the servants here. "The stew? It's a local dish I made myself. More wine?" Jürgen is lounging back, the pet ostrich leaning over his shoulder looking at his plate. Five years earlier, in Saudi Arabia, I am looking at Jürgen in the prince's living room. He is relaxing, his arms back over the arms of the chair in the same gesture. But the prince is not a servant in his own home. A head appears at the far door, a questioning look on his face. A small man appears, moving in a quiet way toward the prince. Two words come from the prince, whose expression shifts from relaxed to stern and commanding. The little man is smiling; his smile never wavers.

I am looking at a slave. I realize that I am in a house that has represented position and wealth of one kind or another for at least three generations, if not for much longer. Household servants are a part of the privilege of the ruling class, and despite the abolition of slavery in Saudi Arabia decades before, they are more than mere servants.[30]

Moments later, the man returns. He offers the same aromatic amber coffee we enjoyed in the café two nights before, and he pours it in the same fashion as the man who greeted us at the café doors. From his right sleeve, small cups appear, as if by magic, and he pours from a pot held in his left hand. But this is an entirely new experience, far more luxurious than the sybaritic café. The prince's "slave" holds me in his eyes as he pours the coffee. His gaze never wavers. He never looks at the cup or the pot; his eyes search into mine. He is looking at me with love. He loves me, I am sure of it.

I am compelled to return his gaze of love. There is nothing in it to make me doubt—it is a complete acceptance of me. I am a guest of the prince, and I am to be loved.

334

Humility.

How can I understand what I am feeling as I am being served by a slave? I enjoy it. I am relaxed in the unconditional love that I feel from the man. My place is unquestioned in his eyes. I am lulled into a feeling of knowing my place in society, a place that is on the topmost rung of the ladder. His eyes confirm it. I see no reason to doubt where I stand in the presence of this submission, this acceptance of my position in society.[31]

This is humbling to me, because I can see how I am like anyone else capable of seeing my truth as the absolute; otherwise, why would I accept this display of obedience laid before me? And how am I different from anyone else? Would not anyone be seduced by such an affirmation? I have been brought up to believe that although we are all equal, I may merit more than others, due, simply, to who I am. I have come to believe that this is a development coming from my actions and that therefore it is deserved. But am I capable of asking how much is due to my being a member of the ruling class?

335

Plato criticizes the excesses of democracy. Avoiding the need for a ruling class that has grown up with the right education and experience, shunning a dominant elite with members who are fair and wise, will inevitably lead to the society self-destructing, he says. Tyranny will result from too much liberty.[32] But all measures of success accepted by Plato and his class are the measures defined by the elite, so what is the meaning of "straying from the good solutions"?

I have no other standards myself. I know that I accept and revel in my European heritage, and I feel deep down my superiority. And yet, how can I reconcile this with what I know is a lack of justice? I realize that my perception of the world comes from only one point of view.

My deep-seated belief in my own culture cannot stand up to scrutiny. There is no Great Chain of Being, not even in the natural sciences, that would unravel the secrets of the universe. Therefore, can there be one theory that will stand above the others? No, I know now that all knowledge is dependent on the immediate, the local circumstance.

But I am trapped in my paradigm, even though I can see the trap.

My reconciliation of this dichotomy begins with my acceptance of my imprisonment in the paradigm of the west. The only route out is the slow one of my own travel into the landscape, shaping my world as much as it shapes me, accepting the intimate private interchange and not expecting to shift the trajectory of the entire world. Discoveries that I make in my explorations will change everyone else but little. They are but paddles up a stream in my canoe, of no greater significance. This is learning humility, and it is not easy. The closer scientists in the west come to what they believe is the complete story, the truth, the more they feel the intoxication of the power of a ruling class that has defined the parameters and that has made their efforts inevitably successful in our society. But these successes are false.

Though we believe in it, even if only secretly, there is no absolute truth.

336

I drain the amber coffee. I cannot believe I have done this. I am in the prince's home and he has graciously agreed to see us, and we have been served coffee. At least I should wait politely for my host to finish his cup of coffee first before gulping mine down. Jürgen and Joe are sipping theirs. Lawrence is twitching in the corner, not even touching his cup.

Years later, I think I understand. I wanted the slave to serve me again. I wanted the prince to summon him back for my needs. And he does. Prince Sultan looks at my empty cup and smiles. He claps his hands and the little man returns. Moments later, we are all served carrot juice, large glasses of it, cool and refreshing. The slave's eyes look into mine again as he hands me the glass. I almost drop it because I can't stop gazing into his eyes in return. I sense there is a new look in them this time. I imagine that they reveal even greater respect for me because I am being honoured with food from the prince's home for a second time. I follow the slave's movements as he moves through the room and leaves us.

CHAPTER NINE

THE ENDS
OF THE
EARTH

A man travels the world over in search of what he needs and returns home to find it.

– GEORGE MOORE, *The Brook Kerith*

337

"I CANNOT SIT BACK and accept that we can talk about *any* form of special Arab science. Science is universal. Our children need the exposure to science as it is being developed and taught in European and North American schools and universities." The man is perhaps the least conservatively dressed in the group, but his head is nevertheless covered and his robes are of the whitest white. I think maybe everyone here is dressed for the film cameras that keep swivelling to catch whoever is speaking at the moment. He continues, shaking his finger in my direction. "Science hasn't progressed in Islamic countries since the fourteenth century." The very religious members of the group are not nodding in assent, but neither are they objecting.

We are participating in the brainstorming session arranged by Prince Sultan; we are to come up with a theme for the new science museum being built mainly for children in the centre of Riyadh. The prince isn't here. No one knew he wouldn't be attending—we all came in anticipation of his presence. His absence is responsible for an unexpected frankness in our discussions—we are all a little less polite than we had intended. I have just arrived from Canada, having had little sleep in the past day and a half. Joe is here from San Francisco, and there are many others from all parts of Saudi Arabia and the nearby United Arab Emirate states along the Persian Gulf.

I am bleary with fatigue, and Joe isn't helping my attempts at broadening the perspective of the group on the definitions for science. He expounds with western logic. "We know what works—we've done it for years. We know how to turn kids on to science in our museum in the States, and we know that developing similar approaches here in Saudi Arabia will open the door to the world. Your children will have better links with the rest of the world and be able to communicate with others learning the same science in the United States and Europe." There is *one* path to the understanding of reality, he is telling them—sometimes there are missteps or wrong directions, but on the whole the western approach to unravelling the secrets of the universe is working. And I am not surprised to see adherents of that logic even in the heart of Saudi Arabia. The scholars with whom we are meeting today have all been educated in European and American universities, whatever their religious beliefs. But I know Joe has made a fatal mistake in his argument—he has mentioned the need for better communication between cultures of the world. That is the mistake westerners often make—they assume that the maps of two cultures can be conjoined, can relate to each other. Joe has not been along the same route that I took to get to Riyadh. He has not questioned the arrogance of western science in the face of exploited Khanti people from Siberia as I was forced to do. He has not seen that the maps of two disparate cultures are distinct, even if they occupy the same piece of the earth's surface, as I realized when I met the gas drillers and the reindeer herders of the Yamal. I see in the eyes of the more conservative religious men in the room, the ones whose heads are covered with simple unadorned cloths, a stiffening at Joe's words about communication between the cultures of the world. I know that this means the invasion of American values to them. They may want the science of the west, but they don't want it combined with what they consider to be a decadent lifestyle. They do not want American clothes, they do not want American television. They hear, contained in Joe's invitation for communication through sharing American know-how, the threat of intellectual assimilation.

I start again. "Can you not consider that although it may be true that there has been a virtual takeover of scientific intellectual development by Europeans since the fourteenth century, that there is still room for a distinctly Islamic approach? Can you not also consider that the future, the next century, the next century's intellectual achievements, could belong to Islam? Could not an Islamic point of view inform the logic of discovery? Is there anything in the Qur'an that prevents learning?" On the contrary, I am aware that learning is perhaps the central issue in Islam, and that an understanding of the workings of the universe, as they are revealed to us, is perfectly in keeping with the religious practice. So why must we separate the development of science from what is the heart of a culture and the driving light behind its inspiration? I am on risky ground. Who am I to teach them their religion? But this is my message too. I believe that there can be learning that reflects the culture, even the religion of a people; in fact, I believe that such a connection cannot be avoided. I cannot stay silent.

At the foundation of this discussion is the question, Is science universal? The countervailing question asks whether it is feasible to consider a personal development of reality, a compact between the observer and the observed, and one that is not governed by the strict universals that western scientists seek, by the ultimate parameters of a "theory of everything." In Saudi Arabia I was confronted with those who are among the most fierce defenders of a universal science, the educated elite of a culture that desires to gain access to the inner temple of western science. The educated of Saudi Arabia were gathered to discuss the theme of a new science museum, one that would inspire their young people. It was the intent of many of them that this inspiration be western in character; it was my intent that a westerner bring the message that we should be wary of believing we have achieved knowledge that approaches "the mind of God."

338

Edward Said, in his book *Orientalism*, confronts the west's depiction of the Arabic people. The history of cultural clashes is a long one. Said makes the argument that there is a mythology that has developed surrounding the "Oriental," and that this mythology has been created largely as an excuse for the colonial pursuits of the Europeans. The issue is, however, can there not be scientific perspectives that are culturally centred, not in a value-laden sense, not suggesting that orientals are primitive with respect to their culture, to their science, but in the sense that there could be different sensibilities that lead to new forms of questions for the scientist? It is this possibility that prompted me to be so bold in the brainstorming meeting of scholars in Riyadh in 1992.

Could this apply to virtually all sciences that are not intrinsically western? Are there points of view that have been forgotten or dismissed? The historian and scientist Henry Bauer, in dissecting the western scientific approach, disparages the possibility that there could be more than one main road to understanding the world.[1] He notes that there are essentially two perspectives in the study of scientific developments and approaches. One is the "internalist" point of view that characterizes the pursuit of science as the achievement of pure thought, unaffected by human concerns, and the other is the "externalist" framework that considers that human history and bias will affect science just as they do every other aspect of human endeavour. Bauer suggests there is a place for both points of view. Internalist perspectives develop the basic precepts of what we call "textbook" science, the quantified observations, the exacting of "universal laws," while externalists are important at the frontiers of science, where human error is an important part of the history, and where pure rationality cannot be easily deciphered from all that is happening in the messy work of first discovery. Despite his acceptance of the role played by the externalist approach, however, Bauer is dismissive of the likelihood that such a humanist perspective could ever produce a new and different logical interpretation of the world, a new "reality," as it were:

> In reality and quite obviously, internalist and externalist positions are both right and both wrong, because some bits or aspects of science lend themselves to internalist explanation whereas others yield naturally to externalist exegesis. Textbook science is best understood through an internalist approach that illuminates the intellectual history of the growth of ever more reliable knowledge. Externalist criticism is pointless here unless it could be shown that, say, a Marxist, feminist, or third-world science could incorporate a different Periodic Table of the Elements (a nonperiodic one, that is to say), or some other equation than $E=mc^2$, or some nonentropic system of thermodynamics, or something equally beyond the bounds even of science fiction.[2]

I believe that Bauer's concerns stem from the fear that the existence of valid alternative sciences would attack the very foundation of western science—a foundation characterized by the belief that there is only one reality out there and that western science is *progressing* ever closer to an understanding of this reality.

339

The herbalist's store on Diagonal Street is a wall of smell. Three baboon carcasses, gutted and drying in the sunny doorway, act as sentries. I had wanted to walk through the streets of Johannesburg on my own, but at the last minute Monty announced he was coming with me. "Just a better idea, all in all. You never know. Anyway, I can show you places." The shop on Diagonal Street has a pretentious name: Museum of Man and Science. Inside, the ceilings are low; we have to stoop as we walk through the main room. There are thousands of dead animals. Hides and carcasses hang into our hair as we make our way to the medicine dispensing counter at the back of the shop—animal heads, fur, feathers, all kinds of animal parts preserved in liquid, boxes of bones, powdered bones, whole bones, powdered organs, dried organs, skulls, and severed monkey's hands are piled in bins around the edges of the room. Lining rows of labelled shelves are seeds, dried plants, and plants preserved in murky liquids. The smell stops the air from entering my lungs, but I persist.

"Let's talk to the man behind the counter." There are three people dispensing combinations of powders and dried plants and animals to an old woman in tattered clothes and a young man in a suit. Both customers are black. Dr. Naidoo is the owner of the shop. He has a patient waiting on a chair next to the counter, but he dismisses him when we come up for information.

"Please come back tomorrow," he tells the man. "It is not urgent, you know." Then, turning to us, he remarks, "He is here every day. My medicine takes time. It cannot work overnight, I tell him." Monty introduces me and tells Dr. Naidoo that we would like to ask him about his medicines; Dr. Naidoo is clearly flattered that we are here to see him. "You are from Canada? Please come into my office." His science is old, he tells us. He is called on to deliver his skill and his information by university professors. His sources are the hinterlands of Africa. His family, who came from India, has been the bridge to African herbal and psychological science for three generations. There are many sources of this information. It would take years to discuss it.

It is when science takes this form that western scholars begin to doubt there is anything of value outside the narrow confines of the western logic. But what knowledge is there in this shop? Apart from the possibility of herbal effects unknown in the west, is there logic that would prove daunting to the western mind but that nevertheless would produce a new physical perspective on the natural world?

Monty and I continue our walk through downtown Johannesburg. Some of the sights are startling. A woman selling peaches from a mat on the sidewalk has white paint covering her cheeks in two large patches. She stares back at me as we go by. I am conscious that we are the only whites here. Monty is straightforward. "The way you walk is important. We have somewhere to go, so we look purposeful, although I confess that I do not make a habit of touring the city by foot." We are off to see an Inyanga, a medicine man, who practices in a little hut under a freeway exit in a marketplace devoted to herbal potions.

"Zulu, not English, Zulu, Zulu." The Inyanga will not talk with us.

"Yes, but surely . . ." Monty starts, ineffectively looking around for help from the gathering crowd of curious street hawkers. Monty asks me if I will pay the man.

"Of course. How much would he want, do you think?"

"Rather too much, I suspect. Here, my good man." Monty commandeers a young man sitting nearby. "Most young people speak a little English. I say, would you mind interpreting for us? We would like to pay the Inyanga for a conversation about his practice. Would you, aah, would you oblige us by interpreting?" The interpretation is not of the highest quality, but we proceed, paying both the Inyanga and the interpreter. I ask for a session. The Inyanga looks me up and down and retires into his hut for a moment, then returns wearing a priest's cloak, complete with a large cross on the back. "They mix religions here a fair bit, I'm afraid." Monty keeps a straight face so as not to reveal his amusement to the Inyanga. Yet despite the incongruous religious outfit, I am intrigued. The Inyanga takes out a little round child's mirror, its frame made of pink plastic. He looks at my reflection in the mirror from an angle, then he returns to his hut. Whistling is heard, and he comes back outside. "Usually they use bones and feathers. I've never seen this mirror routine before. Notice that it has a crack through the middle of it?" Monty is standing politely behind me, providing commentary.

I ask our interpreter, "Why is he looking at me in the mirror?"

"It is his medicine. It must come through you to him. Now he is breathing you in." The Inyanga is inhaling deeply. Suddenly, he scoops up a large quantity of powder from one of his bags, using a long skeletal birdbeak as a spoon. I'm glad he is not resorting to the severed monkey hands that seem to be abundant in this particular marketplace. He sniffs up a large quantity of the powder, inhales deeply again, and stands stock-still, waiting.

"What is in that powder?"

"It is . . . I will write it for you." Our interpreter writes in capital letters very slowly, "ALLANIMALPARTS." The Inyanga pounds his chest, then he repeats the procedure, each time looking at me from the mirror. Some powders are accepted by him and put into little bags for my use later on, and some are rejected. "The Inyanga says you are not strong. You must take powerful medicine to gain strength."

Later, I will deliberately lose the powdered animal parts on the plane ride home to Canada. I get nervous thinking about what I will say to the customs people, should I be asked about the contents of my smelly little plastic bags. All in all, I feel a little foolish about the session. I know that what I witnessed would be dismissed by modern scientists without hesitation, but there is the essence of a basic approach that has possible merit even though it is foreign to the western way of thinking. As I sat with the Inyanga, I knew that the exploitation of an ancient knowledge was well past any real recovery—too many years of European colonization had elapsed for there to be knowledge that is purely African, and too many tourists like me spend time looking for "authentic" experiences. Yet I saw something in his actions that made me think again of the conversation I had in Riyadh with the Islamic scholars and scientists. Was there something in the movements of the Inyanga that speaks of a different logic, something beyond the contents of his bags of powdered animals and plants? He breathed me in and he took the medicine meant for me into his own body. What is good for me is good for you, we are all one body, he seemed to be saying. Or to bring it around to the philosophical foundations, in the west we can see an external reality and therefore can see the patient as a separate entity from the medical practitioner, but in African medicine was I seeing something else? I interpret the Inyanga's methods to reveal a different sense of reality—he and I were occupying a *blended* reality. And I was not "external" to his personal space.

340

Abd al-Halim Ibrahim Abd al-Halim and Rasem Budran were the two architects of the project in Riyadh. Abd al-Halim I. Abd al-Halim is Egyptian—his beautifully balanced name, with two identical parts, at the beginning and end, acting like pillars at a gateway, is the perfect identifier for an architect. Rasem Budran is Palestinian. Both of them have studied in the west, but both are committed to understanding the science and culture of the near "orient." To some extent, it was their work that inspired my call for an Islamic approach for the new science museum in Riyadh. My impassioned speech came after a break for coffee. The rush for the doughnuts and pastries, a wall of white robes surrounding the table of food, was too daunting for me. I sat in a corner of the room, and Rasem Budran took the opportunity to show me his designs.

The new building was to line up with the stars, a likely orientation for an Islamic science museum, considering their history of astronomy, but there was more. There were strange pits at the base of the building, angled to catch as much sunlight as possible. "These are sun pits. The sunlight collects in these architectural pockets, and they become very hot."

"But why? In a country where heat is to be avoided, why trap it?"

"We have a philosophy that works in this instance." Rasem is watching me anxiously as he speaks. "Submission to the course of events in the natural world leads to a favourable outcome. Go with the heat and it will care for you." The heat collected in the sun pits creates a strong upward draft, and conduits channel the hot upwardly moving wind through the building to chimneys in the roof. Along the conduits there are openings that allow the air from inside the building to flow into them as the hot wind rises. So the wind scoops up the passive air in the building, creating a current that draws out the trapped hot air that has collected. Cooler air comes in from openings along the shaded periphery of the building. "At least that is the theory. We have developed the concept from a combination of traditional architectural approaches and our own thoughts on the matter. We think that we will only have to augment the cooling by using a fraction of the artificial air conditioning we would normally employ."

I am moved by this display of counterintuitive logic. "But you have done something much more important, you have employed a perspective that is unique to the region, to the climate," I respond—unique to a people who had to look at the natural conditions of heat and desert in an entirely novel way. "Has it occurred to you that your passive, aah, submissive architecture, if I can put it that way, is different from western concepts that are usually concerned with defeating the climate?"

A shrug, well, yes, but please do not make too much of it, it is only a theory, we haven't built it yet. The reply was like the architecture, humble. For me, it did not matter whether the design could be perfected; it was in fact the nature of the theory that intrigued me. It embodied a different set of values and the possibility of a different scientific path entirely.

Later I would walk along the cool covered passageway of a long building. The building's walls are made with two layers, like the double glazing of Canadian windows, but open at the bottom and the top to allow air flow, the upward movement of cooling passive winds. As with the sun pit concept, the upward flow of air is powered by the heat of the sun. "But it owes a lot to Frank Lloyd Wright." Rasem is not about to claim a purely middle-eastern origin for these architectural developments. Yes, but it is an approach that is at home here, exemplifying the philosophy of this part of the world.

341

"What is this? Only one of us can get into this door at a time?" Jim is squeezing in between the two doors of the building in downtown Johannesburg. They are built like an airlock; the outer door swings open only when the inner door is closed. Once you are in between the two doors, the outer door firmly locked, the inner door will open and you are inside the office building. And each person has to be buzzed in individually by the office staff communicating with us from the tenth floor through the intercom at the door. There are nine of us waiting to enter—Jim, Jürgen, and I, along with Monty and our other South African host, Dirk, and two black women with their two barefoot children. It takes several minutes for us all to get through the doors. This is architecture reflecting a philosophy far different from the one I saw in Riyadh. The separation of the people inside from the people outside is dramatic.

Upstairs, through windows that go from floor to ceiling, we look out over a 360-degree view of Johannesburg—the Magaliesberg Mountains to the north, Soweto to the southwest, and all the central downtown core at our feet. Right beneath our gaze, covering much of the central core of Johannesburg, are huge long hills of beige dirt, tailings from the gold mining that created the original settlement. "They're filled with poisonous chemical compounds, cyanide, and such things," Monty told Jim and me on our first day as we drove through town. The wind blows toxic dust over everything and everybody, especially toward the black townships to the south. "They're trying to grow grass and other plants on the hills to keep the dust down, but as you can see, it doesn't work so well."

First the airlock doors and now the mine tailings. We are being confronted by a philosophy that is not passive, not submissive. South African industrialists are aggressive. Their architecture keeps people out, their industrial projects attack the earth. The mines are dug out right in the neighbourhoods of the workers. The hills of dirt are evidence of a most unsubmissive approach to life.

How telling these mining remains are for me. They are so clearly the product of an uncaring civilization—digging out the actual earth itself in a brutal struggle against nature. And the aggression is projected onto the people of Africa, who are also seen as something to be conquered and something to control through the technological manifestations of our western science.

342

Mine tailings are a form of excrement. Such hills in Johannesburg cover the city, evidence of an enormous confidence in the superiority of the white invaders of Africa. Later we see excrement used in a far different way on an excursion to the north of Johannesburg. Monty, his wife, and his older son, Stephen, take Jürgen and me into the Ndebele district. I want to see the geometric designs the Ndebele women use in their beadwork and as designs in their homes.

"Wait." Stephen is cautioning us to hold off from walking through the gate of the highly decorated home; geometric designs cover the inner and outer walls and the wall surrounding the compound. "I'm afraid that this isn't a museum—it just looks like one." We are invited in. The designs are truly mathematical in form. I feel that they reveal an understanding of pattern as sophisticated as anything produced in Europe or Asia. But what catches my eye immediately are the floors.

"Is this a kind of cement?"

"No." Stephen is an expert on the art and culture of his country. "It's cow dung. They harden it into a very tough mixture—makes great floors. And notice the wonderful designs. They're made by brushing the floor with a wet brush or rag after they're set. The water brings up a slightly different colour. Of course artificial colouring made from local plants can be added, but that is reserved mostly for the walls." The matriarch asks us if we would like to see her in her full Ndebele wedding costume. This is her home. I feel we are intruding a little too much, but it is impolite to say no, as we are guests. We wait half an hour and she returns, a garment of extraordinary beadwork covering her entirely.

343

I wrote to Henry Bauer after reading his book on the scientific method of the west. I wanted to know whether he would consider sciences like ecology as alternatives to the more classical forms of western science, the ones that are based primarily on hypothesis testing. In my letter to Bauer, I termed ecology a "systems" approach, one that considers all parts of a system as equal and that cannot allow for perturbation experiments, as this would alter the entire system profoundly. Thus, I was asking him whether he could see, in western science—for the time being forgetting about science from other cultures—alternative approaches that could eventually offer different formulations and descriptions of the world that are more than merely general. I see the systems approach as a form of non-teleological investigation because it does not involve creating a series of hypotheses that will be tested against a preconceived design. The purely ecological approach is highly dialectical and non-hierarchical, in that it assumes that elements within a system are defined through mutual interaction, and that in actuality one can not speak of "elements" within a system, except in a temporary, expedient fashion, because their definition entails such intermingling with one another as to make them entirely indistinguishable as separate units.

I saw an instance of an ecological experiment in South Africa. The reasons for it were noble, and the outcome may be gratifying, but the premise is flawed. Cheetahs are becoming extinct in South Africa. Brian told us why when we visited him on his farm: "They hunt by day and so are an easy target for anyone interested. Now, leopards—that's a different story. Leopards sneak into the farms every night around here; they are really dangerous."

The de Wildt Cheetah Centre in the Magaliesberg Mountains north of Pretoria is an ecological experiment, an attempt to breed the cheetahs back to their former numbers. But a cheetah is more than a beautiful creature accepting hunks of raw meat tossed out of a pail by a keeper while a busload of tourists watch; the cheetah is both the animal and the environment that surrounds it. Even so, the cheetahs were awfully real. "Jeesh, they're jumping right up here!" Dirk had let me sit by the open side of the bus to get a better view as we drove through.

"Ah yes, they are rather close aren't they? I'm sure they know what they're doing here, though, don't you think?"

The open bus is in the compound for the young male cheetahs. The keeper stands his ground. "You have to face them down. It's a natural instinct for them *not* to attack you directly, head-on. They like to chase their food down from behind." Practical information, valuable for the keeper, but I think the reliance on instinct as an explanation gets a lot of ecological experimenters off the hook—if there are instincts encoded in the genes, you can argue that the environmental influences are not so strong, and then maybe you can isolate an animal from its habitat and breed a proper population of cheetahs. I doubt it's that easy. I see the cheetah as integral to its environment, so I think the breeding experiments are intrinsically flawed. And there will be serious inbreeding from such a population anyway, which the natural habitat would have prevented from being a concern—so much for even the purely genetic aspect of the experiment.

Bauer replied to me that he wouldn't want to rely on general theories for practical results, especially since he himself is a practical scientist, a chemist. Systems approaches, he said, are not going to give us anything very definite in the way of measurements. We can't actually *do* anything using a systems approach. Now I don't agree with Bauer on this. I will admit that the systems approach would not produce the mines of Johannesburg very easily; one has to ignore a lot to dump cyanide hills everywhere. At the purist levels, of course, systems approaches allow for only observing an environment, since any change will make a profound difference. But systems people can be practical too; the ideal of not perturbing the environment is mitigated by the realization that living in it, no matter how carefully, will effect change inevitably, but the question is, how much? Living *gently* on the earth will at least allow a civilization to last longer than it would if the philosophy were characterized by struggle and defiance of the natural world. For example, the Nientsi and Khanti people of the Yamal peninsula region in Siberia have lived for hundreds of years dragging their reindeer-powered sleds over the tundra without leaving a mark. The skin-covered runners do not gouge the epithelium of the permafrost the way a modern tractor does. The traffic of our modern vehicles is leaving the region permanently scarred. We could be quite successful with a gentler, ecological approach. We could learn from the environment. But perhaps the resistance we have to this less invasive way of life lies in the fact that it does *not* leave a mark. Leaving a sign of our passage may be just too important to us.

344

There is another lesson I learned in Saudi Arabia. The discussion with the scholars and scientists *assumed* that there could be different points of view with respect to how one approaches an understanding of the natural world. Although there is still an ultimate design inherent in their stated belief that learning can bring one closer to the "truth," the Islamic scholars did, nevertheless, see western science as being merely one method among many. It was new for me to hear scientists speak of their *awareness* of the paradigm in which they are working. Most of my experience in laboratories in the west has shown me that scientists do not see their point of view as a point of view at all; they see it as living in reality. Muslims learn the discipline of a foreign western science while still maintaining their cultural and spiritual values, and maybe that is what allows them to see that one always speaks from a frame of reference, from a perspective that may not match that of someone else. The philosopher al-Farabi, who lived in the tenth century and who exemplified the unification of the religious and the philosophical/scientific man, believed that reason could allow a learned person to achieve understanding, presumably through any number of sources, judging by the eclectic thinkers the Islamic centres of learning gathered from across the middle east, Africa and Europe. I found much open-mindedness with respect to the diverse sources of scientific philosophy that day in Saudi Arabia, more than I often do in similar discussions in the universities and museums of North America.

345

Our western science is derived from the perspective of a particular civilization that will eventually be eclipsed. There will come a time, according to Laura Nader, an anthropologist who studies scientists in much the same way as Margaret Mead studied Pacific islanders, or other anthropologists studied the people of the Amazon basin, when the accomplishments of our science over the past centuries will be turned into difficulties and sources of societal and environmental destruction:

> It is a humbling experience for us to know that civilizations rise and fall, flourish and disappear, and to know also that the same happens with science. . . . Great scientific traditions, too, after periods of productivity, decay. . . . The societies that have nourished the extraordinary rise of modern Western science in the last three centuries are those having to face problems for which science has as yet no answers; problems that stem from changes often directly traceable to science and technological achievements.[3]

346

What is the message here? It is to realize that our reality is known through our filter, through our map. We may imagine an external Platonic ideal, but we will live at the level of the intimate encounter where we cause changes to the landscape as much as it changes us. The interface of the observer and the observed is where we live. The route we take is an arduous one. It is not the survival of the fittest, it is the intimate pact we make with the world as we live it, as we travel over it. We create the map as we move; we do not live a predestined design. The final end, the τέλος, is not lying in wait for us.

347

I am standing on the edge of the lake, the same lake I crossed in an ice storm when I started into the bush, alone in my canoe, a few days before. I need to return to the base camp now. The trip is almost over. I am due to travel back down the highway to Toronto later in the day.

I am looking at a choppy lake, feeling the cool breeze lift from the surface of the freezing water and cut across my face. It will be a long paddle. I decide to use my life preserver as a cushion under my knees. If I fall in, it's too cold to live through the experience anyway, with or without a life jacket, I reason.

As I start out, the wind is constant at least, from the northwest. I position the point of the canoe into the waves to cut across them at a slight angle. I am paddling on my left side, with the prow a little to the left of the wind, so each stroke moves me back into line, toward the right, and I don't risk being swung around completely. It is five miles that I'll be blown down to the south end of the lake if I lose control of the canoe. One false move and I will be.

This is not a test for the survival of the fittest. This is a personal intimate arrangement between me and the wind and water. The path I will take is not predestined, I remind myself. Every moment is a covenant with the nature around me, my reality the interface I make with the surface of the lake. I can feel the dialectical nature of the exchange in a very powerful immediate way here in my canoe. And no one is here to watch; there is nothing existing beyond this experience.

348

I think back to Sasha. He is an Arctic explorer. He walks over treacherous ice breaking away beneath his feet, chasms opening, open water appearing. He makes a pact with the nature around him. He may say he is being challenged by an immovable force, the Arctic, that there is no exchange, just the puny exertions of a man against nature. I would counter that his journey is a meeting of two equal entities, the man and the environment; what occurs is a secret between the two. And the reality that is experienced in the moment is very real; there is nothing else, only the dialectical exchange between Sasha and the icy wilderness, the one defining the other.

349

At what level do we actually live most of the time, and therefore, from where do we draw our inspiration, where does our reality come from? My physical experiences may be dialectical, but my interchanges with the people around me are influenced by the hierarchical nature of my civilization. Should I stop all action that reinforces the hierarchy? Does this mean I should stop enjoying the fruits of the European civilization?

It is 1986; I am in London for a week on my own. It is November, and the weather is miserable. I read that Gustav Leonhardt is playing a harpsichord concert in Goldsmiths' Hall. He will play the compositions of Orlando Gibbons, Thomas Morley, William Byrd, Couperin, Rameau, Scarlatti, all from the time of the Age of Discovery, when Europe was colonizing the face of the earth. But it will be pure pleasure for me to hear this exuberant music. I am looking forward to it.

"But I am afraid that the concert is closed to the public. It was advertised only for members of the hall." I am stopped at the door. "There isn't even an admission charge, so you see we are not set up for this."

"I'm here from Canada . . . I rarely have an opportunity to hear Gustav Leonhardt. . . ."

"Yes, well . . . I tell you what, please come in as our guest this evening. We are honoured that you came out on such a night." I am admitted into the temple. I am a card-carrying member of our civilization, of the highest order. No one but a member of the elite would choose to come out for Leonhardt, a musician's musician playing the music of the foundation of our modern civilization in the most careful and yet robust fashion.

Before he is to play, the golden chalices and other treasures of the hall are brought on stage from the vault by a contingent of guards. There are plates of solid gold the size of picnic tables. At intermission they are removed and then brought out again for the second half of the concert. This gold may have been mined by workers in Johannesburg, toxic mountains of mine tailings left behind and plates of solid gold brought out for my pleasure in Goldsmiths' Hall in London.

Is this equivalent to enjoying the love of a slave in a prince's home? I do not know. I choose to think that taking pleasure cannot in itself be wrong, but doing so at the expense of others is. But this is problematic—our civilization has the leisure for elevated pursuits simply because we have colonized the world. There is no easy answer.

350

In Leningrad in the summer of 1990, the summer before my frozen January walk through the city with Sasha, I stroll through the streets with Fiona and Jim and I am filled with enjoyment. I am looking at a beautiful city, a wonder, built on canals along the Neva River, extraordinary pastel yellow and blue buildings belonging to the time of Europe's greatest flourishing. Again, I am getting pure pleasure from the fruits of our western civilization.

But this is not the real Europe of the 1700s I see here. Peter the Great founded the original city, St. Petersburg, about 1703 in an attempt to wrest Russia from the "orient," to drive the Russian citizens toward the education and progress offered by western European science and technology. St. Petersburg was a *copy* of western civilization. But copies can often be more idealized, and more "real" to the observer than the originals. And more than the architecture and the institutions of learning and industry and science were copied. Like its model cities in Europe, St. Petersburg was conceived and built to reflect a hierarchical society. A great chasm lay between the wealthy and the poor workers and peasants of the city and its surroundings. The marshland on which it was built was so treacherous that many died during the city's construction. It is said that St. Petersburg was built on bones—a true hier-archical model, in other words. Nevertheless, Fiona and Jim and I felt uplifted by the perfection of the city. Our walk was an antidote to the deprivation we had left in Siberia, a place built on the same model but lacking the charm. Siberia was akin to Johannesburg with its mine tail-ings, the detritus of a civilization, its back alley. Leningrad was London and Paris, the suffering that goes into making such a beautiful capital of a civilization well hidden.

351

Many people would say that a "photograph" of the earth's surface taken from space is the best map you could ask for; it is rendered per-fectly—there are no distortions. However, just as the city of St. Peters-burg started off as a copy of the great cities in the European civilization, the photograph is only a copy of the earth below, and copies are ideal-ized. At the moment the copy is made, there is an effort to capture the ideal. Peter the Great of Russia tried to capture the best attributes of the emerging European society of the 1700s and render it in his city. Just so, the photograph portrays a static moment, or series of mo-ments. It is not a better map than one that is useful to navigators, such as the Mercator map, for example, it is not a map that reflects the inter-ests of the head of gas drilling in the Yamal, it is not a map that records the history of conquests around Africa. A map is the filter required by the user; it leaves out as much as it leaves in and it distorts judiciously so as to render the map intelligible to its user. The photograph is an idealized picture, not always a useful map. And a photograph, in cap-turing only a moment, is not a map that reflects the ongoing exchange between the traveller and the landscape.

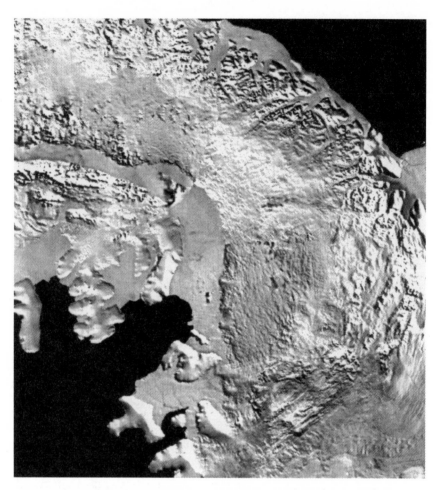

Satellite Image of the Antarctic Peninsula (between 60 degrees and 70 degrees west longitude, south of the Antarctic Circle). This is a composite made from detailed satellite images. The United States Geological Survey (USGS) created this image map with advanced very high resolution radiometer images, using sensors on the National Oceanic and Atmospheric Administration satellites. The images that make up the mosaic of the image map were collected from 1980 to 1994. The error level of the final image, representing ca. 450,000 square kilometres, is estimated at less than 2.5 km². The image has been downloaded from the USGS website (http://TerraWeb.wr.usgs.gov/TRS/projects/Antarctica/AVHRR.html). Grateful acknowledgement is given to the USGS team members: Pat S. Chavez, Team Leader; Jane G. Ferrigno; Miguel G. Velasco; Jo-Ann Barell; Stuart C. Sides; Cheryl Hallam; Rosendo R. Gonzales; Deborah L. Soltesz.

352

Photographic maps are symbols of an ideal; they are not reality, despite their appearance. They are attempts at creating an image of the perfection we aspire to. The trouble is, the journeys we take through life are usually far too difficult to allow the time for philosophical gazing toward the idealized end. Instead, the exchange with the landscape is immediate and it is humbling. There is a reality that is constantly defining itself, that cannot be captured by a photograph, and that cannot be sublimated into the self-fulfilling completion of a preconceived end point.

Standing on the edge of the lake before setting off, I did imagine the completion of my journey, but that soon passed. The reality of the lake passage is harsh, and the idealized ending is not so sure now. The wind has picked up a little. I cannot hesitate for even one paddle stroke—I must keep the canoe pointed in the same direction, just off to the left of the wind's direction. Every stroke is an aching moment, every thrust forward is met by a wind that would send me back, that would turn the canoe around and push me to the end of the lake. And that is if I'm lucky. The waves are very big, bigger than I had imagined they would be. Water spills into the canoe and threatens me with capsizing. I wish my life preserver wasn't a sodden pillow under my knees now. If I fell into the freezing water wearing it, the bright orange colour would at least ensure that I could be seen by someone who might be on shore before it was too late. I can't take the time to put the life preserver on, I can't even take time to push my hair out of my eyes—the paddling rhythm can't stop for a second.

I shift my body ever so slightly to get a better purchase on the paddle stroke. I have to kneel higher in the canoe. It rocks dangerously, close to flipping over. My muscles are numb but I cannot stop. I know that if I waver now, the canoe will definitely capsize—it will not just sail down to the end of the lake.

Every move of the canoe and the waves is an intimate exchange, a constant give and take. I am conscious that this is not a dream—every second is a tangible present tense—but the realness of the event makes me wonder how often I am unaware at other less intense moments in my life, trusting my reliance on the endpoint to carry me through a journey. The anxiety and the immediacy of the danger and the pain are bringing the dialectic to life for me.

353

Two years before the lake crossing in my canoe, while I walked through the 1990 summertime of Leningrad, the idealized picture-map was more apparent to me than any personal dialectical struggle. Leningrad was sunny and beautiful and life seemed predictable. Our driver, Vladimir, had asked us to bring him back some morozhano, ice cream made with condensed milk. "Vladimir! You want ice cream?" I hold out the little bar, already melting in my hand.

"Ah, yes!" He is thrilled.

On nearly every corner, Leningrad citizens lined up at kiosks to buy this delicacy—ice cream in the midst of the ideal city, but ice cream being enjoyed while starvation sits at their door—a starvation I would experience myself the following winter when I would walk through a colder and less idealized Leningrad with Sasha.

354

"It looks like Karnak."

"Well, yes, it has been modelled to some extent on Karnak. It is monumental, of course." Abd al-Halim I. Abd al-Halim and Rasem Budran are walking us through their most recent architectural enterprise in Riyadh. It is the combined central mosque and palace for the king, together costing nearly US$800 million. Neither building is completed. We are allowed to make a rare tour. The rooms in the palace are so huge that in the evening light there is a gloom that shadows the end walls, giving the sense of being outside in a city street. There are no domes in either the palace or the mosque. This is the Nadj region of central Arabia, where only mud was used traditionally, making domes impossible. The architects have been true to that tradition.

It is the shape that has reminded me of pictures I have seen of Karnak in Egypt, remnants of an ancient civilization, but one that is not foreign to these architects. Massive square stones on top of giant pillars act as a roof to rooms that appear narrow because the ceilings are four storeys high. And at the end of the room that lies in partial darkness, there is one lone image, a painting of Karnak. My impression had been correct, the message is so strong.

I am faced with the monuments of a civilization far older than my European one. When confronted with the quiet magnitude of a Karnak being built in the 1990s, how can we be so arrogant as to think that we have the only way of knowing? I know it too is hierarchical, but it is a hierarchy that does not admit the elite of the western laboratories. Faced with the realization that there are many ladders climbing to a truth, might we not admit to there being several different truths?

355

Monty and I are walking through yet another marketplace in central Johannesburg. In among the monstrous hills of mine excrement we find the beginnings of a new civilization. There are no white people from the suburbs here, only people from the black townships surrounding the city. They have come into town to work and some to live and to create a community.

"This is the library." Monty is taking me up the steps of a monumental building, obviously designed to support the cultural and intellectual needs of the former white regime. Inside, we see every desk and carrel in the enormous ground floor room occupied. A hundred black faces look up from their studies. We leave them; I am embarrassed for having stared so intently.

We pass an outdoor beauty salon, several clothing stalls. "The merchants in the department stores and shopping centres can't do anything about these street hawkers. Who knows what will happen here?" Monty is equivocal.

"But this is a vibrant community, exciting."

"Oh yes indeed, but is it viable?" Suddenly women at one of the stalls start to trill in loud voices, like birds. A young man runs terrified between the racks of clothing next to us, then he leaps over a bin of plastic sandals and runs and runs. About ten women are chasing him. A woman next to us, dressed in an American flag design, is laughing, doubled over. Monty asks, "What happened here?"

"Woman is strong, man is weak." She continues to laugh.

"Yes, yes, I suppose . . . you women are indeed very strong, but what did he do?"

"He take from stall over there, but that is last time."

I turn to Monty. "What will they do to him if they catch him? Turn him in to the police?"

"I doubt it. I think they'll beat him rather badly, actually. You notice that the community here is very unified, and that it is almost entirely run by women. Men are welcome as customers, I guess, but not tolerated on the whole."

356

It is humbling to learn that our place in the hierarchy is a result of the structure of our civilization. People are not born to rule by some genetic predisposition.

When we choose to think that our culture is superior because our science is so provocative, we lose sight of the fleeting nature of success. Our western science has produced as many problems as it has successes. And it is not the pathway to the ultimate understanding of the truth, because there is no absolute truth.

357

The passage to understanding lies in gaining humility. In the face of the many individual maps of reality that must exist for each and every thinking person, it is arrogant to expect that the concepts of a few will lead to an understanding of everything, to a "theory of everything."

Despite the arrogance of our elitist establishment, violence against the perpetrators of a hierarchy that seeks to control everyone on earth through its science and technology seems not to be the answer. Violent solutions meted out to colonialists and the intellectual elite re-enact the regimes that have sought to label people as "essentially," or genetically, disposed to exploiting the common people, such as was claimed by the Nazis of the Jews. Violent solutions are inherently hierarchical.

The solution lies in submission to the world around us, allowing for the interface between the traveller and the landscape, choosing the path that is not a struggle for survival but is rather a mutually defining journey. The traveller is changed as much as the landscape; each alone is nothing, but together they are a unit of life.

It is like the architecture of the desert that Rasem Budran showed me in Riyadh. The heat of the sun is not avoided but sought out, and the dynamic interchange with the sun forms a new, surprising outcome. The encounter is mutually defining, but most of all it is passive and submissive and from that submission comes enormous power.

It is Gandhi and not Fanon. It is the struggle of passive resistance, not because this will eventually cause the perpetrators of violent rule chagrin, as is often said of Gandhi's approach to protest, but because the acceptance of the journey as a mutually defining dialectic between the traveller and the landscape creates a powerful entity, a reality that cannot be overthrown by the false realities of those who would project their future idealized end points onto the destinies of a society's citizens.

Striving to perform in order to adapt to what is perceived to be an unmoving landscape, the struggle to prove who is the fittest, is the non-passive approach that leads to violence. It does so because it continues the belief that if the system can be seen to change in the natural course of historical events, then it can forcibly *be* changed to exemplify a more equitable model. But the revolution of a system most often involves the installation of new self-defined superiors in a society; and the old system, the old order, does not change in that case, but perpetuates itself.

Does the more passive route allow the elite to go on as before, unhindered? In quiet revolutions, there is always the worry that the old ways persist, and that the oppressed masses, compelled to resist violent upheavals, will therefore gain little in the end. But what will they gain with violence? If we look into the smaller arena of the sciences, which is after all a microcosm of the civilization as a whole, what can be gained through upheaval, through the attempted overthrow of the established paradigm?

On one level, the scientific community is like a river. Its flow cannot be dammed, or its course easily redirected. It will flood the banks, in any case; it will travel the path of least resistance. Changes in the paradigm occur at times, but they occur at the level of the science community as a whole, felt only distantly by the individuals that make up the ranks of scientists. The system of science cannot change without altering its entire state, its entire collective of internal and external interrelationships. To surgically interfere with the system is to risk total destruction. Therefore, I think it unlikely that any actions could be taken to constructively change the natural course of scientific ideas. The dialectical course of action that I am advocating takes place not at the level of a society or a community of scientists but rather at the personal level, at the level of intimate everyday judgement, for that is where we live our lives. Tempting as it may be to confront arrogance at the social level, such a massive change is an impossibility.

358

Models that seek to synthesize broad areas of observations are filter maps that help to develop a paradigm. In leaving out parts that interfere with the clarity of the interpretation of the natural world, they become robust and are effective in the development of technologies. Gas and oil drilling in Siberia and gold mining in Johannesburg are examples of the power of singular ideas. But they are not reality. If it is reality we are seeking to study, the phenomenological interface between the observer and the landscape is very real, is the highest level of reality attainable. We bring to this interface all that we are; we change what we see and it changes us.

359

I have kept the canoe headed into the waves, keeping the same angle for an hour now. I have not been able to shift over to the other side to give my muscles a rest. I have made it across. The last few strokes are the hardest I have ever undertaken, but the pain is delicious. Now I am heading into shore.

On shore, the sun is warm, and the wind seems light to me. The Native helper at the base camp of the outfitters comes out, takes my bags out of the canoe without noticing their weight, and flips the canoe over his shoulders in one motion. "Nice day, eh?"

"Yeah." What would this arduous journey mean to him? He's here every day.

A short time later, I am driving down to Toronto, several hours ahead of me. My muscles are in so much pain that they are warming me. I feel buoyant and happy.

360

"We were taken into Alexandra Township just outside of central Johannesburg by car. They put me in the back seat with two body-guards on either side, and they put my colleague into another car with two bodyguards. They were armed to the teeth. There have been so many murders there during the past few years that they didn't want to take any chances. We were important people, and they knew we had a reception later that day in Pretoria. Mandela himself showed up for it. Anyway, we inspected the shanty houses and the terrible living conditions of the people in Alexandra. We just drove in like a convoy and did our thing and left quickly." The head of a Canadian museum design firm is telling me his story of visiting the wretched of South Africa. Monty and I did our walk without bodyguards. Yes, there was danger, but then we couldn't very well see much or talk to anyone from a speeding car, so we walked.

361

When we walked along the Gulag railroad in Siberia, we were walking in danger. The danger had left long ago, but the bones were still under our feet, as in Leningrad. The civilization that I enjoy is so completely founded on this legacy of the hierarchy, the oppression of the conquered, the colonized.

A few years after the Gulag experience, working on an exhibition that explores the roots of prejudice in the history of the practice of science, I am with Ali Mazrui, a visiting professor at the State University of New York at Binghamton, a black African Muslim scholar from Mombassa. "Slavery had benefits for some, of course. The civilization of America was built on it."

I ask, "Do you think the descendants of slaves want to take pride in the work of their dead great-grandparents, considering that the slave work was not done out of choice?"

"The civilization is what it is, and they were and are a part of it. Take it as you will—they have contributed and that should be acknowledged."

The civilization is what it is. I enjoy the Gustav Leonhardt concert; I am a part of the civilization. What conceit on my part to think that I can change anything, especially my own personal tastes and pleasures. But what arrogance to forget its roots.

362

"Can you believe it?" The woman is standing in the small hut, out of the wind, where they serve coffee and sell souvenirs. "People were actually walking on the graves out there. I mean, how crass." We are in Hå, on the coast of Norway. Hå is a burial site from about the year 400. The graves are of high-ranking women from a settlement of seafarers. These are the ancestors of my northern European civilization. The Norwegian forays into the sea marked the beginning of the truly European colonizations. I was one of those who walked on top of the huge mounds, the partially excavated graves of Hå. I walked on their old bones to feel something from them, to feel the history of the conquests that foreshadowed the Age of Discovery. Besides, I was used to walking on bones—I had walked along the railroad in Siberia.

363

From my horse, I can see into the second floor of these elaborate shanty houses. They are made of cardboard and planks, but they have electricity; there are television sets in all the homes. Aerials stick up everywhere, and they have colourful wall hangings, beds and chairs. I am riding through with my guide, José. He doesn't usually come this way, he says. We have been touring the hills around the resort in the Dominican Republic where Danielle and I are staying. She told me to go on this excursion on my own. "You're the horseback rider. I want to enjoy myself on the beach." There is a mesh of wires covering the whole village. I reach up to push them out of the way, they are so low.

"Don't touch those wires!" José shouts at me. "They are live! The people here—they all tap into the main power sources and string in the wires. It is very dangerous." They have made homes here out of almost nothing, it seems to me.

A few years later, Monty and I are nearing the end of our walk through Johannesburg. The abandoned turbine building in front of us is huge, like an industrial cathedral, with one giant interior room, tempered glass ceilings forty feet high. "They've even started to take the large glass sheets from the top to build their shanty homes. It's a real tragedy." Monty is rubbing his eyes against the sun as he looks up. We are a few hundred feet from the building, on the street. The walls of the turbine building are covered with thousands of little glass windows. Every one of them has been broken, shot out with bullets. The building looks like a church after the bomb raids of the Second World War.

"At least they're enterprising. Anyway, how on earth did they ever climb up to get those huge glass sheets, and why weren't they broken like the other windows?"

"Too strong, tempered glass. Look, I'm an architect, and I have to say that this shanty business can be awfully destructive. How will we ever begin to rebuild this city with this vandalism going on?"

We walk closer to the building. There is a back entrance up a grassy hill that separates the building from the roadway. I glance at Monty. "Do you think we could look inside the building?"

He is squinting. "Yes, well, it is daylight, I suppose. Still, it's filled with shanty dwellers, you know. We probably look like government inspectors or something, not likely to be very welcome."

I persist a little, and we walk up to the building. I am conscious of an old memory. When I was five years old we lived in an ancient farmhouse. A pig barn was on the property. "Don't go there—the old sow escapes sometimes; she'll kill you if she can." I recall the smell of the back entrance to the barn. It was a grassy rise, an entrance for the tractor. The scent of grain mixed with the odour of pigs, sweet and terrifying. I went there whenever I could, unwatched by my mother. Now in Johannesburg I smell the barn, I tingle with the fear of the five-year-old still inside me.

"Good, let's go, then." Monty is walking back down the grass. We have peeked into the enormous room, lined along the sides with shanties all of equal size, people sitting in the shade, filtered sunlight coming from the thousands of windows.

"Can we meet some of these people?"

Monty looks at me, then at his feet, and starts to say something, "Loo—" Then, "Why not?" He shrugs. It is Monty who approaches the young couple standing outside of their little house. "I have a guest here from Canada, and he would like to talk to you." We talk, and I am invited into their home. There is room for one narrow bed, and a stove. Above the bed is a calendar with a picture of two little blond girls.

"We haven't cleaned up. I am sorry for the mess." The man collects cardboard for recycling depots. "Two years I've been here, yes."

"Do you enjoy living like this?"

"I have my family back home. I hope to do better soon. There is still work for an honest man."

I am conscious of the eyes of fifty people looking at us from their shanty homes. We turn our backs and walk slowly away.

364

The most important aspect of dialectical maps is that they are personal, made as the journey progresses. Keeping our eyes open for the delicious, surprising possibilities of the journey is the delight of the dialectical map.

Khallid is taking us to the desert. We are on the highway outside of Riyadh on our way to the royal reserve. The signs above us, written in Arabic and Roman characters, look not unlike the signs I see on highways in southern Ontario, except they tell me that this road, if we were to stay on it long enough, would take us to Mecca and Medina. On the hillsides we see tents, flowing in the wind, and camels nearby. Bedouin camp outside Riyadh, waiting to go into the marketplaces.

Ahead of us is the open road. Except for the Bedouin, there is absolutely no one else in sight. The next town is a very long way, we are told.

There is something white on the roadside far off. As we get closer, I see it is a truck selling soft ice cream. There are colourful pictures of vanilla and chocolate cones painted on the sides. We pull up to the truck. Khallid turns to us. "What flavour would you like?"

τέλος

NOTES

1. Stephen W. Hawking, *A Brief History of Time* (Toronto: Bantam Books, 1988), 175:

    However, if we do discover a complete theory, it should in time be understand-able in broad principle by everyone, not just a few scientists. Then we shall all, philosophers, scientists, and just ordinary people, be able to take part in the dis-cussion of the question of why it is that we and the universe exist. If we find the answer to that, it would be the ultimate triumph of human reason—for then we would know the mind of God.

2. The concept of the things of the world, living and non-living, existing on a ladder of achievement, or having a ranking, goes back to before the Middle Ages. Aristotle describes a descending hierarchy from live-bearers such as humans down to grub producers such as insects. In his *De Generatione Animalium II*, 732b 27-33, and 733a 32, 733b1-16 (found in Aristotle, *De Partibus Animalium I and De Generatione Animalium I (with passages from II. 1-3)*, trans. D. M. Balme [Oxford: Clarendon Press, 1992], 59–60.), Aristotle writes:

    [T]he viviparous are those animals that are more perfected in nature and partake in a purer source. . . . The more perfected are those that are hotter in nature and wetter and not earthy. And the mark of natural heat is the lungs. . . . We should note how well and consecutively nature brings forth generation. The more per-fected and hotter animals bring forth their young perfected in respect to what sort they are (though no animal does so in respect of size , for all increase their size after birth), and these are the ones that generate animals within themselves immediately. The second grade do not generate perfected animals within them-selves immediately (for they bear live young after first producing eggs) but exter-nally they bear live. The next generate not a perfected animal but an egg, and this egg is perfected. The next, having a nature still colder than those, generate an egg, but it is not perfected: it becomes perfected outside, in the manner of the scaly kind of fishes and the crustaceans and cephalopods. The fifth and coldest kind does not even lay eggs out of itself, but this kind of affection comes about in this case outside, as we have said: the insects bear grubs in the first place, but the grub after development becomes egglike (for what is called the chrysalis has the capability of an egg) and then out of this comes an animal, gaining in the end its generation in the third change.

It is important to note here that hierarchy, as it is being used in this book, refers to a ranking of organisms or units that exist on the same organizational level. This is important because hierarchies can also describe levels of organization such as atoms as components of the more complex higher level of molecules, which are in turn components of tissues, which in turn constitute the organism. There are problems associated with that type of hierarchy as well (as will be discussed in later chapters), but for the most part, hierarchies that will be examined are associated with ranking, the perceived "political" organization of living things.

3. Shakespeare's *Troilus and Cressida*, act 1, scene 3, Ulysses. The full quote is as follows:

> The heavens themselves, the planets, and this centre,
> Observe degree, priority, and place,
> Insisture, course, proportion, season, form,
> Office, and custom, in all line of order;
> And therefore, is the glorious planet, Sol,
> In noble eminence enthron'd and spher'd
> Amidst the other; whose med'cinable eye
> Corrects the ill aspects of planets evil,
> And posts, like the commandment of a king,
> Sans check, to good and bad: but, when the planets,
> In evil mixture, to disorder wander,
> What plagues and what portents! What mutiny!
> What raging of the sea! Shaking of earth!
> Commotion in the winds! Frights, changes, horrors,
> Divert and crack, rend and deracinate
> The unity and married calm of states
> Quite from their fixure! O, when degree is shak'd,
> Which is the ladder to all high designs,
> The enterprise is sick! How could communities,
> Degrees in schools, and brotherhoods in cities,
> Peaceful commerce from dividable shores,
> The primogenitive and due of birth,
> Prerogative of age, crowns, sceptres, laurels,
> But by degree, stand in authentic place?
> Take but degree away, untune that string,
> And, hark, what discord follows!

4. In the century since Darwin, there have been opinions that blow hot and cold with respect to the power of his theories. During the beginning of the pursuit for root causes, attention moved away from Darwin's theory of natural selection toward the search for the subunits of heredity. These units, now known as genes, were speculated on by Darwin, who referred to them as "gemmules." A series of concepts was developed at the end of the past century and the beginning of the present one. The English philosopher Herbert Spencer (1820–1903) termed them "physiological units," and then there appeared the "idioplasm" of the Swiss botanist and physicist Karl von

Nägeli (1817–1891), the intracellular "pangenae" of the Dutch botanist and geneticist Hugo de Vries (1848–1935), the "idents" of the German biologist August Weisman (1834–1914), the "idioblasts" of the German zoologist Oscar Hertwig (1849–1922), and the "plasomes" of the German biologist Johannes von Wiesner. Because of the perceived need to understand root causes, the more outdoorsy and naturalist theory of natural selection was not particularly favoured at the time when genetic science was emerging. Today, however, there are attempts by theorists to bring together the different elements involved in studying, on one hand, the relationship between an organism and its component genes, and on the other, the relationship between an organism and its fellow creatures in the population. New concepts that consider slow change, along with major shifts at periodic intervals, have brought back a re-examination of Darwin's theory of natural selection, re-establishing it as a major element of scientific consideration. But the grander legacy is the twentieth-century version of Darwinian theory, the genetic movement.

5. Charles Darwin, *The Origin of Species* (New York: The Modern Library: no date—original publication, 1859, although the reference to Wallace only appears in the second edition, 1860, and subsequently), 371.

6. The Canadian historian of science Michael Ruse follows the development of the theory of evolution with respect to its link with the western cultural belief in "progress." He points out that in public, or popular, science, such as would be seen in a museum, the cultural concept of progress (which can include the concept of a hierarchy from the lowest animals to the highest humans) is still very much in vogue today. In the conclusion to *Monad to Man* (Cambridge, Mass.: Harvard University Press, 1996), 526, Ruse writes:

> The significance of the cultural value of Progress to the history of evolutionism has been confirmed, many times over. Evolutionary thought is the child of Progress, and for its first hundred years was but a pseudo-science, supported and justified by its cultural content. . . . For nigh two centuries, evolution functioned as an ideology, as a secular religion, that of Progress—usually against, although sometimes with Providence. Moreover, let there be no mistake that at the popular level, which for most people is the beginning and the end of their acquaintance with evolution, Progress continues to ride high. I have yet to find a museum or a display or a chart or a book which is not overtly progressionist.

7. Charles Darwin, *The Descent of Man and Selection in Relation to Sex* (Chicago: William Benton, 1871), 1971 reprint, 566–67.

8. Charles Lyell, , *Sir Charles Lyell's Scientific Journals on the Species Question*, ed. L. G. Wilson, (New Haven and London: Yale University Press, 1970), 373.

9. Phillips Verner Bradford and Harvey Blume, *Ota Benga: The Pygmy in the Zoo* (New York: St. Martin's Press, 1992).

1.   Aristotle, *Physics* II. 3, 194 b16 to 194 b32, trans. Robin Waterfield, (Oxford and New York: Oxford University Press, 1996), 38–39.

Aristotle (384 BCE to 322 BCE), in his *Physics*, lays out a description of the four causes as a prerequisite for understanding the nature and disposition of the natural world. All the causes, including the fourth (the teleological cause), are necessary for the thinking person who wishes to grasp this understanding. The relevant passage describing the four causes reads as follows:

> [T]he point of our investigation is to acquire knowledge, and a prerequisite for knowing anything is understanding why it is as it is—in other words, grasping its primary cause. Obviously, then, this is what we have to do in the case of coming to be and ceasing to be, and natural change in general. Then, once we know the principles of these things, we can try to analyse anything we are looking into in terms of these principles.
>
> One way in which the word "cause" is used is for that from which a thing is made and continues to be made—for example, the bronze of a statue, the silver of a bowl, and the genera of which bronze and silver are species. [This is the first cause—What something is made of.]
>
> A second way in which the word [cause] is used is for the form or pattern (i.e. the formula for what a thing is, both specifically and generically, and the terms which play a part in the formula). For example, the ratio 2:1, and the number in general, cause the octave. [This is the second cause—What is the form of something, or where does something exist in space?]
>
> A third way in which the word [cause] is used is for the original source of change or rest. For example, a deviser of a plan is a cause, a father causes a child, and in general a producer causes a product and a changer causes a change. [This is the third cause—whence did it come to be?]
>
> A fourth way in which the word [cause] is used is for the end. This is what something is for, as health, for example, may be what walking is for. If asked, "Why is he walking?", we reply, "To get healthy", and in saying this we mean to explain the cause of his walking. And then there is everything which happens during the process of change (initiated by something else) that leads up to the end: for example, the end of health may involve slimming or drugs or surgical implements; they are all for the same end, but they are different in that some are actions and some are implements. [This is the fourth cause—What is the purpose of something, or why is it here?]

2.   Bill Mason, *Path of the Paddle* (Toronto: Key Porter Books, 1995), 63.

3.   Conrad Hal Waddington, *Organisers and Genes* (Cambridge: Cambridge University Press, 1940).

4.   Ellen Larsen and Hooley M. G. McLaughlin, "The Morphogenetic Alphabet: Lessons for Simple-Minded Genes," *BioEssays*, Vol. 7, No. 3 (1987).

5.   The Human Genome Project was officially begun in October 1989 with the establishment of the National Center for Human Genome Research under the auspices of the National Institute of Health. James Watson was the first director, with a mandate to

map out the entire human genome. Watson and his colleagues believed that the map of the genes would reveal the key information necessary for the understanding of life on earth, particularly human life. The fact that genes interact with each other, and with the environment in a dynamic way, and that they cannot be seen as separate from the "system" which is life, does not stop researchers from believing that genes are the "blueprint" for life. The goals of the Human Genome Project are very close to the beliefs I heard Watson espouse in his discussion on the discovery of the proteins of a living cell. When I heard him speak in the early 1980s, Watson theorized that a list of the proteins in the living cell would reveal the workings of a cell. Similarly, in the Human Genome Project, he is looking for a list, a map of the chromosomes, and believes this to be a blueprint for life, the dynamics of genes within a living system notwithstanding, it seems.

The Human Genome Project has received more attention than any other biological project in history and more money. (See James D. Watson, "The Human Genome Project: Past, Present, and Future," in *Science*, Vol. 249 (April 6, 1990): 44–49, and Joan H. Fujimura and Michael Fortun, "Constructing Knowledge across Social Worlds: The Case of DNA Sequence Databases in Molecular Biology," in *Naked Science: Anthropological Inquiry into Boundaries, Power, and Knowledge*, ed. L. Nader, (New York and London: Routledge, 1996): 160–173.

6. Albert Einstein, letter to Max Born in March 1947 from "Quantum Spookiness Wins, Einstein Loses in Photon Test," in *Science*, Vol. 277, (July 25, 1997): 481.

7. *Science*, Vol. 249: 481.

8. *Photons* are light particles. In quantum mechanics, light can be understood as a particle and as a wave simultaneously. Photons are talked about as quantifiable "pieces" of light.

9. Map is redrawn from *Science*, Vol. 249: 481.

10. *Morphogenesis* is the generation of physical shape, or form, in a growing, developing living organism. *Dialectical morphogenesis* refers to the model described here, one that allows for a reciprocal relationship between the organism and its genes. The genes do not hold the blueprint for the ultimate shape of an animal or a plant. Neither does the shape reside strictly outside the genes. "The genes are necessary but not sufficient components," as my colleague Brian Goodwin has noted, just as the flesh, bones, and other tissues of the organism are necessary components, or at the level of the genes themselves, just as the proteins and other molecules are necessary but not sufficient components of the living system. In a dialectical morphogenetic model, there is a constant give and take, a contrapuntal reciprocal action between components, no one element dominating, but the system as a whole acting as a whole tangled unit.

11. *Regeneration* studies are concerned with the regrowth of a limb or a spinal cord after it has been injured or cut off. The regrowth of a body part or its extensive repair are not unlike the original growth seen during the embryonic stages; thus, regeneration is investigated in laboratories devoted to the study of embryos.

12. *Embryogenesis* is a term referring to the earliest stages in the life of a living organism. It means the beginning of the embryo, the genesis or origination of the incipient living creature. An embryo has all the components that will eventually grow into the mature organism, but in a somewhat unformed and uncommitted state.

13. Redrawn from information presented in Knud J. V. Rasmussen, "Iglulik and Caribou Eskimo Texts," in *Report of the Fifth Thule Expedition*, Vol. VII, Part iii (Copenhagen: Gyldendalske Boghandel, 1030); sketch map III, facing p. 98., as found in John Spink and D. W. Moore, "Eskimo Maps of the Canadian Eastern Arctic," *Cartographica*, (Toronto: University of Toronto Press, 1972).

14. Redrawn from John Spink and D. W. Moore, "Eskimo Maps of the Canadian Eastern Arctic."

15. Redrawn from "Iglulik and Caribou Eskimo Texts," sketch map X, facing p. 158.

16. Redrawn from "Eskimo Maps of the Canadian Eastern Arctic."

CHAPTER THREE: The Dark Wood

1. The Gulag refers to an initiative of Josef Stalin's in the Soviet Union. According to my Soviet friend and associate Sasha, the word *Gulag* is an amalgamation of three terms: G for *gulavnoye*, meaning "main"; U for *upravlenye*, meaning department; and *lag* from *lager*, meaning "camp." The Gulag was a system developed by the agencies that eventually became known as the KGB—the Committee for State Protection, in the Soviet Union. For decades, between the 1920s until a few years after the death of Stalin in 1953, the Gulag was a major industry. Millions of people, sometimes whole villages, were arrested and sent to work in camps across the Soviet Union. By far the largest contingent went to Siberia. Camps for political prisoners did not stop after Stalin, and some believe that the system lasts to this day, even after the dissolution of the Soviet Union. However, the peak of activity was under Stalin, especially during the 1940s.

2. The term *America* was first used on a map of the world in 1507. The map was drawn up by Martin Waldseemüller, who had read the account of the voyages of Amerigo Vespucci, published as *Mundus Novus* in 1503. During this time, Columbus never gave up the idea that the West Indies were the gateway to the east.

3. The map was drawn with reference to Peter Whitfield, *The Image of the World* (San Francisco: Pomegranate Artbooks, 1994), 44–45. The original is housed in the Biblioteca Estensa, Modena.

4. Stephen Lamoreaux, *Physical Review Letters*, 1997.

5. Stephen J. Gould and Richard Lewontin, "The Spandrels of San Marco and the Panglossian Paradigm: a critique of the adaptationist programme," *Proceedings of the Royal Society of London*, b205, 581–98, 1979.

6. C. S. Coon, S. M. Garnand and J. B. Birdsell, *Races* (Springfield, Ohio: C. Thomas, 1950).

7. B. T. Shea, "Eskimo craniofacial morphology, cold stress and the maxillary sinus," in *American Journal of Physiological Anthropology* 47 (1977): 289–300.

8. Dr. Pangloss goes so far as to say that even his venereal disease is to be considered a perfect development, as it can be traced back to the discovery of riches from the New World. Without his venereal disease, there would have been no chocolate.

> It is indispensable in this best of worlds. It is a necessary ingredient. For if Columbus, when visiting the West Indies, had not caught the disease, which

poisons the source of generation, which frequently even hinders generation, and is clearly opposed to the great end of Nature, we should have neither chocolate nor cochineal. We see, too, that to this very day the disease, like religious controversy, is peculiar to us Europeans. The Turks, the Indians, the Persians, the Chinese, the Siamese, the Japanese as yet have no knowledge of it; but there is a "sufficient reason" for their experiencing it in turn in the course of a few centuries. . . .

– From Voltaire, *Candide*, trans. John Butt (London: Penguin, 1947), 30.

9. The Great Chain of Being refers to the ranking of all living (and non-living) things, from the lowest to the highest, the human being existing just below the levels of the angels and God. Arthur O. Lovejoy in *The Great Chain of Being* (Cambridge, Mass.: Harvard University Press, 1936) traces the concept back to the Middle Ages with roots in Plato and Aristotle.

10. I would dispute the constant references made by adaptationist thinkers to the concept "purposeless." Stating it does not let them off the hook. There is nothing purposeless in a process that is moving everything up some preconceived ladder leading to perfection.

11. The song referred to is "Tell Me Why."

12. Daniel C. Dennett, *Darwin's Dangerous Idea: Evolution and the Meanings of Life* (New York: Simon and Schuster, New York, 1996), 511, 520.

13. "The Spandrels of San Marco and the Panglossian Paradigm."

14. The map was redrawn from information supplied by and with grateful acknowledgement to the Dean and Chapter of Hereford Cathedral and the Hereford Mappa Mundi Trust, and from information in P. D. A. Harvey, *Mappa Mundi: The Hereford World Map* (Toronto: University of Toronto Press, 1996).

15. "The Spandrels of San Marco and the Panglossian Paradigm," 593.

16. Paul Davies, "The Mind of God," in *Physics and Our View of the World*, ed. Jan Hilgevoord (Cambridge: Cambridge University Press, 1994).

> Page 231: Science emerged from mediaeval Europe, under the twin influences of Greek philosophy and the Judaeo-Christian religion.

> Page 233: Very few scientists, however, stop to wonder where these laws come from, or why they have the form they do. In particular, they do not question the fact that we human beings are apparently capable of knowing these laws. Yet the entire scientific enterprise is founded on the assumption that the Universe is rationally ordered and that we, as rational beings, can come to know that order through the processes of reasoned inquiry that we call science. For Newton and his followers this was no mystery. They believed that Man was created in God's image, and so shared his divine rationality, albeit in diminished form. Thus Man is able to discern this same rational structure reflected in Nature, because the physical world is also a product of God's rational plan. But if the laws are no longer regarded as thoughts in the mind of God, the success of science seems baffling.

Paul Davies, professor of natural philosophy at the University of Adelaide, formerly held the chair of theoretical physics at the University of Newcastle upon Tyne and is the author of *The Mind of God* (New York: Simon and Schuster, 1992).

17. Ibid., 238.

CHAPTER FOUR: Paris and America

1. The Mall refers to the large grassy area between the Washington Monument and the Capitol building. On either side of the grass, which covers several football fields of room, are the museums associated with the Smithsonian Institution. The Smithsonian is the centre of much of the world's museum activity.

2. PET stands for positron emission tomography. A person's blood is infused (usually through inhalation) with a radioactive isotope of oxygen or another relatively low-level radioactive material, such as Xenon gas, that emits elementary particles called positrons; the positrons are traced through the brain. Sectors of the brain that reveal more positron emission are also areas with more blood flow, indicating more mental activity, and this activity shows up on the PET scan. The scan can be set to look at layers of the brain, in much the same way as the more common CAT (computerized axial tomography) scan. In the case of the PET scan, changes occur in less than a tenth of a second, indicating new active areas—a new emotion, a new thought being worked out, a new visual or auditory experience, and so on.

3. John Hinckley Jr. was committed to St. Elizabeth's Hospital after attempting to assassinate President Reagan in 1981.

4. *Prefrontal* refers to the front-most section of the brain, and *dorsolateral* to those parts of the frontal sections that are set slightly off the centre line. It is these areas that are associated with the personality or affect of an individual. When the dorsolateral prefrontal cortex of the brain is chronically not in communication with the rest of the brain, the individual has characteristically little affect and little ability to understand how to plan or to communicate with others. The flat affect, social withdrawal, lack of goal direction, poor motivation, and behaviour dominated by immediate rather than long-term needs are typical traits in someone who is not using the dorsolateral prefrontal cortex. These traits are also characteristic of patients suffering from schizophrenia. The experiments being performed using the brain imaging techniques were aimed at describing the function of the prefrontal regions of the brain; the most revealing studies compared the brain scans of normal individuals with those suffering from schizophrenia. On the day we attended the experimental sessions, the subject was a patient diagnosed with schizophrenia, who was also receiving neuroleptic drug treatment designed to control hallucinations and other symptoms. (Details on the experimental procedure can be found in Daniel R. Weinberger, Karen F. Berman, and Ronald F. Zec, "Physiological Dysfunction of Dorsolateral Prefrontal Cortex in Schizophrenia: I. Regional Cerebral Blood Flow Evidence," in *Archives of General Psychiatry*, Vol. 43 [1986]: 114–24; and Karen F. Berman, Ronald F. Zec, and Daniel R. Weinberger, "Physiological Dysfunction of Dorsolateral Prefrontal Cortex in Schizophrenia: II. Role of Neuroleptic Treatment, Attention, and Mental Effort," in *Archives of General Psychiatry*, Vol. 43 [1986]: 126–35.)

5. I am aware that many areas of scientific endeavour have used networks to describe phenomena. However, in western science, the predominating model is still hierarchical. A network model, wherein every element holds an equal position and a balance is sought between all the elements, is not typical, or at least only represents a minor aspect of the more global hierarchical model. Nevertheless, networks have been used for modelling

such areas of study as machine intelligence, human brain circuitry, the ecosystem, and even the immune system.

I recall thinking of Indra's net one other time in my scientific work. I was studying immunology with Alastair Cunningham at the University of Toronto in the late 1970s, when he brought up the work of Niels Jerne, the Danish immunologist. He had developed a network theory that explained the observations that immune cells, which produce antibodies against disease or other foreign substance, and also stimulate other cells to form antibodies against the original antibody-forming cells themselves, thus anti-antibodies. And in turn, there are eventually anti-anti-antibody cells and so on. Every so often, one of the links would be a node that would also have antibody properties against a foreign invader. The effect would be as follows: an invasion of foreign substance would stimulate not only the body's production of antibodies but would also stimulate a ripple effect throughout the entire network of interlinking cell reactions. (N. K. Jerne, "Towards a network theory of the immune system," in *An. Immunol.* [*Paris*] 125C, 1974: 373.) Despite the effectiveness of describing the immune system in terms of an interlaced network, however, the predominant model (which even overlies Jerne's model) is one that describes "fighting off" foreign invaders, thus invoking the concept of something always being superior to something else in nature. This concept of superiority is the hallmark of the hierarchical scientific model that, I maintain, subsumes all other models in western thought.

6. Georges Cuvier, *Cuvier's Animal Kingdom, Arranged according to its organisation; Forming the Basis for a Natural History of Animals and an Introduction to Comparative Anatomy. Volume 1.* (1817) (London: Wms. Orr & Co., Amen Corner, Paternoster Row, 1840), 49.

7. *Sir Charles Lyell's Scientific Journals on the Species Question*, ed. L.G. Wilson (New Haven and London: Yale University Press, 1970), 347.

8. In the Wisconsin card sorting task, the subject tries to discover the rules for sorting playing cards—rules that have been arbitrarily set by the experimenter. In the computer version of the task, the subject responds to images that differ in colour, shape, and number (like playing cards). A subject is asked to match each image by using an electronic switch labelled with the same colours and shapes—all the time trying to match according to the as yet obscure rules for sorting. Feedback as to the correctness or incorrectness of the response is given by a green or red light, respectively. Once the "rule" for correct matching is discovered and a series of at least ten correct responses is recorded, the rule changes without warning and the subject has to decipher the new rule, and so on.

Concentrating on solving this task characteristically activates the dorsolateral prefrontal cortex region of the brain and allows for an image of the "planning" brain to show up on the PET scan. This type of planning is also characteristically not found to be common in subjects suffering from schizophrenia.

9. Philip Lieberman, "Peak Capacity," in *The Sciences*, November/December 1997: 22–27.

10. It was thought at the time of Saartje Baartman's dissection in the early 1800s that the labia of Khoi women were evidence of a lower order. Their extended shape was proof of this to anatomists such as Cuvier. Suspicions that the Khoi people may even have intercourse with apes was also entertained. This belief that African people were something less than human probably affected the observation skills of the scientists of the

time. If there were differences in the genitalia of Khoi women compared with European women, they may have been due to the small sample size that anatomists used for such comparisons. Alternatively, they may have been due to sexual practices that involved pulling down the inner labia, which over time led to a slight extension of the tissue. This type of practice seems less unusual when we consider the nipple rings, cock rings, and pierced labia of western people today. Any genetic differences postulated by investigators have to be seen as products of overactive imaginations of the European scientists involved, people rather too interested in the sexual organs of exotic foreign women. On the other hand, Stephen Jay Gould (in *The Flamingo's Smile: Reflections in Natural History* [New York and London: W. W. Norton and Company, 1987), 291–305] claims to have been shown the Cuvier dissection (in the storage area of the Musée de l'Homme by Professor Yves Coppens); Gould's straightforward description of the item appears to give some credibility to the possibility that genitalia may vary slightly in appearance from one group to another, perhaps just as faces do. In this regard, Saartjie Baartman was also known for her large protruding buttocks. Just as individual families will have a characteristic appearance, the tribal group of Saartjie Baartman may have had particular traits. I suggest that we find these differences much less alarming today in our world of multicultural societies.

CHAPTER FIVE: Southern Africa and Leningrad

1. David Hume, *A Treatise of Human Nature* (first published in 1739), ed. Ernest Mossner (London: Penguin Books, 1969, reprinted 1985), 52.

2. Ibid., 231.

3. Ibid., 233.

4. Karl R. Popper, *The Logic of Scientific Discovery* (first published in German in 1934), author trans. (London and New York: Routledge, 1959, reprinted 1992), 27.

5. Ptolemy's work was rediscovered by Europeans in the 1400s, having been preserved by Islamic scholars. His map of the world, which was superior to the medieval religious-based maps used for centuries in Europe, was republished in 1477 and had considerable impact on mapmakers. The Martellus map relied heavily on the Ptolemy map, but added details supplied by explorers such as the Portuguese travelling on Dias's voyage around the Cape of Africa. In Martellus's map, Africa appears for the first time as a continent that is not connected to Asia by means of a long unexplored southern land mass.

6. David Hume, "Of National Characters," in *Philosophical Works III; Essays: Moral, Political & Literary*, eds. T. H. Green and T. H. Gross (1882 edition, first published in 1748), 252

7. Immanuel Kant, *Observations on the Feeling of the Beautiful and Sublime* (first published in 1763) trans. John T. Goldthwait (Berkeley: University of California Press, 1961), 110–111.

8. Popper, *The Logic of Scientific Discovery*, 53–54.

9. I forget the name of the hotel now. It was to the north and west of Leningradski Prospekt. I remember the taxi driver taking pity on me and taking me where I would find others who felt as desperate as myself. He left me at the door, assuring me, in Russian, that no Russians were allowed into the hotel. Unlike my rather unhappy visit to the Savoia Hotel near Red Square (related in Chapter Two), this outing left me at least filled with food and drink by the end of an evening.

10. Popper, *The Logic of Scientific Discovery*, 40–41 (Italics Popper's).

11. Rodney W. Nichols, "The Scent of Science," in *The Sciences*, September/October 1997, New York Academy of Sciences: 6.

12. Walpole Island had a sign at the entrance stating that it is "Unceded Territory," meaning that it is not considered to be a reserve by the residents. The area is under dispute.

13. Any open piece of land can be inhabited by squatters in present-day South Africa. By law, the inhabitants cannot be moved until better accommodations are found. However, there are increasing demands by other residents to move the squatters from the downtown area, which is filling up with hawkers who sell on the streets and do not pay rent—for their homes or for their businesses. The accommodation found for the Braamfontein squatters was considered adequate compensation for burning up their homes. (Inside many of these squatters' huts are comfortable homes, a real attempt to make something out of nothing.)

14. Popper, *The Logic of Scientific Discovery*, 42.

CHAPTER SIX: Leningrad and White River

1. Pronounced, "teh´ los." Aristotle used the term τέλος meaning the "end," a concept related to the "completion" or "perfection" of a thing. Questions pertaining to the purpose, or end use of a thing or a process (what something is "designed for") are asked in the form of a *why* question. They are termed teleological questions, derived from Aristotle's use of the term τέλος. Teleological questions have been the basis for much philosophical debate over the centuries.

2. Aristotle, *Physics* II. 8, 198 b16 to 198 b17, trans. Robin Waterfield (Oxford and New York: Oxford University Press: 1996), 50.

3. *Physics* II. 8, 198 b17 to 198 b30, 50.

4. *Physics* II. 8, 198 b32 to 199 b33, 51–53.

5. Thomas S. Kuhn, *The Structure of Scientific Revolutions*, 3d ed., (Chicago: The University of Chicago Press, 1996, originally published 1962), 18–19.

6. Ibid, 148. The complete quotation refers to a few examples that help to bring the point out more clearly:

> We have . . . seen several reasons why the proponents of competing paradigms must fail to make complete contact with each other's viewpoints. Collectively these reasons have been described as the incommensurability of the pre- and postrevolutionary normal-scientific traditions, and we need only recapitulate

them briefly here. In the first place, the proponents of competing paradigms will often disagree about the list of problems that any candidate for paradigm must resolve. Their standards or their definitions of science are not the same. Must a theory of motion explain the cause of the attractive forces between particles of matter or may it simply note the existence of such forces? Newton's dynamics was widely rejected because, unlike both Aristotle's and Descartes's theories, it implied the latter answer to the question. When Newton's theory had been accepted, a question was therefore banished from science. That question, however, was one that general relativity may proudly claim to have solved. Or again, as disseminated in the nineteenth century, Lavoisier's chemical theory inhibited chemists from asking why the metals were so much alike, a question that phlogistic chemistry had both asked and answered. The transition to Lavoisier's paradigm, like the transition to Newton's, meant a loss not only of a permissible question but of an achieved solution. That loss was not, however, permanent either. In the twentieth century questions about the qualities of chemical substances have entered science again, together with some answers to them.

7. Ibid, 66.

8. Ibid, 56.

The more complete quotation is valuable as an insight into Kuhn's interpretation of the paradigm-shifting thinking of Lavoisier, and serves as an example of the power of theories over the intellectual map of an individual:

> Grant now that discovery involves an extended, though not necessarily long, process of conceptual assimilation. Can we also say it involves a change in paradigm? To that question, no general answer can yet be given, but in this case at least, the answer must be yes. What Lavoisier announced in his papers from 1777 on was not so much the discovery of oxygen as the oxygen theory of combustion. That theory was the keystone for a reformulation of chemistry so vast that it is usually called the chemical revolution. Indeed, if the discovery of oxygen had not been an intimate part of the emergence of a new paradigm for chemistry, the question of priority from which we began would never have seemed so important. In this case as in others, the value placed upon a new phenomenon and thus upon its discoverer varies with our estimate of the extent to which the phenomenon violated paradigm-induced anticipations. Notice however ... that the discovery of oxygen was not by itself the cause of the change in chemical theory. Long before he played any part in the discovery of the new gas, Lavoisier was convinced both that something was wrong with the phlogiston theory and that burning bodies absorbed some part of the atmosphere. That much he had recorded in a sealed note deposited with the Secretary of the French Academy in 1772. What the work on oxygen did was to give much additional form and structure to Lavoisier's earlier sense that something was amiss. It told him a thing he was already prepared to discover—the nature of the substance that combustion removes from the atmosphere. That advance awareness of difficulties must be a significant part of what enabled Lavoisier to see in experiments like Priestley's a gas that Priestley had been unable to see there himself. Conversely, the fact that a major paradigm revision was needed to see what Lavoisier saw must be the principal reason why Priestley was, to the end of his long life, unable to see it.

9. Ibid, 71.

10. Ibid, 150–51. The Max Planck quotation is cited in Kuhn as Max Planck, *Scientific Autobiography and Other Papers*, trans. F. Gaynor, New York, 1949, 33–34.

11. Ibid, 205–206.

12. The effects of culture and language on the interpretation of scientific "facts" are to be found throughout Toulmin's long list of publications spanning four decades. Stephen Toulmin, *The Philosophy of Science*, (London: Hutchinson University Library, 1953), 129:

    To talk . . . of theoretical physics . . . and to ask for the facts and nothing but the facts, is to demand the impossible, like asking for a map drawn to no particular projection and having no particular scale. . . .

    [I]t is possible to show, with a very little technical explanation, how the acceptability of statements which at first glance seem to be pure matters of fact may depend, rather, on the technique of representation employed in a physical theory.

    Stephen Toulmin, *Cosmopolis: The Hidden Agenda of Modernity* (Chicago: The University of Chicago Press, 1990), 201:

    Even at the core of 20th-century physics, idiosyncrasies of persons and cultures cannot be eliminated. The quirks and backgrounds of creative scientists are as relevant to our understanding of their ideas as they are to our understanding of the work of poets or architects. There are things about Einstein's general theory of relativity, for example, that are understood best if we learn that Einstein was a visual rather than a verbal thinker, and things about quantum mechanics that are best explained if we know that Nils Bohr grew up in a household where Kierkegaard's ideas about "complementary" modes of thought were . . . discussed at Sunday dinner.

13. Toulmin, *Cosmopolis*, 15–16:

    Even now, historians . . . still treat the early 17th century as the transition point from medieval to modern times. . . . Looking back at the "received view" of Modernity after fifty years, my inclination is to retort, "Don't believe a word of it!" From the start, that whole story was one-sided and over-optimistic, and veered into self-congratulation.

14. Stephen Toulmin, *An Examination of the Place of Reason in Ethics* (Cambridge: Cambridge University Press, 1950), 127:

    [N]o scientific theory can modify the experience it explains. The sun still looks red at sunset, although we know that it is not *really* red; physics may explain why a stick looks bent. And even to say, "No explanation *can* modify the corresponding experiences," may be misleading, for it is the logical conditions we impose on "Scientific Observations" rather than any feature of the "physical world" that accounts for the impossibility—no experience which could be altered by a change in one's beliefs alone would be acceptable to us as "scientific observation."

    It is of interest that Stephen Toulmin was a student of Ludwig Wittgenstein, who analyzed the relationship between "reality" and the communication of this reality.

15. Aristotle, *The Politics*, Book VII, Chapter vii (1327b18–1328a21) trans. T. A. Sinclair. Revised and re-presented by Trevor J. Saunders (London: Penguin Books, 1981), 410.

16. See David Lewis, *We, the Navigators, the ancient art of landfinding in the Pacific*, 2d
     ed. (Honolulu: University of Hawaii Press, 1994), 173–179; also see Ward H. Goode-
     nough, "Navigation in the Western Carolines: A Traditional Science," in *Naked Sci-
     ence: Anthropological Inquiry into Boundaries, Power, and Knowledge*, ed. L. Nader
     (New York and London: Routledge, 1996), 29–42.

17. Information for map adapted from David Lewis, *We, the Navigators, the ancient art of
     landfinding in the Pacific*, 2d ed. (Honolulu: University of Hawaii Press, 1994) 173–79.

18. Dava Sobel, *Longitude* (New York: Walker and Company, 1995). It is true that sailors
     travelled out of the sight of land before the 1700s, but not with any confidence. Meth-
     ods for determining the longitude position were not accurate before the chronometer.
     Most ships hugged the coastlines of continents.

CHAPTER SEVEN: Escape

1. One could argue that capturing the reins of one's own destiny is hardly purposeless,
    but in the sense that local actions do not seek to achieve a world as conceived by a
    higher being, or designer, they are "purposeless" with regard to the universe as a
    whole. Meaning can be found, but it exists at the very personal self-generated level of
    the individual in her or his landscape.

2. Hooley M. G. McLaughlin, Michel P. Rathbone, Richard A. Liversage, and Danielle
    S. McLaughlin, "Levels of Cyclic GMP and Cyclic AMP in Regenerating Forelimbs
    of Adult Newts Following Denervation," in *The Journal of Experimental Zoology*, 225
    (1983): 175–85.

3. Hans Spemann worked in Germany in the first half of the century studying the embry-
    onic "organizer." The organizer was isolated in a particular sector of the very early em-
    bryo, and was believed by Spemann and his associates to "control" the initiation of
    the embryo. It is significant that the transplant of this organizer into another host em-
    bryo was seen, because of the subsequent embryonic organization noted in the host
    tissue, to be proof of an organizing essence. This theory is antithetical to my proposal
    that any organizing in the embryo comes about not from one or more dictatorial orga-
    nizers but from the general "dialogue" among the many tissue types.

    Spemann published his definitive work on the subject of the organizer in 1924:
    Hans Spemann und Hilde Mangold, "Über Induktion von Embryonalanlagen durch
    Implantation artfremder Organisatoren," in *Roux' Archiv für Entwicklungs mechanik*,
    100 (1924): 599–638. He won the Nobel Prize for Physiology and Medicine in 1935,
    largely based on this work.

    It is of interest that an "organizer" was the basis of a theory for embryogenesis in a
    German laboratory during the 1920s and 1930s. The concept of a dominating tissue
    type is certainly reminiscent of the politics of the time. Spemann's student and succes-
    sor to the directorship of his Freiburg laboratory in 1937, Otto Mangold, Hilde's
    husband, supported the Nazi Party (see Viktor Hamburger, *The Heritage of Experi-
    mental Embryology: Hans Spemann and the Organizer* [New York and Oxford: Ox-
    ford University Press, 1988], 57). There is a certain symmetry to the fact that the

Germany my wife and I witnessed in 1970, with all its destructive symbolism left over from the Second World War, was also the source of our later laboratory work in embryology.

4. G. W. F. Hegel, *The Philosophy of History*, trans. J. Sibree (1899, The Colonial Press, put together by students of Hegel's from lectures delivered 1830 to 1831) (New York: Dover Publications, 1956), 78.

5. I worked on the chick embryo experiments by day as well, but it was the nighttime surgical sessions that allowed for so much pure observation of the living embryos. During these times, I began to think about the embryo system as a whole, something that could not be broken without changing the entire system of the embryo utterly. Therefore, these nighttime sessions marked the change in my experimental practice. During the day, I worked on the analysis of the work, the care of the animals and the embryos, and on setting up the apparatus needed for the nighttime sessions that took place only once or twice a week. As it turned out, the chick embryo work became the topic and theoretical basis of my Ph.D. thesis, "Morphological patterning and stability in the regenerating spinal cord of the chick embryo," 1985, University of Toronto. This work, although in many ways it deviated significantly from the traditional approach of perturbation experimentation, was strongly supported by my supervisor, R. A. Liversage, and by my colleagues.

6. Johannes Holtfreter, "Neural induction in explants which have passed through a sublethal cytolysis," in *The Journal of Experimental Zoology* 106 (1947): 197–222. It is interesting that I should find inspiration in Holtfreter's work, since he came from Spemann's laboratory, where the prevalent hypothesis concerning the organizer, a concept diametrically opposite to my ideas, was being developed. However, opposite concepts often have the same source. It should be noted that I also came from a laboratory that can be directly traced back to Spemann's.

7. *Prespinal cord* refers to the embryonic tissue that will eventually become the hollow tube that is the spinal cord, complete with all its nerves and other specialized cells. In the prespinal form, it is a long flat area, not yet characterized by nerve and other special cells.

8. C. D. Stern, "A Simple Model for Early Morphogenesis," in *Journal of Theoretical Biology*, 107 (1984): 229–42.

9. Hooley M. G. McLaughlin, "Morphological patterning and stability in the regenerating spinal cord of the chick embryo," Ph.D. thesis, University of Toronto (1985): 137a.

10. Hooley M.G. McLaughlin, Ph.D. thesis, University of Toronto (1985): 140a.

11. The shape of growing embryonic tissues and organs has its roots in both the tissue/inner-environmental interchange and in elements like the genes. The genes are a part of the system as a whole, their role in designating protein production within the context of the local environment closely associated with the eventual shape of the embryo. In the case of early embryonic spinal cord formation, for example, the cells that line the inner tube of the brain and spinal cord are epithelial, or skin-like, in nature. As such, they tend to form a surface that is juxtaposed with an open space, perfect conditions for such things as tube formation. The genetic component in this developmental process is therefore a necessary one, but it cannot be supposed that *all* the shape conditions are somehow held within the genetic code. The experiments described here

indicate that shape is very much a condition of the interchange between the developing tissue of the embryo and its inner landscape or environment.

12. Hans-Georg Gadamer, *Hegel's Dialectic: Five Hermeneutical Studies*, trans. P. C. Smith. (New Haven and London: Yale University Press, 1976) (excerpt from "The idea of Hegel's Logic"), 86. First published as *Hegels Dialektik* (Tübingen: J. C. B. Mohr, 1971).

The first part of Chapter One of Hegel's *Science of Logic*, trans. A. V. Miller (London: George Allen and Unwin, 1969), 82–83, reads as follows:

Being

A. Being

Being, pure being, without any further determination. In its indeterminate immediacy it is equal only to itself. . . . Being, the indeterminate immediate, is in fact *nothing*, and neither more nor less than *nothing*.

B. Nothing

Nothing, pure nothing: it is simply equality with itself, complete emptiness, absence of all determination and content - undifferentiatedness in itself. . . . Nothing is . . . the same determination, or rather absence of determination, and thus altogether the same as, pure *being*.

C. Becoming

I. Unity of Being and Nothing

Pure being and *pure nothing* are, therefore, the same. What is the truth is neither being nor nothing, but that being—does not pass over but has passed over—into nothing, and nothing into being. But it is equally true that they are not undistinguished from each other, that, on the contrary, they are not the same, that they are absolutely distinct, and yet that they are unseparable and inseparable and that each immediately *vanishes in its opposite*. Their truth is, therefore, this movement of the immediate vanishing of the one in the other: becoming, a movement in which both are distinguished, but by a difference which has equally immediately resolved itself.

Hegel has articulated his dialectical approach distinctly here. Opposites are both different from and identical to each other, they define each other, and ultimately they define "Becoming," essentially a new principle, which is inevitably developed from the existence of anything, since any "thing," or "Being," must be defined by its opposite, even if that opposite is "Nothing." All this happens as an immediate here-and-now activity. There is no map laid out for the process, it is inherently non-teleological.

13. *Chuang Tzu Basic Writings*, trans. Burton Watson (New York and London: Columbia University Press, 1964), 35.

14. Chuang-tzu is arguing here with another philosopher, Kung-sun Lung, who has written about how one cannot define an object through its attributes. Kung-sun Lung argues that a "white" horse is not a horse because then all horses of a different colour could not fit the definition of "horse," since it has been first based on a horse with the "white" designation. The basis of Chuang-tzu's argument is somewhat different. By playing with the concepts of Kung-sun Lung, he is bringing out a deeper point, pointing to the

fact that a thing has its definition in its opposite. Before the horse reference, Chuang-tzu refers more explicitly to the need for opposites in definitions. He also refers to the juxtaposition of death and birth, or the generation of new orders out of the destruction of the old, reminiscent of Hegel: "Everything has its 'that,' everything has its 'this'. . . . '[T]hat' comes out of 'this' and 'this' depends on 'that'—which is to say that 'this' and 'that' give birth to each other. But where there is death there must be birth." (*Chuang Tzu Basic Writings*, 34-35.)

The similarity between Hegel and Chuang-tzu has not gone unnoticed. Wing-Tsit Chan in *A Source Book in Chinese Philosophy* (Princeton: Princeton University Press, 1963), 183, writes of Chuang-tzu's "horse" passage: "Things are not only relative, they are identical, for opposites produce each other, imply each other, are identical with each other, and are both finite series. In some respects Chuang Tzu is surprisingly similar to Hegel and Nagarjuna (c. 100-200 C.E.) [Nagarjuna was a philosopher writing in India on the nature of the original coming into being of all natural things.] It must be quickly added, however, that both the dialectic of Hegel and the relativity of Nagarjuna are much more conceptual than Chuang Tzu's synthesis of opposites."

In my case, the development of dialectical concepts, the non-teleological map, had its roots in part in my studies of Chinese philosophy. I did not discover Hegel until many years later, when I was working as a biologist.

15. Richard A. Liversage, Danielle S. McLaughlin, and Hooley M. G. McLaughlin, "The hormonal milieu in amphibian appendage regeneration," in *Regulation of Amphibian Forelimb Regeneration*, ed. R. E. Sicard (New York: Oxford University Press, 1985), 54-80.

16. Gadamer, *Hegel's Dialectic: Five Hermeneutical Studies*, 26.

17. Plato, *Sophist*, 243e to 244a, from *Plato: The Collected Dialogues*, eds. Edith Hamilton and Huntington Cairns, Bollingen Series LXXI (Princeton: Princeton University Press, 1989), 987. (Originally from *Plato's Theory of Knowledge: The Theaetetus and the Sophist*, trans. F. M. Cornford, London, 1935, with passages from the translation by B. Jowett in *The Dialogues of Plato*, 3d ed. Oxford, 1931, first printed in 1892.)

18. G. W. F. Hegel, *The Philosophy of History* (trans. J. Sibree 1899, The Colonial Press, put together by students of Hegel's from lectures delivered 1830 to 1831) (New York: Dover Publications, 1956), 341. It should be noted that there is a footnote to this section that has expectations for the underlying nature of humankind. It reads: "The Supreme Law of the Universe is recognized as identical with the dictates of Conscience—becomes a 'law of liberty.' Morality—that authority which has the incontestable right to determine men's actions, which therefore is the only absolutely *free* and unlimited power—is no longer a compulsory enactment, but the free choice of human beings. The good man would make Law for himself if he found none made for him."

This does seem to indicate a strong belief in the free will entailed in the development of one's personal non-teleological map for life. But at the same time, it indicates the innate morality that is a trait, and not a relative one, of all human beings. I will return to this subject at the end of the book, but it should be noted here that although this may be arguable, Hegel couches the belief for universal morality within his conviction that not all peoples express the trait equally. References to non-European peoples especially are filled with descriptions of low morals.

19. Ibid., 18.

20. Ibid., 81.

21. Ibid., 93.

22. Ibid., 99.

23. Ibid., 98–99.

24. Plato, *Timaeus*, 37d–38a, ibid., 1167.

25. William Shakespeare, *Troilus and Cressida*, act 1, scene 3, Ulysses.

26. John Milton, "Samson Agonistes," lines 1687–1707, from *The Portable Milton*, ed. D. Bush (New York: Penguin, Middlesex), 662– 663. Written in 1671, near the end of his life, perhaps when concepts of death were not so foreign to him.

27. Frantz Fanon, *The Wretched of the Earth*, trans. C. Farrington (New York: Grove Press, Inc., 1963), 35 (first published 1961 as *Les damnés de la terre*).

28. Ibid., 48–49.

29. Gail M. Presbey, "Fanon on the Role of Violence in Liberation: A Comparison with Gandhi and Mandela," in *Fanon: A Critical Reader*, ed. L. R. Gordon, T. D. Sharpley-Whiting, and R. T. White (Oxford: Blackwell Publishers, 1996), 284.

30. Ibid., 296.

CHAPTER EIGHT: Arabia

1. His Royal Highness Prince Sultan ibn Salman ibn 'Abd al-'Aziz, our host in Saudi Arabia, is an important man in the Kingdom of Saudi Arabia for more than one reason. He is high-ranking with respect to the succession to the throne—Abd al-'Aziz refers to the first king of the country—and Prince Sultan is world travelled and educated. He has been one of the few non-Americans to travel as an astronaut in one of the shuttle missions. His vision for a scientifically literate nation was responsible for my visit.

2. Ludwig Wittgenstein, *Tractatus Logico-Philosophicus*, trans. D. F. Pears and B. F. McGuinness (London and New York: Routledge, 1974), 5. (First published in *Annalen der Naturphilosophie*, 1921.)
The passage reads:

1	The world is all that is the case.
1.1	The world is the totality of facts, not of things.
1.11	The world is determined by the facts, and by their being *all* the facts.
1.12	For the totality of facts determines what is the case, and also whatever is not the case.
1.13	The facts in logical space are the world.
1.2	The world divides into facts.

Wittgenstein's *Tractatus* has had a formative effect on the logical positivists and others in the twentieth century who have sought a purely empirical basis for scientific practice and its relationship to the discovery of ultimate truth. (It has been argued, however, that Wittgenstein himself was not, even during the time of his writing the *Tractatus*, an adherent of the pure logical positivist stance.) Logical positivists are encouraged by statements in the *Tractatus* confirming that to understand a proposition means to know the conditions under which it is true.

> 4.02   We can see this from the fact that we understand the sense of a propositional sign without its having been explained to us.
>
> 4.024   To understand a proposition means to know what is the case if it is true.
> (One can understand it, therefore, without knowing whether it is true.)
> It is understood by anyone who understands its constituents.

This passage gives confirmation to the positivists' desire to limit discussions in pure science to empirical investigations; approaches that render propositions that cannot be "verified" are considered to be meaningless. (Karl Popper modified this approach to allow only hypotheses that can be potentially "falsified," but it is along the same lines.) However, according to scholars examining the history of Wittgenstein's thought, he considered this truth verification to be useful only as a general approach, not as a firm, unmoving law of logic. (See J. Hartnack, *Wittgenstein and Modern Philosophy*, trans. M. Cranston [London: Methuen and Co. Ltd.,1965], 36-47.)

3. Ibid., Proposition 2.0121, 5-6.

> 2.0121   ...
> Just as we are quite unable to imagine spatial objects outside space or temporal objects outside time, so too there is *no* object that we can imagine excluded from the possibility of combining with others....
> See also proposition 4.2211.

4. Ibid., Proposition 2.02, 7.

> 2.02   Objects are simple.

5. I found out later that with regard to Saudi Arabian bureaucracy, a code word for Jewish is *non-Muslim*, and that many Jewish businessmen travel freely to Saudi Arabia. However, at the time of my travel there, I did not know these nuances, and religion was an issue of some level of concern to me. I contemplated not going at all, but then decided I would be better to accept the label of Christian and see what it was really like in Saudi Arabia. I am not Jewish, but close members of my family are, and I was aware, as I sat in that Ottawa embassy, of my need to explore this area of the world that locks out my friends and family.

6. *Tractatus Logico-Philosophicus*, 8.

7. Ibid., 9-10.

8. Ibid., (Bertrand Russell, introduction), xi.

9. Here, I find some support in Wittgenstein's argument that objects contain within them all *possible* relationships:

> 2.0121
> It would seem to be a sort of accident, if it turned out that a situation would fit a thing that could already exist entirely on its own.
> If things can occur in states of affairs, this possibility must be in them from the beginning.

(Nothing in the province of logic can merely be possible. Logic deals with every possibility and all possibilities are its facts.)

Just as we are quite unable to imagine spatial objects outside space or temporal objects outside time, so too there is *no* object that we can imagine excluded from the possibility of combining with others.

If I can imagine objects combined in states of affairs, I cannot imagine them excluded from the *possibility* of such combinations.

This proposition emphasizes, to some degree, the *creation* of reality rather than the acceptance of an already formed one. On the other hand, there is also the tacit assumption here that there is an infinite preformed reality, containing all possibilities, and that interpretation is definitely not a dialectical one.

10. Plato, Letters VII, 342b-342d, from *Plato: The Collected Dialogues including the Letters*, Bollingen Series LXXI, ed. E. Hamilton and H. Cairns, trans L.A. Post, (Princeton: Princeton University Press, 1961), 1589-1590. (The italicized words are my emphasis.)

11. Plato, *Republic VII*, 514a and passim, in *Plato: The Collected Dialogues*, 747 and passim.

12. A number of map projections are used by navigators on the oceans and in the air; some keep the shape of the land masses and oceans more or less accurate; others, like the Mercator projection, sacrifice the accuracy of the shape of the land masses to allow the navigator to maintain a straight path along the map when plotting a route between two points. (Mercator projections become extended in both east-west and north-south directions the closer one moves to the north or south pole. At the poles themselves, the projections are infinite in size; no Mercator projection attempts to map the poles themselves for this reason. Nevertheless, despite the distortions, the Mercator maps allow for two points on the map to be joined by a straight line that will be in line with a constant compass direction for a navigator. These rhumb lines of the ocean navigators of centuries past are still understood and used to a degree by all navigators today.) For aviation purposes, there are other projections that allow the navigator to plot the shortest distance between two points on the globe—gnomonic projections, for example. See Mark Monmonier, *How to Lie with Maps*, (Chicago: University of Chicago Press, 1996), 8-18. Gnomonic projections are only good for limited areas, however, becoming greatly distorted when large regions of the earth are projected. (On other, more common, two-dimensional map projections, the shortest distance between two points will appear as a gentle curve. One can calculate the shortest distance between two points on a globe by stretching a string between the two points. A string stretched between Toronto, Canada, and London, England, for example, will arc gently to the north. Most routes of aircraft steer into the northern regions for this reason, trajectories that are rather counterintuitive for the average passenger.) More and more, map projections of large sections of the world are being used less and less. In very recent years, the global positioning system (GPS) has come into use. When satellite signals from a number of cross-referencing position-guiding satellites are used, virtually every part of the world can be tracked to an accuracy of a few centimetres. In any case, the point can be made that the accuracy of a map, its relationship to a known reality, depends on how it is to be used. A map that is relatively accurate as regards the shape of the continents will be less useful than a Mercator-style map that keeps lines between the points of travel straight. (For this information and general

sense of maps and navigation, I am indebted to my father, Capt. Ted McLaughlin, who, in his profession as a military and commercial pilot, has navigated aircraft in virtually all regions of the world for over four decades.)

13. Edward Said, *Orientalism* (New York: Vintage Books, Random House, 1979), 49.

14. Ibid., 46–47.

15. Ibid., 331, in 1994 Afterword.

16. The Truth and Reconciliation Commission (TRC) is not a court, and it cannot reach a verdict of guilt or innocence. It was set up to allow the perpetrators of past wrongs done during the period of apartheid to come forward and confess. Archbishop Desmond Tutu, the chair of the commission, appears interested in people asking for, and receiving, forgiveness. It is hoped by many that this process will cleanse the country of South Africa and lead to a non-violent revolution. It is hoped that reprisals for past injustices can be avoided. Therefore, the TRC can give amnesty to those who come forward and testify freely. However, Tutu was quoted on November 25, 1997, as saying that certain cases would perhaps be referred to the attorney-general for prosecution. This statement was made just as the hearing into allegations against Winnie Madikizela-Mandela were under way. She is accused of being responsible for a number of serious crimes, including murder and abduction, while she was operating her infamous Mandela United Football Club in Soweto in the late 1980s, a political organization fighting apartheid but that also targetted people who were apparently collaborating with the brutal government then under the leadership of President Pik Botha.

As I complete this writing, in the summer of 1998, I read that the Truth Commission has finished its two-year mandate and is drawing to a close—the TRC started on April 15, 1996, and had the last official testimony on July 31, 1998, when it heard from the scientist Wouter Basson, who testified regarding experiments designed to create chemical and biological weapons aimed specifically at blacks. It is ironic that the last testimony should be from a scientist whose experiments reveal the age-old ignorance of the true foundation of "race." Race is political, *not* biological. No biological weapon could ever target "blacks" as a group. Anthropologists today do not segregate people into racial colour groups biologically. This testimony is another example of how the Truth Commission has allowed old apartheid theories to be on display. Even if there are confessions of guilt from the scientists involved, unfortunately, at the hearings, the "science" of race is not being disputed.

Botha was put on trial for refusing to testify before the Truth Commission. The Amnesty Committee of the TRC can still hear his testimony, as they will be working well into next year. On August 21, 1998, Botha was fined 10,000 rand (US$1600) for contempt of court and ordered to face the Amnesty Committee. Failure to do so will result in a possible twelve-month jail sentence. Botha is appealing the conviction.

17. Winnie Madikizela-Mandela, interview with Newton Kanhema, reported in *The Star*, Johannesburg, November 17, 1997: 13.

18. Winnie Madikizela-Mandela was accused of assaulting and being an accessory to the December 1988 kidnapping of fourteen-year-old activist Stompie Seipei. (Stompie was associated with the Mandela United Football Club, and was accused by Winnie and others of breaking trust with them and being a police informer.) Winnie was acquitted of the assault charge, but convicted of conspiracy to kidnap and fined 15,000 rand (about US$4,000). Her associates Jerry Richardson and Katiza Cebekhulu were

charged in connection with Stompie's kidnapping and murder. Richardson was convicted of murder, and Cebekhulu went into hiding and returned to South Africa when I was there in November 1997; under the protection of a former British M.P., Emma Nicholson, he came to give evidence at the Truth Commission. Richardson and Cebekhulu were both prepared to give evidence implicating Winnie in Stompie's murder. During my November stay in Johannesburg, the Truth Commission's hearing into the activities of Winnie Madikizela-Mandela occupied most of the news time every day.

19. Fernand Hallyn, *The Poetic Structure of the World: Copernicus and Kepler*, trans. D. Leslie (New York: Zone Books, 1990), 281–82.

In referring to Copernicus, who devised the sun-centred planetary model that superseded the earth-centred Ptolemy model, and that was credited with changing the course of western science, Thomas Kuhn, cited in Hallyn's *Poetic Structure of the World*, points out that Copernicus's sun-centred system could not be perceived as the ultimate truth at the time it was developed (or since for that matter), as it did not solve the planetary model problem, nor was it more simple or accurate than Ptolemy's model that had been accepted as doctrine for centuries: "The preface to the *De Revolutionibus* [by Copernicus] opens with a forceful indictment of Ptolemaic astronomy for its inaccuracy, complexity, and inconsistency, yet before Copernicus' text closes, it has convicted itself of exactly the same shortcomings. Copernicus' system is neither simpler nor more accurate than Ptolemy's. And the methods that Copernicus employed in constructing it seem just as little likely as the methods of Ptolemy to produce a single consistent solution to the problem of the planets. . . . Even Copernicus could not derive from his hypothesis a single and unique combination of interlocking circles, and his successors did not do so." (Thomas Kuhn, *The Copernican Revolution: Planetary Astronomy in the Development of Western Thought* [Cambridge, Mass.: Harvard University Press, 1957], 171.)

And even though there were observations, pointed out by Galileo, that were solved by the Copernican model (such as the phases of Venus), there were other models, earth-centred ones, that solved these observational problems equally well. The Tycho Brahe system holds the earth at the centre, has the sun orbiting the earth, but has the other planets orbiting the sun and thus the earth as well; and this system solves the issue of the phases of Venus in as satisfactory a fashion as the Copernican model. As Kuhn states: "The Tychonic system is, in fact, precisely equivalent mathematically to Copernicus' system." (*The Copernican Revolution*, 202.)

The issue of developing a scientific revolution seems to lie more in the need to prove that progress is being made toward the understanding of ultimate truth. Therefore, new theories are treated as keys to the kingdom of knowledge, secret formulae that will reveal hitherto unknown truths, and thus they are given the image of an alliance "between God and man."

20. Richard Winfield, *Overcoming Foundations: Studies in Systematic Philosophy* (New York: Columbia University Press, 1989), 13–14.

21. Jean-Paul Sartre, Preface to *The Wretched of the Earth* by Frantz Fanon, trans. C. Farrington (New York: Grove Press, 1963), 13.

22. This map was drawn using information from Peter Whitfield, *The Image of the World* (San Francisco: Pomegranate Art Books, 1994).

23. William Makgoba, "Academia should also be made to face the music," in *The Star*, Johannesburg, November 21, 1997: 17.

24. *The Wretched of the Earth*, 48.

25. *Tractatus Logico-Philosophicus*, 74.

26. In light of my non-hierarchical definition of dialectical ideology, it should be noted that dialectical political models have often been linked with hierarchical *progress* models, and these, in turn, have, according to the analysis of some historians, been used to create models for the natural world. For example, the Canadian historian and philosopher of science Michael Ruse (in *Monad to Man* [Cambridge, Mass.: Harvard University Press, 1996] claims that biologists who espouse dialectical alternatives to the "self-fulfilling" progressionist Darwinian model of adaptationism are themselves tied to "progressive" models via Marx and Hegel. On page 522, Ruse states:

> [L]et us not forget that a Darwinian-type progress is not the only kind of biological progress we have encountered. There is also a Hegelian-transcendentalist-type of progress, a hierarchy driven by a kind of historical necessity, with humans at the top. This is the kind of progress a Marxist should understand, and there are at least hints of sympathy with something like it in what [population geneticist Richard] Lewontin writes. He is committed to a hierarchical view of nature: "As against the reductionist view, which sees wholes as reducible to collections of fundamental parts, we see the various levels of organization as partly autonomous and reciprocally interacting." (From Richard Levins and Richard Lewontin, *The Dialectical Biologist* [Cambridge, Mass.: Harvard University Press, 1985], 288).

But here Ruse confuses a consideration of *levels* of organization *within an organism or society* with the *ranking* of *like-sized* organisms—the *comparison* of people to a society as a whole, versus the *ranking* of one type of person to another, for example. The quote from Levins and Lewontin is an accurate description of an aspect of the dialectical approach—the whole is not reducible; and it is interacting with all its parts. To be fair, Ruse's example may not be perfect, but his point could still be analyzed. He is suggesting that dialecticians perceive humans as the top of a history of progress—which would indeed be a model based on organism-to-organism *ranking*. With regard to this matter, my interpretation of the "transcendental" qualities of Hegel's thought—which do lead him to propose not only the ascendance of humans to the top, but also of Germans to the top of the human ranks—is that, in the first place, Hegel's best thoughts are suffused with his personal chauvinism; and second, and more important, Hegel talks of a "new principle" that emerges from the dialectical background. This new principle does *not* dictate a *rank*, it indicates a *change*, a move to new rules of interaction not to be associated with the old order of organizational interactivity between elements within a system. The new principle exists outside the ladder of ascent associated with hierarchical, *progress*-laden models—in effect, the new principle leads to a discarding of any ladder that may have been imagined, since that ladder is illusional, as eloquently suggested by Wittgenstein in proposition 6.54 of the *Tractatus* (see section 327).

27. Edward O. Wilson, "The Biological Basis of Morality," in *The Atlantic Monthly*, April 1998: 70.

28. Edward O. Wilson, "Consilience Among the Great Branches of Learning," in *Daedalus: Journal of the American Academy of Arts and Sciences,* Vol. 127, No. 1 (Winter 1998): 131.

29. In Islamic culture, one eats with the right hand and never with the left. Greetings are also made with the right hand. The left hand is used for cleaning oneself after using the toilet. The need to be very formal about this was drilled into us. I found myself having great difficulty eating in public places, discovering how much I use my left hand without being conscious of it.

30. I was told in Saudi Arabia that slavery had been abolished more than twenty years before our 1992 visit. However, the servants in a household would be members of a family that would have been slaves for generations, or, if not strictly slaves, then members of a subservient class that would be seen as essentially slaves by anyone from my culture. In other words, the concept of their rising above their station in life, their level or degree on the ladder of the natural world, would not even be contemplated. The physical differences in stature and in body language alone, between the servant and the prince, were enough for anyone to decipher the relationship. Although it is true that in our western society we have a distinct class system, it is much more obvious in Saudi Arabia, marked as it is with a very definite quality. It is clear that there can be no movement between classes. In the west, we harbour the illusion that there is the possibility of moving up from a lower to a higher class.

31. Plato writes about the need for a social structure that keeps slaves obedient. This indicates that the love that I saw in the eyes of the prince's household retainer was only an indication of his great ability to perform his duties, attitudes and expressions that should not be taken as the mark of someone who is thoroughly accepting of his lower status. Plato imagines that if a household with slaves were to be transported instantaneously to a remote land, where there was no longer the protection of the slave-owner by the state, that the head of the household would, under these new social conditions, have to ingratiate himself to his former servants in order to survive. (Plato, *Republic* IX, 578e–579a.)

    However, I saw no reason to believe this to be the case during my visit to the prince's home in Saudi Arabia. I can only surmise that I was doubly seduced, on the one hand by the eyes of the slave, and on the other by my desire to believe that I was right in being placed in such a position of privilege. Taking a slightly different viewpoint, could not the slave have grown to believe in his position in society as much as I do mine?

32. Plato discusses the roots of tyranny as coming from a too lenient attitude to those who are beneath the ruling class. Indeed, from Plato's perspective, the foundation of some forms of tyranny seems to be the development of democracy, where all people, in spite of differences in ability and merit, are treated as equals.

    > And a democracy . . . comes into being when the poor, winning the victory, put to death some of the other party, drive out the others, and grant the rest of the citizens an equal share in both citizenship and offices—and for the most part these offices are assigned by lot.

    > .   .   .   .

    > And the tolerance of democracy, its superiority to all our meticulous requirements, its disdain for our solemn pronouncements made when we were found-

ing our city, that except in the case of transcendental natural gifts no one could ever become a good man unless from childhood his play and all his pursuits were concerned with things fair and good—how superbly it tramples underfoot all such ideals, caring nothing from what practices and way of life a man turns to politics, but honouring him if only he says he loves the people!

.   .   .   .

These and qualities akin to these democracy would exhibit, and it would, it seems, be a delightful form of government, anarchic and motley, assigning a kind of equality indiscriminately to equals and unequals alike!

.   .   .   .

[I]s not the avidity of democracy for that which is its definition and criterion of good the thing which dissolves it too?
What do you say this criterion to be?
Liberty . . . this is best managed in a democratic city, and . . . that is the only city in which a man of free spirit will care to live.

.   .   .   .

[I]s it not the excess and greed of this and the neglect of all other things that revolutionizes this constitution too and prepares the way for the necessity of a dictatorship?
How? . . .
Why, when a democratic city athirst for liberty gets bad cup-bearers for its leaders and is intoxicated by drinking too deep of that unmixed wine, and then, if its so-called governors are not extremely mild and gentle with it and do not dispense the liberty unstintingly, it chastises them and accuses them of being accursed oligarchs.

.   .   .   .

[T]he climax of popular liberty . . . is attained . . . when the purchased slaves . . . are no less free than the owners who paid for them.

.   .   .   .

[F]inally they pay no heed to the laws written or unwritten.

.   .   .   .

This . . . is the fine and vigorous root from which tyranny grows . . . any excess is wont to bring about a corresponding reaction to the opposite in the seasons, in plants, in animal bodies, and most especially in political societies. (Plato, *Republic*, in *The Collected Dialogues of Plato*, ed. E. Hamilton and H. Cairns, Princeton University Press, 1989, trans. P. Shorey, *Republic* 557a, 558b, 562cd, 563b, 563e, pp. 785, 786, 790-792.)

I am struck by this reflection of my dilemma in the prince's home. As I was enjoying the attentions of the slave/servant, my belief in my position in society was being positively reinforced. Plato discusses the avidity for liberty as is seen by those who advocate democracy as being an outgrowth of an acceptance of the equality of all, even those who have not studied and who do not deserve the respect of the noble, the wise, the scholars who can apparently run the society best. The fact that the knowledge, the education, that is judged to be best will always be that of the ruling class, and that no other point of view will have a chance, is missed in this argument, it seems to me. Nevertheless, Plato's description of how tyranny grows from democracy is intriguing to me as it describes a Hegelian self-destruction of a society and it also describes the inward feelings that I must have been sensing as I accepted the position of a superior being in the presence of a professional slave. My western ideal of equality is but a mask for my real western need to reinforce the status quo that dictates that there is a hierarchy, and that there is a destiny that is preordained, one that dictates the path along which we all travel. The status quo leads me to my most comfortable position in society. While I protest that we need equality, I find myself most happy and satisfied when I am being served as the master, when I am being loved by a slave. This is a humbling and somewhat unnerving realization for me.

CHAPTER NINE: The Ends of the Earth

1. Henry H. Bauer, *Scientific Literacy and the Myth of the Scientific Method* (Urbana and Chicago: University of Illinois Press, 1994), 101–140.

2. Ibid., 112.

3. Laura Nader, *Naked Science: Anthropological Inquiry into Boundaries, Power, and Knowledge* (New York and London: Routledge, 1996), 274.

INDEX